WHORE
BY DEFAULT
™

A story of love, lust, DEATH, sex, life....real life.

respectfully, ROSSANA

1stBooks - rev. 7/22/03

Sneak Preview

IN MY DREAM, the day dream that kept me lolling in bed this morning until ten am, I'm invited to Kevin's house for what I think is an innocuous dinner. After a nerve-wracking, cuticle-biting drive on black ice, I arrive only to walk into an awkward moment- a confrontation in an environment no one planned. After kissing Kevin and Sal hello and being introduced and reintroduced to the other four, my cousin walks in laughing. As she is as wide as she is tall, I didn't see who is behind her. It was him! Ten feet away. Why? He should be in California or some forgotten city as far away from me as his endless bank account could buy.

The smile leaves my face. I just stare, wide-eyed and opened-mouthed. I'm at first bewildered and then my knees begin to shake as it dawns on me. My face turns red and tears begin to form in my eyes. I'm losing control, losing control in a room full of HIS friends. I quickly run past; pull open a door to find it's the kitchen. Where's the bathroom? I can't control my emotions, emotions which have been, until this moment, in tact... As I'm washing cool water over my face, he walks in. I'm cornered. What will he do? Take me in his arms? How will I react? Succumb to him? My mind is racing. What will he say? He begins to speak, whispers that he is separated. Déjà vu? This is the same set of circumstances under which I met him the first time. He continues. The syllables have not yet escaped his lips as I run past, through the kitchen, outside. Where am I going? What am I doing? All rational thought has left me as I'm overcome with a sense of helplessness, running down a dark, snow covered mountain...

He's behind me. He grabs my arm. "I'm sorry." he says. "No!" I state as I spin around and start pounding his chest, the tears free flowing. "No," I scream. "I'm sorry. I realize I miss you. I want you back," he croons. "Noooo!!" I cry. Pain? Torment? Grief? I don't know as I collapse into him. I manage to shout as the pitch is carried by the wind for all to hear: "You need to tell them." Sob. "Tell them what happened." Double sob. "Tell them how you deprived me of my grief!" Sob. Sob. Sob. Sob... At this point, I'm hysterical- everything held in suddenly burst through a wall of stone. Someone throws a blanket over the two of us and leaves us be- me pounding his chest, crying, rocking as he holds me. He lays my head in his lap and strokes my forehead, the way a mother calms her newborn, gently, gently, gently he caresses me, consoles me. The below freezing temperature had not yet penetrated my crippled soul for I was still angry. Still hurt. Still- I didn't know.

As the snow begins to fall, my tears continue but don't flow as freely. I close my eyes and try to sleep. Maybe I'll wake up and he'll be locked away, thrown into a dark, deep chamber in my heart where he belongs. He lets me be. Five minutes? Ten? Time is insignificant. He pulls me to my feet, hugs me as we walk into the house, into a room that seconds before was buzzing with laughter and is now quiet.

We sit on the hearth of a monstrous fireplace, wrapped in a blanket, me cradled in his lap, weak, eyes swollen. He begins to speak in a tone of one who must confess and be judged. As I lay there, in a trance, I do not need to listen to what he has to say, to humiliate himself... It's for them... They all sit, stand, meander but with the same expressions on their faces, mouths open, listening...

"She is the innocent victim... After all of us went to dinner in NYC that night in September..." He begins to tell the story. The story that they have never heard. A story of how he cried across 3000 miles, of how he bawled like a baby, of how he took away from me my ability to feel...

"I want to marry you," he says. I sit up and gaze into his green eyes, deep into his blackened, cold soul. "Do you love me?" I ask between short, gasping breaths. I waited so long to hear these three simple words. I needed to hear them from him. From anyone. It had been so long. "I love you. Will you forgive me? Will you marry me?"

The room quiet. The moment suspended in time. Just as I'm about to speak, to reveal my answer... Sal jumps in and says with conviction as someone who's kept quiet for too long, someone who's wanted to speak and be heard: "I love you. I always have but my friendship with him is my life and I didn't know how to divide myself."

"I love you, Rossana" coming from across a dark corner of the room. Kevin had been getting a drink.

And there they were in a circle around me. Three men in one minute had declared their love for me... I needed to get up from the bed when the realization of this event ever taking place was beyond my sanity, farfetched into a stellar atmosphere. In actuality, my bowels rumbled and my stomach lurched. How we dream....

I told you... I am a hopeless romantic...

To my family and friends...
(too numerous to list)

My stream of conscience:
where the present, future, past
tenses intertwine....

"Words are just words
unless there is
a heart and soul behind
that which is read to
that which is written."

-rossana

PS- May my angels keep watch over you.
****

A special thanx to my mother and father (who are
not allowed to read this book)- however still
encourages me and inspires me...

Table of Contents

<u>Introduction</u>

I have "fuck me" written on my forehead like a tattoo, engraved. No! -deeper, chiseled like that on a tombstone. As the lines on my forehead become more pronounced, the words "fuck me" become more evident... I don't think of myself as beautiful, possibly pretty, though I am often described as sexy. If beauty is in the eye of the beholder, then why is it a commonality of perceptions that all viewed me in that lustful manner, as if I was no more than passion's infinite plaything?

MAYBE, IT'S MY sultry voice, the raspiness of it a suggested aura of self-confidence, sensuality, sexuality. For years, people, strangers, acquaintances, former friends have approached me, a blast from the past where I can't quite place the circumstances of our meeting, they've stated: "I know you. It's that voice!" It's deep, it's energetic, it's nasal, it's intonations change depending on my allergic environment. (Achew! Why are you wearing that perfume? Achew! Were there raspberries in that pie? Achew! Do you have a cat? A dog? Achew! Achew! Achew!)

Adorable, little mischievous me with a smirk I can't hide and an expression of warmth that's always inviting...Or it could be my gesticulating mannerisms, lively and animated, which I'm told can be mistaken for a hidden agenda. What agenda? Tell me. My friend Brian (I've known him since I was a child of seven.) says I have that certain naïveté that men want to dominate, let lose the woman! I possess that vivacious personality (you want to emulate) and a garrulous tongue (you may wish to smack me for!). I am the luminescent girlfriend, bright, witty, sparkling, upbeat. Men love me for some reason, women hate me...until they get to know me. Body language- it can be misinterpreted. I think this is an innate quality; after-all, I am Italian and I doa talka witha mya handsa.

As for my eyes, they smile and they are piercing. Depending on my mood, they fluctuate from a warm chocolate brown to a tantalizing gold, the color of 24 carats. I'll look directly at you when we're talking which may cause you to look away. I tend to gaze into your eyes, lovingly, with affection, with kindness or possibly with disbelief. (I haven't quite figured out how to read the dilation's of the pupils to tell whether you are being honest or not.) Anyway, I look at you because I am always interested in what you are saying.

"Oh beautiful me" is about me. By me. I superimposed the poem on top of a charcoal self-portrait. My mother exclaimed, upon discovering my Renoir, sitting pretty on the easel: "Oh! It's a beautiful you." Thanks, mom.

"Oh beautiful me"

Amber eyes of gold, reflecting
a million points of light...
Above which stands the Himalayas,
whose boundaries- arched peaks.

Hair like the chameleon, changing
to reveal mood and environment,
Red, like fire, temperamental at best,
Interwoven with corn's silky threads,
a sunset's glare.

Waves like the ocean's crests and troughs
neither overpowering nor gentle bearing
just a forceful nature.

The voice's sultriness,
emanating from deep within...
Outward-spoken words of meaning,
Kindness of thought or
tones sharp as a double- edged sword.

The nose,
roundness of curves,
size of no delicate proportion
Yet, not exceedingly large.

Lips as soft as a child's sandbox,
Sensual in shape...
The smile that radiates
like a full moon
on peaceful water.

Two dimples, the indentations
of a paragraph's commencement
in an adventurous short story...

Since I was 15, my friends have told me I look like a certain actress, famous today for her outspoken, lascivious(?) character... (She's married to that Matthew guy. You know him best for his role as the truant, "playing hooky from school one day" and causing a hell of excitement throughout Chicago.) Anyway, I sported the same bangs and dark curly waves when she appeared on *Square Pegs*. The only difference is that she portrayed a nerd and I was the utmost in cool. I simply do not see the resemblance even though after twenty years, I still get "you know who you look like..." I'm not skinny, I don't have perfect abdominals and arms, nor do I have blue eyes... They say it's the way we talk. What does manner of speech have to do with looks? You got me...

As I stated, I am not beautiful. I am sexy. Men find me sexy. I should just accept this. I am sexy. I am SEXY! I AM SEXY!! Self-confidence=sexy. But, shit... I am so insecure. I'm caught between having it (self- confidence) and being the shy, demure me.

My body- ahhh, my body. I should have left alone to nature that which I paid a high price to change. My body. You can bounce a quarter off my butt. In fact, I am very accepting of my heart-shaped ass. The rest of me, well... that leaves something to be rectified... My body, which has been recently enhanced, is now disproportionate. I am my own best critic and find fault where need not be; however, once again my mother pointed out: "You had a better body before the liposuction." Thank you, Mom. Just what I needed to hear- the truth. My thoughts exactly but it's up to me to voice them not be affronted by you. I know, she means well...

Inside thighs- out! Chub-rub- no more. Forget the jelly arms- gone! The lower bulge- removed! Or so I thought, so I wanted... I had my flanks, lower abdomen, and "then some" diminished. I thought I was having my love handles removed. *Wooooooooooooooooooshl* (that's supposed to be a sucking sound) Now, I would be able to wear hip huggers- *oh so low, how low do you go!* Yeah, right. Brittany Spears, that's the body I would be! Anyway, by doing so (*woooosh*), I now have two lovely fat deposits that sit on my hips and an upper belly protrusion which didn't exist (I-swear-I-have-the-photo's–to–prove-it) pre-surgery.

The weight of my huge breasts, 36 full C ("full" being the operative word), have left two folds of flab underneath them. The slouching has intensified, the rounded shoulders are becoming obvious, the lower back pain intolerable. I need a personal trainer to teach me how to sit, walk, relax with the new me. In addition, my equilibrium and center of gravity have been altered. How will I ski this season?

So now I'm... I'm?... *"I'm a little tea pot, short and stout, here are my handles, here is my spout!"* Curvaceous. Full figured. Voluptuous. Big. If only I had the height to justify the horizontal alignment- I mean misalignment!

I'm being hard on myself because you would never think from looking at me that I had $12,500 of added improvements, an upgrade plus the cost of new bras ($24.00 a pop), and new clothes. (I had to give away all my trendy suits and vintage frocks.) I am that tomboy who one day decided to switch gender roles when I accumulated an eye for detail and a flair for style, impeccable style: aka "the poise of Grace Kelly and the style of Audrey Hepburn." I wanted the body to go along with it. That's me (or who I aspire to be). I am still the ravishing red-head; yet, now the obvious buxom stature clearly outmatches my wit!

All curves is what I am though my girlfriends still utilize the word "HUGE" in pointing out my breasts. I get the looks, even when covered from head to toe. I get the envy. I get the wonder-if-its-real eyebrows raised. Looks it. Feels it. Moves like it. Haha...Your husbands would get a handful and then some (and you know your husbands are dying for a "Please! don't squeeze the Charmin!"). .

I am not your recent middle aged divorcee, trying to capture my lost youth, beauty that's gone. A white gown and me have nothing in common. I'm more of the scarlet letter type of woman... a big R across my chest: ravishing, robust, red-hot, raunchy, restless. Or is that reserved, respected, resilient, re-known? Maybe, rolly-polly, my childhood nickname. R! The big R in red. That's me.

One day, I went out and got a boob job (and some liposuction) because my Mother coerced me (well, that's part of another story). She kept up her usual nagging-did-you-make-an-appointment-yet. I've been talking about it for years and had started noticing some undesirable effects. I might as well do something for myself (no one else will) and I had the money to do just that. I only wanted fuller, rounder breasts. I wanted to be able to go bra-less. I wanted to wear a tank top without having gravity dominate the look. I wanted to sport a bikini without any padding. I wanted to ENHANCE not TOPPLE!

I should have just let things be and paid for a trainer, 1/10 of the cost. Now, I'm told a lift is in order. Giddats! I'm going to become one of those women who are constantly undergoing the knife to achieve near perfect results. Plastic surgery. Addictive? You bet. So, *"Dr. F,"* excuse me, while I direct this question to him...*"If a lift is in order, will I now look fuller, rounder, with the perfect décolletage? Or will I succumb, once again, to pointy, tubular breasts that sag and jiggle with lollipop scars that can't be hidden?"* God most definitely died at the Spa...

My virgin breasts have been manhandled in the past one and a half years since their birth (but only by three):

1. A 28 year-old (great catch!). The sensitive type in touch with his feminine side. My first, and that's only because my friend, DJ, kept harassing me: "Don't you want to know what they think? if you have sensation?..."
2. A 39 year-old most definitely gay male (who needs to J-U-M-P out of the closet). What a waste of my chastity.
3. A 46 year-old divorcee who claims he wants another wife. He'll have to kick that anti-depressant habit first.

Yes, you will read more about them.

My biggest fear was what would John think? John was my last endeavor. Would he know? Chances are he hasn't been with a lot of women and my added padding would camouflage the bubbliness. Bubbliness? Under close surveillance (and careful handling as if touching a newborn), one breast- too much, too full, not enough play. The other breast feels like a balloon left out in the sun for a few days. Once round and perfect, it's now deflating. Giddats. I should have just let things be....

Does anyone have a bicycle pump handy???

God Died at the Spa (Prologue)

God died at the Spa. I was reminded of this as I adjusted my saline breasts to stand upright. Did I need another visit to Dr. F. to fix what should have been left alone to nature?

God died at the Spa (gid-dats):
where vanity has taken precedence over basic moral obligation.

For just one second, stop yelling at your children. As usual, you're being too overprotective. They're not misbehaving. Okay- so you have the painter coming. He hasn't shown up and you're late for a doctor's appointment. Oops! I think your toilet's overflowing. The phone is ringing. Ding-dong!

This is the last time you'll live your life vicariously through me. Why is it that you married ones always want one more single excursion? I'm not in your house five minutes and the first thing you ask is "So- what have you been up to?" meaning "So- who are you screwing now?" I would do anything to switch places with you- even steal your husband. NOT! Don't get your panties in an uproar. It never crossed my mind. I think that a visit into my past will help you... help you capture the vision of what a wonderful life you lead. Your life, its ups and downs, chaotic, always rushing around. Your life- but at least you're not alone. It's ten years of my life that I confess to. Don't judge me. Understand me.

My friend Cristina says that I'm in love with the idea of being in love. She says I've always been that way and I've known her also since we were seven years old. Does that make me a hopeless romantic? So what. Someone has to be. We (yes, I'm including you) are a gender descriptive majority, untouched by outside elements, though small scars (male induced?) have left an indelible impression on our hearts. At least my heart, lots of scars...

This brings me to my point..."M*ommy*...MOM*my, MOMMY!!*" Pay attention to your three year-old. She's pulling your shirt. I can wait...

My untamed spirit yet kindred heart has led me to the conclusion that I knew my name change was inevitable- the result of me experiencing too many empty promises, repetitious moments, momentary adornments, temporary passions, and passionate temperaments.

I know you probably want to know who the hell I am. All right, I'll introduce myself now... Rossana T- my last name is up for dispute. How about "traversare" (to cross)? He had to cross through me to get to her... That is who I am: Ross-an-a Traversare. He's somewhere at the beginning. I'm in the middle (waiting with sinful trepidation)... She's at the end. As he passed, he had to encounter me... For all of them encountered me at the apex before spiraling downward to life (or wife) of acceptance, ordinary bliss. They all had to experience me before finding another to settle with. (I never said you'd like what I have to share, what I have to say.)

I always seem to be part of a triangle. Triangles- I try to avoid. I was never the part as the "other woman". I was always "the" woman. Triangles, as part of a day of everyday life as expected. Triangles. What keeps us intriguing? Triangles. I want no part of. Somehow, I'm always in.

Maybe this is why I am single... a single, sexy woman in her thirties... I still have long, youthful hair. I still have fashionable nails. And I most definitely still wear high heels.

Being single sucks. It's not what it's cracked up to be, that adventurous short story. "You live the life of Reilly." How many times have you said that to me? Who's Reilly? And if I live his life- who's living mine? Being single... not what it's cut out to be, especially at an age when you've become "the stereotype". Why are there so many single women in their 30's (asked again and again)? I think (okay- I know) its status has been elevated to a "Sex and The City" episode. "Sex and The City"... you have to watch it. You can't get enough of it. Why are there so many single women in their thirties? Hey- if we all live the lives like those four, why get married? But I believe... there is no answer to a question that should never have been contrived. Who's asking? What standard is "so many" weighed against? Are we talking in the state of NY? The US? The World? Hey, how about: "why are there so many men still single in their 30's?"

So ask yourself... why are there so many single women in their 30's? Why are you still single, you're wondering? How about this for an answer... because. Just because. Because is the answer to everything. Remember asking your mom if you could sleep over a friend's house. "No." "Why?" "Because."

"Because why?" "Just because." No formidable answer- it was just your mom's way of letting you know that she was in charge and you could not go. No reason, no explanation needed. Because. Just because. The next time your child asks if she can go next door and play, careful! "No." "Why?". "Because..." Aahhh, you have to think twice! So the next time you ask me why I am still single... "Because. Just because." It's the answer to everything...

So? 30? Single women? So many? Because (just kidding). Did you ever think that maybe we (single ones) are at a point in our lives where we have one quality so rightfully deserved: self- respect. Is it so wrong to want a man to like me for me first and foremost and to make love to me rather than a quick tryst (well- with me it would be a marathon). I don't need another notch on my bedpost- the bed was about to break! As I said to my last crush, I had too much respect for myself. I chose to be pious though the latent sensuality needed to be awoken and soon! My crush couldn't understand it (maybe that's because he wanted me for himself). No one could.

"You could have any man," one friend told me as I pined for his roommate. Yet, why was it that I was alone? Always alone. I was afraid of growing old alone and I didn't want Jack (the rabbit)[1] as my only friend. "There is nothing better than Jack the Rabbit," my married friend, Kim exclaimed. "Jack the Rabbit is everything!" her very much single friend, Chrissie retorted. Robin, Kim's alter ego, the ying for her yang, chimed in: "Yes, I'll cheat on my husband, every chance I get... but only with Jack the Rabbit!" Great for you- not for me. (I was very much content with my own nimble fingers.)

Getting back to me... you may be thinking: "Stop searching. It'll happen when you least expect it." I am not searching. I was not searching. I will not search. They (the plural intentionally used) had just not found me. That's right- they had NOT found me for they were the searchers, looking for perfection that existed as a figment of their twisted testosterone imagination. Perfection? In their eyes, an infinite license to play, tease, taste, and release. A continual game of

---

[1] Jack the Rabbit is a sexual aid toy.

tag- "catch me, catch me, if you can" followed by "see ya!", as they continue to search. Perfection- get a clue. It doesn't exist.

I realized that maybe I was not a woman for one man. I was too much woman (and I have been told I'm too much):

1. The nun who's thoughts ping-ponged between chaste and impure.
2. The shrew somewhat conditioned.
3. The lady in waiting already been seen and had.
4. The princess in distress- once rescued, twice ignored.

And there had been, quite frankly, too many men. Madame Boverie I am not; however, my excursions and adventures are most definitely of the illicit and dubious nature.

Have you finished asking your four year old to "get out of the tub" in your sweetest I-am-a-good-mom voice "NOW!!" So you think you had a rough day...

Too many men. As my father recently remarked during a casual dinner conversation: "More men have come through this house since the Jew that came for Easter." (The Jew being twenty, at that time, five years and a sexual decade my junior.) So many men, but that's because none of them have gulones (balls). Where were the men with balls?

My mother is convinced our generation has emasculated all the real men. Anyway, I need a man (any man) to take charge and make his move. "Go to Mitsubishi and pick up that obnoxious, cocky salesmen," my Dad remarked. "He'd be bowlegged after a night with me," I said. SMACK!!! on the back of my head from my left (Mom!) I didn't see that one coming. Okay- maybe this wasn't dinner conversation, my ribald statement uncalled for. I was just kidding since I hadn't had a date, a fling, or any man in my life in over a year. Fourteen months of chosen celibacy. I should start a club (since I've been the President many times before)- Born Again... uhmn... the... the Born Again Virgins. That's right. I'm quiet these days. I'd rather read a good book, cuddled up in a quiet corner than join in on the family games. I don't go out and I'd rather spend time babysitting your children than be out on the prowl. What happened to me, the "me" you've come to expect?

Too many men... Their IQ's ran the gamut from the developmentally, disabled inebriate to the sanely-insane genius. Looks that could grace the cover of GQ (my pretty boys) to those that needed the name of a good orthodontist. There was the career bachelor who wined and dined me. The rebound divorcee who wanted to feel needed. The still single 39 year-old... Why are there so many single men in their 30's?

I had gone through them all and most importantly appealed to them all (at least temporarily)...

- The 20-something boy, just beginning his career, an exploration of his masculine self through a continual virile force, round after round. Surely, you recall THOSE nights (and that achy morning thereafter...)
- The 30-something man (men.), making his fortune, spending his fortune, making his fortune, spending his fortune, that vicious circle. That self- assured ass who forgot how to please a woman first, at a time in his life when a good cigar, an extension of his lower extremity (did I say small?), is more savored than a succulent pussy (mine).
- 40. By now, he should be grown up... (Do they ever grow up?) He is much too settled in his ways, the mustache replacing the head of hair gone south permanently, trying to recapture the prowess of his youth by a constant exclamation of how horny he is. Too bad his stamina is a one shot deal that left me begging for more.

There was even the 80 year old (80!), who I accidentally discovered pined for me when I deposited my check. As I endorsed it, I noticed he had written on the back:

R -
You're a lovely woman
    Love,
      -R

I should have framed it for posterity. That November, I rented a cottage on a pond in Sagaponack, L.I. for a sabbatical, life in the country away from the city's grind. I planned on painting, painting frescos. Anyway, Richard was my landlord. He mailed me back my security deposit. It never crossed my mind that he'd be interested in me, interested in me in a romantic nature. [2]

So many men... How can I forget my college roommate's father, who chose his son's wedding to throw me over his arm, dip me backwards, and plant a big, sloppy Miller Lite kiss on my mouth! My roommate and her mother kept dancing, laughing as they looked our way. Help!!! Where was my garlic necklace when I needed it?!

And of course, there is my mother's best friend. At 67, his physical vitality, mental clarity, and youthful appearance were phenomenal. He chose a quiet night, while his wife hit the rodeo in Texas, to declare his intentions... I never took him up on his offer though the negotiations may have been entertaining...

Too many men... They were just passing phases (though not in my eyes). I was trying to get back what I rightfully deserved, what had been taken from me so long ago. Some, I loved (in my own way)... each for something so simple and unique:

- one for his hands and the way he created
- one for sex, just sex, and our culinary explosion of food, wine, and exotic tastes
- one for his mind and for teaching me to climax, again and again and again

---

[2] My ulterior motive for renting the cottage pertained to a certain Stephen, Stephen #8. He's "Mr. June." The cottage was a trial basis since this certain 28 year- old kept asking me, year after year, when I was going to move the 90 miles east to be with him. This trial became a test, to see if he was indeed sincere. I saw him that first stormy night I slept at the pond. I never saw him again though he only lived a mile into the forest. True intentions? He got scared. He never thought I would take him up on his offer. Scared him away by calling his shots... I still think of him quite often since he was the only one to tell me I was his soul mate. Stephen #8, wants to be my soul mate...We've never slept together. He usually calls, out of the blue, on a day when I'm feeling low, like the weekend I lost my job. I've named him "Stephen Revisited". We had fun. Strange. Seven years... from being Mr. June. He still calls me...

- one for his gentleness of being, his quiet self, and the way he absorbed every word I spoke
- one for being my clone and for always making me cry because I was laughing so hard.

I know you are waiting to hear about them, to meet them... Patience. It's a virtue.

I was a bitch and should have remained so. Instead, I became nice, too nice, too non-confrontational. It's a shallow but specific observation of me. I'm told I wear my heart on my sleeve though I don't really understand what that means. You, on the hand, probably didn't give him the time of the day: "I didn't call him back for three days." "I got up and walked out. He followed me." The bitch. Was that you? Play hard to get? I have heard your advice so often. Maybe I should have paid closer attention. You're now married. Me. Nice. Too nice (and I'm still single)... My attitude was that everything's copasetic. I dealt primarily with a sincerity of affection and compassion. I was the one who planted sweet kisses on cheeks in stolen moments, caresses to the face, hand-holding as acts of kindness, a deep hug in time of need. Affection. I gave it willingly. Affection. I wanted it back, needed it in return.

This is what scared them off. I let them take me in (I should have put the guard up), cultivate a relationship, gave of myself 110%, kept things light and whimsical or so I perceived. I didn't play the game. I didn't play hard to get. I should have. I never said those three magical words "I love you" but somehow they all thought I did. Were their ego's so big that they fantasized I loved them? Were my actions misguided? My intentions misunderstood? I only wanted us to be happy. I only wanted us to be real. (Psst... I only wanted what was taken from me so long ago.)

So many men... It's poetic justice, a turn of events, that led me to this solitude and virtuous solemnity. Virtue. How often I've tried to reclaim it.

...As the snow continues to fall on a tranquil Vermont's eve, I sit alone, the fire blazing, the Barn quiet. This room holds memories of so many romantic nights through continuous mornings. The perfect setting for rapturous affairs whose ghosts now lay in another's arms but once held me, made love to me, fucked me, as the embers glow hotter and brighter... Yesterday's thoughts.

Too many men... except for one. Today I give myself to him. As a child, I loved him, embraced his doctrine, turned my back, now fight to embrace him once again.

I enter and genuflect to my betrothed...

Book Second

God Died at the Spa

Chapter i.
Let's Just Call Him Matthew
Awakening

My body was starving for affection, starving for intimacy. It was thirsty for attention. I had yet to "marinate the pheromones"[3] that remained unspiced. I had yet to taste true love. Again. I had yet to hear those three words I had been waiting for. Again. I had yet to listen to the music of my lust. Again. I had an aura of sexuality that remained unseen. I had yet to touch what I was grasping for. Again. I had yet to smell the roses. Red Roses. Long Stem.

---

[3] From some Ali McBeal episode

1993. MY SENSES REMAINED dulled. I did not want anyone to touch me, to be with me, to even acknowledge me. I was cold and dark, the smile never forming, the eyes not seeing, the ears not listening... My senses were dulled. No one would possess me. No one could possess me. I did not want anyone to love me ever again.

"It's not healthy," his best friend Johnny said, spoke to me with compassion, the way a brother looks out for his sister. "It's not healthy," he stated when I told him I would never be with anyone again. I would become like them- the merry group of widows who never let themselves be captivated by another. I would become like them-the merry group of widows. "It's not healthy. He wouldn't want you to...," Johnny said. He had given me the green light. Johnny wanted me to forge ahead. He wanted me to experience again. Johnny gave me his blessing, the way a father does to his soon to be son-in-law.

It had been two years. Two very difficult years of just being with myself. I liked my own company. I didn't need to answer to anyone. I didn't need anyone. Two years. *Red light. Green light. 1,2,3...* A ticket to pass... *go!!* Fast speed ahead, I went. Hold on- my sensual voyage was about to begin...

This was the year that the World Trade Center would prove not to be an impenetrable fortress. The same year that Michael Jackson was accused of fondling a 13 year-old. "Tears from Heaven" by Eric Clapton would be the number one song. It was also the year that my friends were getting married. It was wedding after wedding, month after month. I had no time to experience love, just think about it. It was being thrown into my face. Everyone was ready to take the plunge. Everyone had finally made a commitment. Everyone... except me.

I met Matthew at the wedding of my friends, DJ and Jake. I had known him, well, sort of, always wanted to know him, in college. He was such a cute little boy... always whipping around in that red BMW convertible. He was hot!! He was adorable!! He still was a ladies man with his sandy colored short hair and deep Hershey-kiss eyes that penetrated through you. We were in Annapolis, Maryland. During the rehearsal dinner, he paid attention to me. I don't think he sat at our table, but he came over to it later. Attention. To me. Could it have been my red strapless mini-dress? Maybe he was attracted to the pearls around my neck. Attention. It was nice. (I think DJ planned for us to get together. I believe this was a set-up, an intentional, well thought-out set-up. She mentioned something at her shower, given by Matthew's mom. Maybe Matthew's mom started whispering. I'm almost positive DJ had whispered something into Matthew's ear about me (or maybe Jake did).

Matthew paid me attention even though I never spoke two words to him before this, never struck up a conversation with him. He paid me attention... We continued to party at the local bar in Annapolis. Later on in the eve, he put his blazer around me. (I was cold.) He pulled up a stool, taking it from a friend, so I could sit. (My feet hurt from the stilettos.) He propositioned me, as the beers loosened his tongue, bringing back the frat boy bravado, the SAE (Sigma Alpha Epsilon) bravado. Mathew- a frat boy, still. I was in a room full of frat boys with their tasteless rituals (was Matthew trying to initiate me?), the stupid nicknames they still possessed- Face, Hawk, Frog (Larry, Moe, Curly), the ridiculous consumption of alcoholic beverages (buuurrrp!). Did they all still belong to that 4-F Club mentality, the "find 'em, feel 'em, fuck 'em, forget 'em" mentality? What they all failed to realize was that half of them were fat, receding fore-headed geeks. If not for the fraternity of their equally bald, stupendous brothers, they would be stepped upon by women of higher values. Women who knew better. Their actions were sophomoric implications of their masculinity. Matthew got bold. He wanted me to come back to his room. A proposition. I looked at it more as a compliment than an insult. "Fat chance," I answered, loud enough was all to hear. Let him think about what he was missing, what he couldn't possess. He paid me attention. Me?!!!

He was nice, spoke in a gentle way, possessed the polished mannerisms of boy brought up in a loving household, a respectful home. He was nice to me. I thought nothing of it, even the next day, when he turned around (as if he had been

on the lookout) and looked back at me (captivating my
attention), when he arose and came toward me (as I stood
awkwardly waiting for the ushers), when he escorted me down
the aisle, when he asked me to sit next to him at the
ceremony... Small talk. I was nervous. Small talk. I was a little
uncomfortable. Small talk. My friends beckoned me over to
them. I casually got up, excused myself (for the moment) and
sauntered over to them. I never went back to Matthew, as the
seat next to him remained empty. I was uncomfortable.
Matthew was paying me attention. I wasn't used to it. I guess
he thought I blew him off. It was just the shy, demure me
coming out. The stupid, little girl me. I didn't know how to
handle his subtle, yet gentlemanly advances.

I was wearing a black, bugle-beaded chiffon dress set against
a nude lining. It looked like a spider had spun her web across
my body, accentuating every curve, the back plunging into a
deep "v". In addition to being sexy, it had its conservative
appeal sitting two inches below the knee with a high scoop
neckline; nevertheless, "the web." I should have caught him,
weaved my web, and devoured him. I was thirsty. My body
was thirsty. Instead, I ran away. The stupid little girl...

With a few drinks in me, alcohol as my confidence boost, I got
the nerve up to bust his chops about "the proposition".
Everyone made light of it. I wanted him to ask me to dance. I
was waiting for him to continue his advances, to continue
paying me attention. I waited patiently for his invitation. He
never asked. I was disappointed. I became assertive and went
up to him. He wasn't as receptive as I would have liked. I
guess his ego had been shot down when I moved away from
him during the ceremony. I didn't think anyone had noticed.
(DJ said, "Everyone noticed.")

2.

...I WENT TO Philly to visit my friends. I was always going to
Philadelphia to visit them at Bugtussle, the place the Beverly
Hillbillies lived before they discovered oil. They lived at
Bugtussle, a five-room house, stuck behind a hardware store
on a commercial strip on the Main Line, as different from the
Main Line as you could get. This is why they christened their

home "Bugtussle". Anyway, I wanted to continue what Matthew had started, what Matthew had awoken- a flirtation ritual I wanted a big part in but was too afraid to take the lead. I was hiding in the wings, a bit player, yet the starring role included me. Me? Matthew had entered my life through one of the stage doors, the emphasis on the portal's significance.

One blustery night, Jake and I went to a local bar. (DJ was tired and stayed home. She trusted me with her husband.) Matthew was there, having drinks with his soon to be in-laws. Good 'ole boys from Mississippi. They were partying, a continuation of the wedding festivities, his sister's wedding. Handsome men who hid behind their southern charm (their southern gentlemanly charms), who hid behind their smiles, to hit on me. It was a nice feeling being surrounded by all these men, good-looking men, the type of men that could walk in a room and command attention. They hit on me, yet they never crossed the line of indecency. I wouldn't let them. Jake wouldn't stand for it. Matthew didn't notice. (Or did he?)

She was also there. She kept watching us, from across the bar, giving me evil eyes, sending daggers into my spine even though I had a fortress of strong men protecting me. Ouch! "Who is that bottled blonde?" I wondered. It couldn't be the heinous wench I had heard such negative things about. "So, Matthew. When are you coming to NY?" I asked. Oh no! That troll, broke her way through the testosterone barrier, came up in-between us just as Matthew was inviting me to the concert. "What concert? Who's going to NY?!!" she hissed...

He was coming to the city in the fall and somehow I managed to get myself invited to the Jerry Garcia Concert. Imagine that? I had no rights to this date, no claim to it because the Grateful Dead and I did not get along. We didn't socialize. I didn't know anything about their music (except one song-"Truckin") let alone even understand the concept of their culture. Deadheads. A lifestyle. A culture. Something I knew nothing about. Matthew lived it. I am sure if propriety allowed, he would have traveled the world to see all of their concerts. The Jerry Garcia Band was an offspring. I got myself invited to the concert (even with the wench's interruption). He paid me attention and I liked it. It had been so long...

The concert proved to be a thrilling experience. I got stoned from the second hand smoke and there was a lot of it! Madison Square Garden was full of smoke; you could barely make out the stage through the colorful prism of lights. We were center stage but up high. We were high. I was still nervous, being with him. I was uncomfortable, the sexual tension rising. Was this a date? I hated dates. I never did well on dates. The stupid little girl was coming out, surfacing through the cloud of smoke. "Be cool," I told myself, tried to convince myself. Matthew is cool. Tension. Sexual tension? Sexual tension. Something made me say, "Let's get this over with..." as I leaned toward him and kissed him. I kissed him as the smoke surrounded us, as the musical arena enhanced the moment. I kissed him (one kiss and I could get him going). One kiss as if we were alone (even though we were in a stadium filled with people though the public wasn't all with it). One prolonged kiss. That broke the ice. We listened to the rest of the concert (me on cloud nine), holding hands, swaying...

We took a cab back to my neighborhood, swapping spit as we traversed the boroughs. (I was living alone and was very proud of my apartment, an apartment decorated with antiques, an apartment that possessed a European flair, which could have graced a House and Garden magazine.) That cab ride... cab rides in general- infamous for fooling around and other sexual follies. New York cab rides- infamous for many acts of the indecent kind. We only kissed, hard, passionately. The driver kept watching us. This particular cab didn't have the privacy guard. The driver kept watching us... our prophylactic in disguise as a Pakistani refugee.

Matthew spent the night. A safe night! It was the morning. I always get myself in trouble in the morning. I got up early and took a shower. I crawled back into bed with him, my hair dripping, perfumed from the shampoo, my breath minty, my body fresh. Nothing happened!... except some very contortionistic body maneuvers- the "coffee, tea or me" morning, the sex with your clothes on kind of morning except the clothes didn't exist. I was wearing a silk two piece- my usual pajamas (flannels were never in my vocabulary). He slept in his boxers. What a nice chest he had!! What a nice body he had. We fit so well. He kissed so nicely, warmly, passionately. Kissing... Ahhh...

3.

IF THE WALLS could talk... DJ and Jake were coming to Vermont for the long February holiday weekend. I asked them to get a feel for Matthew before I invited him. They assured me that the invitation would be welcoming. I got a rude surprise though when I called him and she answered the phone, demanding to know who I was, what I wanted. He grabbed the phone from her and apologized. He told me not to worry about her. She had unexpectedly dropped by (uhhh- at 10pm?). She was just visiting (uhhh- he lived over an hour away from her?). I didn't want to impose but he assured me she meant nothing. I asked him to come to Vermont. He said yes. Surprise!

I had spoken to him a few times, and made a trip to Philly that November hoping I'd bump into him. I was always driving to Philly hoping I'd bump into him, never telling DJ to just invite him over. Me- I always had that secret, hidden agenda. I always thought I made my actions looks innocuous. She knew. I should have just told her to invite him over!! A trip to Philly. Just visiting friends. A trip to Philly. Many trips to Philly. I was hoping I would bump into him and that was exactly what happened when I drove up one weekend. Surprise! And I hadn't even been able to fix my lipstick. I think he was as surprised to see me as I was him. After some casual conversation, he had to leave (the reason never mentioned). He was supposed to come back that night and party with the three of us but his girlfriend, ex-girlfriend! (damn triangles!) prevented him. She always seemed to be in the picture, though Jake assured me Matthew didn't want her in his life. Jake assured me that Matthew wanted her out of the picture completely. She was the Wicked Witch of the West and had him in a cage, locked up in her dungeon. Short strings. The evil puppet mistress. He was a spineless wimp. That evil puppeteer had him dancing, bending, kneeling to her every wish. Screaming! Cussing! Yelling! as was her usual form. She had probably threatened to kill herself for the tenth time! He had only broken away, freed himself from her sado-bonds once, with me (in NY)! A short leash she kept him on, with a spiked collar. I was disappointed he didn't come back that November night. I was disappointed she prevented him from doing so. I really wanted to see him. I needed to see him. His loss. He may have been with her but I know he was thinking of me. Jake comforted me with the knowledge that Matthew wanted to be here with me.

Anyway... the trio showed up in Vermont at three am, the weather was horrendous. Ice storm. Black ice. Hail. Sleet. They drove through it all, across Pennsylvania, into New York, up into Vermont. It was three am. I kept planning what I'd be doing when they arrived... I had a lot of time to think and imagine... curled up on the couch, watching television (but not comprehending what I viewed), having a drink (or two). The fire blazing. The lights low. I kept planning what I'd be doing so I would look perfect, act cool, be coy. I was so insecure. I wanted to look good so Matthew would be happy to see me.

It was three am- I had just dozed off. I awoke with a start as they knocked on the window. I must have looked a mess, my hair askew, my eyes tired. I hope my breath did not smell. I was so insecure... I gave DJ and Jake the only bedroom. Matthew was planning to sleep upstairs. Why did he want to sleep in the loft alone? We had already slept in the same bed. I had other plans. (My intentions were still pure.) ...As he helped me open the couch, I invited him into my bed, a bed opened before a roaring fire. I didn't want Vermont to be awkward. I hadn't planned on anything happening. I just wanted to snuggle next to him. He was a great person to cuddle up to! Vermont shouldn't be awkward... I invited him into my bed. It was an open invitation... a very pleasant evening (a very pleasant morning)...

We went to bed. He kissed me goodnight, on the cheek, and I turned my back on him to sleep. He had his back to me but them turned over and put his arms around me. I felt protected, safe. We snuggled. It was so nice sleeping in his arms... We didn't sleep. He was a gentle lover, caring, attentive, slowly turning me on, paying attention to every part of my body, devouring each limb, nibbling, and tasting the saltiness of my skin. He seduced me slowly... Matthew- who aroused me, who heightened my senses, who brought me back to feeling, to seeing, to touching. *Halleluiah! Halleluiah!* Matthew- the first man who went down on me and it was nice. The first man to go down on me and I... I let loose though I was so insecure and I felt fat. (This was probably the skinniest I had ever been- almost a size two and I felt fat.) I didn't stop him. He slowly turned me on, he slowly made me feel secure, he...we slowly consummated the weekend. It had been two years. I was ready, willing, and able with a little convincing. He slowly convinced me...*hal-le-lu-uuuu-ahhhhh!* It was cold outside, the air frigid, yet the fire roared, our passion inflamed, our bodies ignited.

...Stratton Mountain. The days were spent skiing, getting stoned on the slopes, yes- they were still potheads- all three of them! We would take the chair to the very top, ski down a bit, around a bend they would sit. I would be the lookout, a few yards above them. The three of us. DJ was taking a lesson so she missed out on the black diamond tricks. The first day was a trial, almost getting home, almost <u>not</u> getting home because the roads had turned into a bobsled run. The rain had just begun turning the pavement into a slick, dangerous, very dangerous hill. Finally, the snowplow... Still on nerves, we made it back down the mountain, onto the highway and sped south on Route 7. You know a bowl was lit up at the end of that hellish ride. Back at the house, getting stoned, even myself, one puff and I was gone... I didn't smoke. I didn't like to smoke. Pot didn't do anything for me. This was strong pot. I think it was Thai. I couldn't even cook dinner. They found me on the floor in the kitchen, my back against the stove, giggling, laughing, hysterical... One toke, okay it was one hit off the bong, one big hit that Matthew had pulled up for me. One hit... and I was gone... Regardless of the "hazy" atmosphere, these few winter nights were beautiful. Blissful. Matthew was a skilled lover, attentive, caring, compassionate.

...Pearl Jam. That is what I fucked him to the last night. Pearl Jam. Jake said I scared Matthew. DJ asked what got into me. They heard me in the next room. Pearl Jam- all night long... I guess two years is a long time and I just went wild, moving to the music, fucking to the music. Pearl Jam- its heavy metal head-banging music. To me- its heavy metal. Is it really alternative? Anyway, I let the beat take me away, carry me, move my hips, gyrate to the force of the music... Remember, Matthew was a lover, more of the classical type, *softly, softly, softly, higher and higher.* It's not that he liked classical music but he carried himself like the great conductor, made love like a symphony, made love like Beethoven's Ninth Symphony, *Ode to Joy*, building up (*piano, piano*), changing repeatedly during the course of the movement, making love, *piano, piano*. *Legato* (bound together, smoothly connected). He had slowly (*piano, piano*) convinced me. He quietly (*pianissimo*) seduced me. *Allegro* (happy). *Accelerato* (to a peak). The tempo changing. **Da capo al fine** (to begin once again). My body. His body. Pearl Jam. He wasn't familiar with this wantonness, my wantonness. It was complete abandonment on my part. Hey- he brought it out. I had had it under wraps... for two years. I hadn't felt... two years. Pearl Jam!! *and those American thighs...* Oops! wrong song.

4.

IN MARCH, I was supposed to join DJ, Jake, and Matthew in Philadelphia for a *Crash Test Dummies* concert. The trip got canceled because I had to work. My vice president was in town and I was told I needed to be there, always sacrificing my personal life for my professional one. Or maybe it was another set of circumstances that prevented me from going to Philly, seeing Matthew, continuing what was inflamed...

Maybe, the Wicked Witch of the West swept down on her broomstick, sending fireballs my way... The Wicked Witch of the West... always around. She was such a trash mouth, trailer park wench. She was so evil, castrating him continually with verbal tantrums. He was whipped, pussy whipped. He didn't want to be in this "relationship" with her. Jake told me he would have liked to pursue us. Matthew was powerless to escape from her. She had reaped him, stripped him of his masculinity, his virility. She cast her spell on him- the bad kind. I was too weak to fight, to rebel against her in a war of good versus evil. Good remained powerless (for the time being).

The Wicked Witch of the West- who blackmailed Matthew. Jake said she had something on him. What could it possibly be? What could she possibly know that kept him in this sado-masochistic coupling? She caught him and held him captive until he finally married her. She got what she wanted. Don't cross her! She's evil. That bitch. They have two daughters. She's pregnant again... Oh... and he's still spineless...

Pearl Jam.

Chapter
ii.
Let's Just Call Him...
He Whose Name Escapes
Me

Are you "comfy cozy" as your daughter is in her fleece pj's? This will warm up your tender loins...

1994. ONE KISS ON the dance floor and I got him more than happy as he rose to the occasion, still evident when he greeted my brother. "She'll chew you up and spit you out for lunch," my brother warned him, a smirk spreading across his otherwise serious face. "Beware," my brother whispered to his co-worker at Victor Capitol, a man who had more than his share of women (until he met me!). I was in party mode. I looked good, felt good, and took no prisoners. I was tired of behaving myself after the "Philly Mishap". It had been six months since anyone paid me attention, attempted to kiss me. I was hurt because I didn't have it in me to fight for Philly Cheesesteak's (Matthew) ardor. I was spending a guest weekend in Westhampton, Long Island at my brother and sister's house, a house shared with Billy and Naomi (whom my sister, Chiara "Kiki" set up), Peter, Little Debbie, Big Debbie, Dennis and Mary. All still single, all still waiting, all still wanting...

Our playful frolic left the crowded club, the dancing lights, the blaring disco beat, and continued on top of a monstrous sand dune (the landfill) overlooking what once had been Dune Road in Westhampton Beach. This summer's storm had finally (the opportune word) blown away the area into an inlet, an expanse of ocean (the Atlantic) meeting bay (the Peconic) where once houses perched precariously on stilts. As forewarned, the jetty's had not been built to protect the delicate land mass from the water's corrosive ways. We threw "caution to the wind", one too many drinks empowering us, climbing, groping, stumbling our way to the top, at least 100 feet up, not once thinking we were in harm's way, not once believing that the mass at any time could crumble in and bury us. (Well, at least he would have died with a smile on his face, mouth full of sand, and a full-blown erection- not that anyone would have noticed.) Like the mountain climbers on Everest, we had one goal- to reach the summit. Our motivation: happy hour, five rounds of drinks, coupled with our lustful demeanors.

One kiss and I got him hard, his erection a small pup tent. Round after round. Me on top, knees anchored in soft sand. Me on my back. Legs anchored, widespread. My hands digging in. Him utilizing the hill as leverage. Our momentum- a constant pendulum, up and down, down and up, backwards, forwards, a suckle here and there, a constellation-filled sky, the moon set, the sun rose. We had S-E-X. Sex of the safest kind. No birth control. No condoms. Nothing. Rated G: sex with our clothes on, the grinding of bodies, the marathon of positions and contortions, the exposed skin of a g-string under a little dress, lightweight khakis with no underwear beneath. Sex with our clothes on... Tease. Torment. His engorged self. Sex with our clothes on... Tease. Torment. Tantalize. My red-hot-as-cinnamon-spice self.

He- whose name escapes me. He- with whom I had a celestial experience- on top of the world. He- tall, dark, good looking, a player. He– I knew it would never go anywhere. He- had many women. He- I bet he still remembers me. He- he just happened. I only know that it usually happened after a long absence and trying to reclaim my virgin rights. He- one of many that so easily would fall into my lap- no pun intended. Did this make me a slut? I had yet to let anyone "dip their stick". I was good at safe sex- the sex with your clothes on kind. I was great at sucking face.

Only one month later, I went to Bellmore, New Jersey, the joke being that I always met younger men, boys usually five years younger than me. And that night, at some outside beach bar, on the waterway, beset with Jersey's best accents, a type of place that if you imbibed a little too much, swayed just a little to the left, you ended up in the bay. It was the type of place whose patrons were a similar bunch dressed in tank tops, cut off jean shorts, sweat socks and sneakers, and a little too much cologne mixed with sweat that hung in the humid summer air. It was the type of place that you could be lucky to find one well-dressed man (or boy) or at least a few dressed neatly in polo's and khaki's... And that night, amidst my district peers, the District Managers, and a few other well-reputed teammates, I met him, Stephen. Uhmn... Stephen #, maybe it was #7?[4] They were always named Stephen for some reason and they were always younger, much. He couldn't have been no more than twenty-one. I felt confident. I was out with a group. I wasn't looking. I can't recall how I met him. I can't recall who approached who. It just happened... on the beach, a late night walk. On the lifeguard chair. It just happened-well nothing did because I wouldn't let him. Tease. Yes, I was. One kiss and I got him going. One kiss and that's all it would be. He spent the night with me, sleeping on the living room couch while the other twenty-five found accommodations wherever they could. It was your usual beach house with bodies sleeping everywhere. It was the type of house that you never knew who you were sleeping next to or who you would wake up next to. He spent the night, half the night. I sent him home. He got too... Too bad. I sent him home. Tease. Yes, I was... but it was only one kiss...

One kiss and I got him going.

---

[4] Steve. Steven. The Stephen's. They are a chapter on their own that I'm not including. Let's just say that from the time I was a pubescent teen to my mid 20's, they were always named Steve. They were tall, short, white, always white, Greek, German, Irish, Italian, Jewish. They were all named Steve. I started fooling around with one of them (Stephen #?) when I was 19. I started sleeping with him when I was about 28, continuing for once a year birthday flings, dinners, "Want to see a movie?"-nights spent in where we never saw the end of (or quite understood) the plot. It ended when the last great century did. I didn't want it anymore. It wasn't passionate. It wasn't exciting. It wasn't devious since we got caught. Even the kissing became... mechanical. It ended at the last century. He still is a good friend, nothing more. Anyway, people will think what they want to think. They always did about us. They always did about me. They were always named Steve. I had "fuck me" indented into my forehead probably with the name Steve embossed on top.

Chapter iii.
Let's Just Call Him Marcus...
Do You Monch the Conch?

I stood at the bar on an island we were warned was tranquil and reserved - with no night life - an early morning rise and an early eve to sleep. Little did the mis-informers know, that only that afternoon, on the very day of our quiet and calm arrival, we were mistaken for breakers. Breakers? "Yeah- are you guys on spring break?"

I WON THE Christmas sales contest. In actuality, my team of
devoted GapKids employees had pushed above and beyond
normal customer service levels, to exceed our goals and win
for the Region. My prize was a choice of various clichés: 1. a
Tiffany gift certificate – as if I were to buy my own ring (if I
only had a man, then I could worry about buying my own
ring); 2. a shopping spree at a reputable department store;
and 3. a trip for two anywhere in the world. I found out later
that the world became a little bit smaller as limited by a $2500
budget. The world became smaller as the U.S. faced its own
turmoil. It was the year of the Oklahoma City Bombing. The
year that O.J. was found <u>not</u> guilty. The Pope made his tour.
The first cloned sheep became a novelty. Grateful Dead fans
would remain in a glazed-eye stupor as they grieved the loss of
Jerry Garcia. *The Usual Suspects* kept us in a state of who
dunnit?

Who would I take with me on this trip? Since there was no
significant other (no one important enough to be labeled as
such), I decided to take my two best friends- my sisters,
Chiara (Kiki), age 26 and Angela (Angie), age 25. So there we
were-"the troublesome trio". T-cubed. On Grand Cayman
Island! I was the ravishing redhead who hair was slightly
brassy. Angie was my blonde, bookish petite twin- 15 lbs
lighter. Kiki was your typical alluring brunette whose jet black
hair made a stark contrast to her yellow eyes, eyes which
united us as sisters, eyes which reflected the sun's rays and
emulated our own personal warmth. Another lovely adopted
sis– Bobbie, joined us. Troublesome trio plus one! On Grand
Cayman Island!

It was just our luck that the stud who mistook us for four
young, wild, and unencumbered collegiates was a local, a local
who knew all the hot spots on a nightly basis. Anyway- Angie
and Bobbie decided to take him up on the offer to ride in his
boat and go "nerfing"- a combination of water skiing and
surfing on the knees. I, being the mature one, decided to not
partake in these reindeer games. He seemed nice enough but
there was something to his devilish charm that didn't appeal
to me, something insincere. (We found out later he was the

island "player"- week after week luring the innocent to believe they were special- more like a special, limited engagement.)

Nothing to do in the evenings- we thought. On this first day, our itinerary was packed with night after night of debaucherous fun and frolic... That eve, I stood being flattered once again: "Do you have ID?" the bartender asked. At that moment, a tall, dark, and handsome boy-man, observing my license, whispered in my ear: "Are you from NY? So am I!"

And so began NONC- the night of no commitment, affectionately coined by my sisters (but pissing me off), who up until this moment had led pious, catholic school-girl lives (or so I thought). One, Angie, had a boyfriend of nine plus years. She, being younger than Kiki, had a better track record with only one "frat boy" encounter as freshmen at URI[5]. This encounter was a relationship my mother prevented from cultivating by sitting Angie and her (then) ex, Mitch, down at the kitchen table and talking to them about love, being true, commitment, etc, etc, etc... There is nothing better than being subjected to a mother's diatribe. I'm glad I wasn't there to hear her preaching.

The other sister, Kiki, had just broken up with her right arm of three plus years. She wanted to get married. He wanted to play. It was Kiki who had pushed him to give up his rising career as a waiter at Bennigan's, finish his degree, and start a job on Wall Street. Since he was now part of the "boys club" (though he could only fantasize with his Queens accent and street smarts to ever become part of the BBC: the Billionaire Boys Club), he didn't want to be tied down. Kiki was in mourning and needed a good kick in the ass- needed to meet someone who was worthy of her beauty and charm. Boys club, huh! when he could have had her!

NONC soon became WONC- the WEEK of NO COMMITMENT. I still wanted no part in their charades... What was I to do? I tried and tried to enforce their good girl image– you know, administer the catholic guilt. As the elder, I was definitely not

---

[5] University of Rhode Island

one to set the example but I tried. I could only reiterate my own romantic shortcomings-a perpetuity of clandestine maneuvers and passionate play toys. "Stop lecturing us," they said in that voice only understood by sisters: meaning- Fuck off!! "We want to have fun. We know what we're doing. Y-O-U are one to talk..." I saw a side to them I never knew. They were let loose and didn't want to hear it, especially from me the "free spirit". Mom was back in NY and if I was going to act like the bearer of moral fortitude, then I could go back to NY! Nice. I was only concerned for their well being. I didn't want them to make any mistakes they would regret (hindsight is 20/20, most definitely)...

Angie ended up (later) with TDH (tall, dark, and handsome) and began a fling. She would later confess to Mitch (her boyfriend of ten plus years), who would in turn humiliate her by forcing her to confess her actions to our parents and his. Penance? A few Hail Mary's couldn't help her. The humiliation was a far greater act of contrition. Mitch left Angie in a state of misery for many months as he baited her, cheated on her with two younger women at once (that's what we had heard), got even, bought himself a top-of-the-line BMW, basically treated her like shit for her one, and only one act (we consider WONC as a complete unit) of infidelity! It was too much of a burden for one small woman to bear. One night in a restaurant, as a family united in their sister's personal happiness, my brothers, sisters and I prepared the intervention. We informed Angie that tomorrow we were moving her out- no excuses, no exceptions. We were moving her out of their apartment (she was still living with Mitch)- and that would be that! Nevertheless, Mitch beat us to the punch. He proposed. Needless to say, we are not allowed to mention (in the slightest reference), this vacation to her husband, Mitch, the man scorned. Beware of a woman scorned? Men can act just as foolhardy.

Kiki would soon meet her prince charming- literally. He was a graduate of William and Mary College, presently in law school, but was a local whose father was the island's Governor? Barrister? Anyway- someone of high ranking official non-American status. His mother was of English royal lineage. At least this is the story he told us. A prince. We were all enamored by his charm, wit, and especially looks. Blue eyed and petite with a mole on his left cheek, he looked like a young, perpetually tan Cliff Roberts or in a conventional movie star sense, the actor from Love at First Bite-George Hamilton. I particularly liked him because he called and asked my permission to take my sister out the next day... Nick's sick, carefree, swinging lifestyle would eventually be the demise of his "relationship" with my sister. She never did reveal to us what happened in Hedonistic Jamaica- though she denies crossing the lines and "switching teams".

As for me and my NONC/WONC- lets just day vacation... Sloth was the SAE (another one) frat brother of TDH. TDH had been transferred by his company to trade on the island. Sloth was on leave (Spring break) from a Maine, marine-based post graduate school. His goal was to become an engineer on one of the big boats. Before he would ever be commissioned, he would first have to lose his nickname, Sloth. Sloth? What kind of name was this? (Years later, I would understand by his "in-actions" that he was appropriately nicknamed.)

Sloth had the cropped hair of a commissioned officer, dark, almost black eyes that looked deeply into me, the stout body of an offensive linebacker who had one too many beers (just one), but the speech pattern of a teddy bear. Teddy bear? Okay- teddy bears don't speak; however, they are cuddly, affectionate, and bring joy to the holder. He was my prize and I didn't want to play the game. And he was just the sort of man my mother expected me to marry...

(I said I had no significant other that deemed important enough to bring on this trip; however, I had been seeing, back home in NYC, "Mr. Dating Book of Etiquette".
You know- 1st date: drinks
                2nd date: lunch
                3rd date: dinner
Mr. Dating Book... this is main reason I wasn't looking. This is why I wasn't playing NONC/WONC.)

Are you still with me? I know- so many coexisting events...
Back to Marcus... Oops! Did I mention that Sloth's real name
is Marcus? He was christened "Marcus" when his sweaty and
swollen Mother was asked what she wanted to name her son.
He was dubbed "Marcus" (unintentionally) when his weary
and teary Mother read though watery eyes her Doctor's name
tag. He was named (accidentally) after the Obstetrician.
Marcus- my teddy bear... It was hot. The island breezes did
nothing to cool the tempered air... I didn't want to be dealt
into the hand at play. It just happened- a winning hand (or
not)!

It happens when you least expect it... How many times have I
heard that?

2.

AT THE LONESTAR Café... Angie and Bobbie were still satiating
their drunken palates. (We had started the night with Happy
Hour at some other hip happening bar, drank our first
MUDSLIDE, soon to be our favorite drink.) Kiki disappeared
with someone TDH said was married. Kiki did not know this.
"He's not a good guy." I got concerned and so out the back
door and to the lot I stormed. They were sucking face as I
pulled her away. I told him to leave her alone. "She can take
care of herself," he said. "No! She can't!" I yelled.[6] "Fuck off!"
he said. This was getting scary. It was a dark parking lot and
he was a stranger who could do anything. The danger level
was high. With that, TDH came to our rescue, forcing us back
inside. We stood in a circle so that drunken ass could get not
get near Kiki- She was in the middle, surrounded by TDH's
friends, one of them being Marcus... Hanging out, getting
drunk, having fun, the merriment continued as Angie and
Bobbie finally showed up... Last call... Jerk chicken on the
side of the road (it's like ordering Souvlaki from a street
vendor)... The six of us taking a "short" walk back to their
townhouse for more drinks. New Yorkers- we were used to

---

[6] I was always protecting Kiki from the assertive actions of the men who tried to pick
her up. I was always being "Mom" but it was for her own good, her own drunken good.
Anyway, she let me. She liked having her big sister protect her.

partying till four am. Walk. Walk. It was far. "Where do you live?" "Just a little while longer." "It's far." Bobbie and I kept trying to vie for Marcus's attention. (Hey- I found him and all of them first.) He was talking to her. I was behind. I caught up or he slowed down. He was talking to me. He was in the middle of us. Walk. Walk. Walk... "Where do you live?" "Just down the road" "That's it! Something's not right!" someone said (not me). "Good night. See ya. We're going home." Angie and Kiki started to walk away in the opposite direction. We had to catch up. It was a long walk. 15 minutes later... 25? It was long walk. Where were the cabs?

Screech!! They came driving up. "Get in." "No." "Get in. We'll take you home." "Okay," someone said and we all piled in (me on Marcus's lap). It was one-for-all and all-for-one. No one was allowed to walk alone so we all had to take a chance, a chance with these "sober" strangers.

We ended up in our gross hotel room at the Holiday Inn, gross because the maid never showed up until after four pm, gross because it faced the parking lot, gross because it definitely wasn't a five star, let alone a four star resort. The only reason we stayed was because it did entertain one of the best weekly happy hours. Anyway, TDH and Marcus stayed. Bobbie made a move on TDH. He ended up jumping out (or being thrown out) of the bed. Marcus and I ended up in the same bed... sleeping.

It was a hot and sweaty night. And wet... the bed was soaking wet. This is what woke me. I was stuck in a corner of the bed because I didn't want to sleep in the wet spot. He was soaking wet. What was up with that? Hot flashes! Did 26 year-old men get hot flashes? Night sweats? I knew I was hot and one kiss could get them going but we hadn't kissed. Did he have too much to drink? It was his birthday. It was gross. He stripped down to his boxers. He went to the floor.

Hot! Hot! Hot! I followed him to the floor and he hugged me as we slept. Early, early, early as the others lay quiet, TDH was snoring in between Bobbie and Angie, you could hear, if you wanted to listen, soft sighs escaping my lips, as he (Marcus) turned me on, he expected nothing in return, as we kissed and grinded our way to a mutual climax, me stopping him, he continuing, he expected nothing in return, he continued to please... as the island awoke...

(Where was Kiki? Who was she with? Oh yeah- on the floor, on the other side of the bed. Whew!)... And that night began Nonc/Wonc. I wasn't expecting it.

3.

I WASN'T EXPECTING it. I was too old, too mature to be a "breaker", having a fling. I wanted to settle down, get married like all my friends. I wasn't expecting it. The next day, Kiki, Angie, and Bobbie went swimming with the stingrays. I stayed behind. I was too hung over and I hated boats. I got seasick, okay. Anyway, I spent the day at the beach. Marcus had said something about hanging out at the condo. I wasn't ready to take that walk, two miles down the beach, to see him. I wasn't sure if he even wanted to see me. Around four pm, I got restless. I walked the two miles, along the water to Treasure Island, the infamous resort we almost stayed at. I found him alone at the pool, reading. We sat. We talked. It was innocent. He asked me what I did. He asked me about my family. I asked him about school. He was impressed that I understood "torques". It was nice. The getting-to-know-you kind of conversation without prying too much. It was a beautiful afternoon on this sunny island. It was the perfect day to spend alone with him.

"Little Buddy"[7] showed up and we started to drink, Banana Mudslides, since all Little Buddy did was drink. I was having a nice time but I knew I need to call my hotel and check in with my sisters. Kiki was mad that I was partying without her. I told her to walk down the beach. Ever the exercise maniac, a two mile walk was a piece of cake in her eyes. She must have jogged the whole way because before you knew it, she was sitting beside me, drink in hand.

---

[7] Little Buddy is another Frat Boy from UConn.

We started to have a great time as the Mudslides enhanced the jovial arena. We called the hotel. Bobbie was still shopping. Angie was mad because we had made plans for happy hour that evening at the Holiday Inn. She was angry that she was stuck, alone, in the gross hotel room while we were in the midst of an impromptu party. One-for-all and all-for-one. "Sorry. We have to leave. We are going to be at our hotel tonight if you want to join us."

I don't think we saw them that night but this was the night Kiki met her Prince. It was only the second night of our vacation. She had been dancing with this tall, blonde man. Bobbie was also dancing with this beautiful brunette. The music played some Calypso tune, the floral-shirted, sunburned crowd swayed as the sun set across the ocean. One of the men yelled "switch" and Kiki ended up with Nick, Bobbie with Blondy. Nick spent the night with us. NONC! Bobbie didn't. NONC!

I liked Nick from the beginning. The next afternoon, he called and asked me, as the "matriarch', asked my permission if he could take Kiki out to dinner. I liked him for knowing I was protecting my sisters, keeping an eye out for them. I liked him because he treated my sister Kiki with respect and also the rest of us. Kiki disappeared. WONC! and Bobbie, Angie and I went to a barbecue. TDH had invited us the night before. We drank Mudslides. We ate the usual barbecue cuisine. We drank more Mudslides. TDH had a strange group of friends coming and going, reminding me of those California blondes... little surfer dudes, big surfer dudes. Something was going on, something illegal. Someone was probably dealing drugs. We never asked. We didn't have to because none us were interested in doing drugs. Anyway... we ended up at TI's, the local disco, walked right through the condo's backyard to get there. Angie made her move. Or I should say that TDH got excited by Angie's dancing and made his move on her. NONC!

I spent the night with Marcus, nestling, on the unopened couch, his arms around me. Angie spent the night with TDH

(WONC!) Bobbie went back to the hotel and spent the night alone...

We sunbathed golden each day. We partied and drank Mudslides each night. No matter where we were, Kiki, Angie, and I would get in our usual sisterly argument, probably because I was being overprotective. We'd huddle together, arm over arm, in a close circle, three miniatures, as we fought and discussed who was going where and when! No outsiders, including those that had initiated these discussions, were allowed into our sisterly bond.

As for Nick... I said, I liked Nick. He invited the four of us to dinner at his home on the other side of the island, a mansion overlooking the ocean, a Jacuzzi/hot tub in the back yard, Cayman Nanny/Cook at our disposal. Nick was such the gentleman. He was good at entertaining. He was great at conversation with all of us even though he was captivated with Kiki. He made us all feel welcome. (I wanted to be with Marcus, though.)

That eve we went to another disco with Nick and our newfound friends, Marcus and TDH. Little Buddy was in his usual drunken stupor and so remained behind.

Marcus hated to dance but he pulled me out and slowly twirled me around, protectingly held me in his arms, oh-so-closely, lovingly kissed me. I was in love. I felt it. A small twinge. A strong beat! He made me feel good. I knew he cared. We strolled back to my hotel, along the beach, after I made sure my sisters were in safe hands, and Bobbie was happy.

This was the Cayman Islands, no crime, no drugs (supposedly). A safe haven of pristine beaches and happy locals. Marcus and I walked along the water. We stopped and pulled two chairs together and gazed upward at the stars, as he held my hand. He pointed out the constellations that adorned the clear, crisp sky. We kissed. I liked when he kissed me. He had a way about him that was so gentle, tender. Marcus made me feel good. He wanted to please me. I wasn't comfortable with my own sexuality because I wanted more than a fling. He was trying to get me aroused. He didn't want me to STOP when I pulled his hands away. I stopped him because it felt good, too good, so secure. I couldn't handle it. He wanted to please me and expected nothing in return. He wanted to please me. I wasn't comfortable with my own orgasms- too powerful and the full release was something that I held back. Full release- it would open up a slew of other well kept secrets... Maybe it was just that I was a nice girl (at this time). I didn't want to be hurt. I knew I felt something for this man and wanted to behave appropriately. Marcus. He could possess me and he knew it. He wanted to please me. He wanted me to feel! I kept holding back but he slowly convinced me... My teddy bear. We snuggled and fell asleep on one chair, on the beach of another hotel. No one slept in the gross room that night.

The days were spent sunbathing. The nights were spent drinking Mudslides. WONC!

On one eve... Marcus and I decided to take a swim in the alcove, a few hundred feet from the condominium. I neglected to wear a suit and borrowed his boxers and t shirt. It was just him and I as the crowd (eight young) cheered us on from the beach, thinking we were doing it, thinking we were doing it as he held me suspended in his arms, buoyed by the salt water, kissing, just kissing. The spring breakers soon left, probably disappointed by our PG-rated performance. They left us to be alone with the moon, its perfect full circle casting an effervescent gleam on the two of us. They left us to be alone as I held his neck and floated on top of him, as he treaded water and doggy paddled to stay afloat, the current slowly pulling us into the deep, dark, and unknown... A romantic midnight swim in the Cayman Islands, the reef protecting us from the perilous ocean deep. If only we had gone skinny dipping, the water caressing our bare skin, an added tingling to our otherwise aroused beings...

I took a shower. He walked in thinking it was his right. "Get out," the demure me said as I covered myself with the transparent curtain. We had not slept together. Who did he think he was? We slept that night in his bedroom as my sister

Angie continued her WONC in the next room. The beating of my heart continued to escalate...

4.

THE BEATING OF my heart escalated as I got to know Marcus, got to appreciate his kindness, got to appreciate him...

On a day in which I wanted to spend with Marcus, a day which he had planned his fishing expedition, a beautiful day on this island of hot tropical breezes... The troublesome trio plus one had been invited by Nick to seek a new adventure: nude snorkeling on a private beach. I didn't want Marcus to know. I didn't want him to think of me as "wild". I didn't want him to believe I was into WONC...

And so there we were, on the north side of the island, trudging through the water one mile to a desolate cove, a small expanse of sandy beach. We had to be careful. It was illegal to nude sunbathe on the island. This was a trip of firsts for me: the first time I went nude bathing, the first time I bared it all, the first time I bared it all in front of my sister's "boyfriend". Bobbie and Kiki had no issue with stripping off their bikinis. They were exhibitionists, always parading around nude. Bobbie was a bodybuilder with a kick-ass physique (though her breasts were a little small). She had the type of body, a lethal body, that could make men salivate and little boys ____. Her jet black hair grazed the back of her knees. She possessed the look of a wild, exotic flower- ripe, ready, in full bloom.(Unfortunately, antibiotics had left her teeth "dirty".) Kiki- was Kiki. As my mother once said- Kiki was able to get anything she wanted with the bat of an eyelash, the toss of her hair, a quick little smile. Angie was a little bit uncomfortable but she had an adorable 100 lb. body and a taught stomach that she could make ripple. As for me. I wasn't fat. I was in shape but I hated my body. I hated my carbohydrate tummy and my tubular breasts. Oh well. It was only my sisters (and Nick). One-for-all and all-for-one.

Nude snorkeling was exhilarating, a lot of fun but I had to be careful not to sunburn my butt, my big white butt. Nick made sure we all put lotion on. (Nick made sure he got a chance to put it on us.) There were only four sets of gear so Kiki volunteered to stay behind. It was her boyfriend but she would venture later, alone, with him. Nick must have loved it. Him. Three naked women. Alone. Way out to where the ocean broke over the reef. I was afraid of sharks. "Don't worry. They can't swim over the coral." He had a blast, diving under, flapping his body like a porpoise as he swam down deep to touch the starfish, to point out the coral, flapping his six inch flaccid penis as he swam down deep. None of us missed this. We all commented on it later, without Kiki hearing us. It was an experience. Snorkeling. Nude snorkeling.

Nick. The deserted beach. We almost got caught. Once. The kayaks glided by. We quickly lay down on the towels and covered up our red asses. Luckily, Nick had spotted them before they turned the bend. How would we have explained this afternoon to our parents if we had gotten arrested for nude bathing? An experience- one of many...

I wanted to get back though. I wanted to get back to see Marcus. I was enjoying myself but my mind was focused on Marcus. It was his last day. It would be our last night. It was our last night in this island of passionate provincial souls. I wanted him. I wanted to sleep with him to the full extent of its meaning. I knew he cared and I wanted something to remind me of "us"... Nick took us to watch the sunset at Rumpoint, the furthest unclaimed spec at the end of the island. As beautiful as the kaleidoscope of colors extended pleasantly over the water, that patchwork quilt of red, orange, and pink draping the sea... I couldn't enjoy it. I wanted to see Marcus. "Come on. Let's go," I kept pleading... I called him from Nick's house and left a message. Stupid me didn't leave the correct phone number. Tick tock. I was getting antsy. I wanted to see Marcus. I was the ultimate in being a bitch. We finally left and I made Nick stop by the condo. Ding-dong. No answer. Where was he? I saw the note as I was leaving:

Rossana,
I tried to reach you, but was unsuccessful. I was forced
to go out. I'll see you out or talk to you later
Marcus
PS Cranked Conch or Top Falls (TI's)

After taking showers and changing quickly, after two hours of waiting for Bobbie... it always took Bobbie so long to get ready! "Hurry Up!" "I have to dry my hair!" Her hair took forever to dry since he fell down to her knees. "No you don't! Hurry up!" You know who was doing the screaming! "I'm trying." Why did it always take Bobbie so long to get ready? She was still primping while Kiki, Nick, Angie and I sat drinking Mudslides. I was anxious. Why did it take Bobbie so long? She had been the first in the shower. Oh, yeah. She didn't have sisters. She didn't know what it was like to share a bathroom with three others. She didn't know what it was like to be yelled out by the eldest to "HURRY UP!! Get out!"

We finally made it to TI's. I kept searching for Marcus? Where was he? Where had he gone? Of course I wasn't having a good time at the club as my mind became preoccupied on finding him. I kept searching for him. I searched frantically ignoring the crowd we had amassed. I finally left the club and walked to the condo, going in from the ocean path. I woke him up. Marcus had been sleeping there all along. Earlier, when I found the note, he was probably inside, asleep. I knew I should have gone around to the back, the door that faced the ocean, the sliding door that was always ajar. I could have been with him these last four hours instead of wasting the time, in a dark club- looking, searching, pining, wanting...

It was all wrong. I had woken him from a restless sleep. We curled up to each other in the bed with Little Buddy sleeping next to us. It was all wrong on our last night together. Everything up until this moment had been romantic, an affectionate handling of each other, at least a respected friendship, more than friends, a commitment of the heart (or so I believed). We had not yet consummated our time in this tropical paradise. We should never have. It was all wrong as his kissing became mechanical, as he took out the black condom, yes, it was black, as Little Buddy slept (?), as the black condom broke and we stopped what we were doing. Was this a joke? Were we back in college, with the roommate in the next bed, in a house full of fornicating frat boys? He had always been so tender. This was our last night. There was no compassion, no romance, not even carnal sex. He was a different person. It was all wrong as we went into the living room and pulled out the couch (for the first time). He was distant. It was all wrong, a horrible ending to our love story.

5.

IT WAS A horrible ending to our love story. I spent the last day upset, thinking about him, being nasty to my sisters, even getting into a fight with Kiki and Nick, the overprotective sister, the overprotective, very drunk sister. We finally got to meet the real Little Buddy, to get to know him. He was coherent enough to have a conversation with us as we drank Strawberry Mudslides, one after another, as I drank myself oblivious. I slept alone that night in the gross hotel room. I woke up and saw a scorpion on my bed. Was I about to get stung?

I kept thinking about him on the plane ride home. I kept thinking about him as I touched the beads he had placed on my neck. I kept thinking about him and that day I gave him the coral which I had found while nude bathing, a piece of white coral in the shape of an anchor. It was perfect for him, my military man. It was a horrible ending to our love story...

The answering machine was blinking. I could see the red glare from under the doorway as I entered apartment. "Hi. It is me, Marcus... I wanted to welcome you home. I hope you had a good flight. Peace!" He called!! He called!!! Thump, thump, thumpety, thump. His letter arrived a few days later...

20-3-95

Dear Rossana:

Please do not get the wrong idea. This is undoubtedly the first letter I have written in years. I would have called again but I don't want to seem like a bother. I just wanted to let you know how much I enjoyed meeting you...On the plane ride, I had a lot of time to think and I feel I owe you an apology I acted insincerely on our last night together., something I regret very much. My excuse in the morning wasn't exactly truthful. This is difficult for me to say, knowing it was your week of no commitment, but I found myself falling for you in a big way. I knew that I wouldn't be seeing you again, anytime soon and I guess I just snapped. I am truly sorry for my behavior for if I could do it all over again I would. as mushy as it sounds. Try and control your laughter. I understand that this doesn't exactly coincide with your WONC week.... I hope you had a pleasant journey home with your sister- I know how you ladies get-didn't say chicks! Thank you for the coral- I have it on my desk, Have a wonderful party... I find myself smiling a lot when I think about you. Thank you because this school doesn't give me much to smile about. You are truly a special person. And I feel privileged to have met you.... I hope we stay in touch. Take it light.

(peace sign)
Marcus
"Sloth"

Ps I am sober right now!
Pss OH yea- I miss you a bunch.

Maybe now you can understand why I felt something for him. Why I pined. Why I felt that heartbeat!! I wrote back, with deep emotion. There were no games, no pretenses. He initiated it. I wrote back. He never answered. I was confused and hurt. I kept viewing him as this lonely seaman, alone with men. Didn't he want a love interest in port? He was either on "cruise" or up in Maine. Lonely Maine. My lonely merchant marine. He never showed up at my party though he said he might. I kept dreaming... dreaming about this man, a handsome man in uniform, in his dress blues, turning up, sweeping me onto the dance floor as all wondered who he was? It would be my Cinderella moment. I kept watching the door that night of my party, my "Ladies in Red" birthday party, a party he said he wanted to attend, a party he promised to show up at.

My Ladies in Red/Men in Black(tie) Party was my 30th birthday party. The wedding invitation read: "Dr. and Mrs T. invite you to the wedding of their daughter Rossana Robin to H. Evan Knows"... On the flip side: "April Fools! Join us for an evening of Ladies in Red, Men in Black(tie)" My formal birthday bash was like a "coming out" party yet I was far from the debutante. My friend Julie mentioned it was the trendy thing to do- to celebrate adulthood, the coming of age with a big celebration. I was lucky that I was well-dressed the night I was introduced to the 26 year-old owner of the catering hall. The New York City nite clubs had disappointed me by increasing their costs with every added detail I wanted. Neverthless, Jack gave me a top of the line party at cost. I would have continued my school girl crush on him if it had not been for his comment that "women are only good to take on vacation." This turned me off and by my look he stumbled... "You know, I work all the time..." Too late. He would have to eat his words.

Marcus promised me he would attend. I started pining. I kept hoping. I kept looking over my shoulder that nite...

I may have spoken to him once after that night he never showed. He always said "maybe" which I interpreted as yes. I didn't realize this may have just been his way to keep me at bay. I didn't realize that this was a typical way to keep women happy- "maybe." I planned our May rendezvous. My imagination went wild. He was a lonely seaman and I wanted him to feel loved. I sent him the letter and planned it as such...

You're invited on a mission...
Goal #1 Be ready
Goal #2 Get there without getting lost.

I imagined it as his great fantasy come to life... He would arrive in Queens and call me from the corner pay phone so I could finalize the surprise. The front door would be slightly ajar. The note: "Stairs a Stocking" pinned just so.

On the first landing, a stocking, draped casually over a bottle of Veuve Cliquot, the open champagne bottle would be labeled: "Warning. Proceed with caution."

*A note pinned to the upstairs apartment door:
        "Opening this door will change your life."
*A card left on the kitchen door to the right:
        "Happy Hour" "We serve Beer and Conch"
*On the kitchen table, surrounded by candles:
        "Do you monch the conch?" "Not at this hour!"
        *On the bedroom door: "Passion's Playhouse"
        "Do you dare?"
*On the petal covered Duvet: "It's a roll in the hay...
        Will this make you stay?
        I think not!"
*The bathroom door: "Privy"ledges
        (you should come out smelling like roses)

I created the fantasy, our fantasy, his fantasy. I had notes to myself to remember to get the picnic basket from my sister, borrow the votives from my friend, obtain the silver wine bucket from Mommy, buy silk stockings. I wanted him to experience the fantasy. I had a wild imagination. I was "in love with the idea of being in love" as Cristina said. I was in love. I think I was in love. He initiated it. As was the norm, he never showed up. I was always setting myself up for disappointment.

6.

IT WAS ONE and a half years later that I was reminiscing with my sisters about our Cayman experience. We had been drinking Cadillac Margarita's (made with Cognac) at the corner Mexican bar. I decided to call him at school. 411 gave me the number I needed...

411 started what should have been left alone. I still thought of him. I still pined for him. I knew he cared. After-all... he sent me that letter. I thought he cared... He was still the lonely seaman, stuck up in Maine. One and a half years later, I picked up the phone and called him.

Fate. He was coming to New York for a wedding. He would be in town with all his friends and wanted to see me. Finally! Maybe... Was I dreaming again?

I had to work that day but left one hour early to meet him in the village, a few blocks north, but I took a cab because I wanted to get there. I was anxious for our re-union. The cab got stuck in traffic on 6th avenue. It wasn't moving so I got out and walked, ran! the last few blocks. I saw someone, with a bald head, on a pay phone. Nahh. That couldn't be him. I went inside the crowded, packed three-deep bar. I looked around and around. I hated going into bars alone. It made me feel uncomfortable, like I was out on "the prowl". TDH grabbed my hand as I was passing, looking, and kissed me hello. Marcus had gone outside to call me. So that was him. Strange coincidence. Two ships passing in the night... Out of nowhere, someone grabbed me from behind, picked me up and threw me over their shoulder, twirled me around. He finally placed me down and gave me big kiss. God! I was so happy! He was happy! It had been one and a half years. I changed out of work clothes into a navy stretch low rider, navy woven, with my belly button exposed just so. I had gotten very sexy since the current fashion dictated that I be a petite size four. Marcus noticed (and so did his friends). I really liked this group. All of them conversed with me. Oooh, Marcus. They left us alone, alone as we sat and talked on the swing, oblivious to the noise of a NYC happy hour in progress, oblivious to the World Series being aired. Me and Marcus. Finally!

It started in the afternoon around four thirty, continued elsewhere until ten and then I took control. My confidence level was high and I wanted him. I wanted him to make love to me. I wanted to consummate what should have happened in the Cayman's. "Marcus is coming home with me!" I dictated to his friends. I made the first move. I know this surprised him. This change in who wanted whom. In Cayman, Marcus always made the move, the first kiss, the first fondle. I usually pulled away. My confidence level had taken a sudden boost. I felt pretty. I felt sexy. I no longer had to worry about being the ugly one standing alone. I made the move. I was good at it. No one ever turned me down. One kiss and I got them going. One kiss and I got him going. We took a cab back to my brother's apartment uptown...

...It was fantastical night and an even better morning. I always get into trouble in the morning. I woke him up as I stretched my leg across him, as I massaged his strong ass, running my fingers gently over him. I aroused him as I climbed on top of his back and licked him from top to bottom. He could feel the silk of my blue negligee against his back. Sensual. Soft. I turned him over and kissed my way slowly up to the top of him and then down again. Up and down. I moved my body. Up and down he responded. AHHHHH. Marcus. Three times.[8] He gave me a bear-hug goodbye. My lonely seaman. Alone. In Maine. I slipped my g-string in his coat pocket. I wanted him to remember our night. I wanted him to remember me.

I wrote a journal during this time. Marcus was that important in my life that I wanted to remember him. The next few months are best followed by my entries, sober, drunk, happy, sad, mad! You can form your own opinions... I thought he cared. I thought he told me what I was waiting to hear for so long... I though he did. I really did.

---

[8] "It was the best sex I ever had," he would tell me months later.

-*October*

Marcus,

This is a letter you'll never read considering I made a fool of myself sending those 2 letters last year. It felt great seeing you-more than you'll know. I didn't expect the feelings to be so overwhelming. It seemed we fit so well together and your friends added to the mutual connection. I was a little scared, intimidated about meeting the boys but they're great. You're a lucky man to have friends just like yourself. I miss you and I only wish you'd let things steer their course in a natural direction. The distance should not be a factor. Once again, I could see by the morning, you were already distancing yourself- for reasons I do understand. Your career is your focus. Good-luck, my sweet friend.

Love, Rossana

PS Its very difficult the second time around to realize this relationship isn't going to be cultivated. I always will think about you.

PPS. I'm reading a letter to my mom- In it, I placed bets that our relationship will work.

He told me his Dad found the panties. I was flabbergasted. He was just kidding. He got a good laugh out of it.

10/24

I spoke to you today. I know now what you meant when you said you were miserable two years ago. How our feelings are reversed. I think about you and want so much to see you- to tell you how I feel. I love you and I feel it deep inside. I want to see you. I only wish you'd invite me up to Maine or to Connecticut. You'll be home for Thanksgiving. I wish you'd call. Sorry you

went to class and were thinking of me. I wish you'd run with your feelings instead of away. Come to me and let's live our lives together. We are such a fit.
-r

ps It's a shame that we can't be honest with each other. Why don't you surprise me and come to my Halloween Party- Two years is a long time to wait. It's in your hands sweet thing. If I have so many boyfriends, why am I alone? I'm lonely, I want you!

As usual, I continued to pine. I continued to wait. I continued to want. I kept dreaming he'd show up and surprise me at my Halloween party... Kiki, Angie, and I went as the three witches. You know "double, bubble, toil and trouble..." And what a party it was. The type of night where all just pass out one by one, leaving the candles flickering and the door ajar... What a party!

11/7
Marcus,

For some reason, you called me Saturday and how positive you were! When I said we had unfinished business, you replied with "who's to say its unfinished?" You asked me to be your "mistress" and live in Denmark with you. "Lover" would be more appropriate. If only you knew I'd do it in a second. I made a reservation (on Amtrak) to come see you, surprise you. When I called you on Sunday, you wouldn't speak to me. You said you'd call me later but you never did. I'm contemplating whether to tell you (about the ticket)- most probably our paths wont cross and I'll only dream about you.

You told me you wouldn't call me at Thanksgiving because you had to study. I hope you'll come into NYC one night.

Hey Marcus-I have this feeling you only look at me as this "wild thing". If you only knew I could be the lady you want me to be. I guess leaving the undies didn't do me justice.

-R

12/1

I sent you an invite- a dinner we should have gone to two years ago. Asking you to dinner was only a gesture. I called you twice, once in Maine, once in Connecticut. You weren't receptive. I wanted to see you but you blew me off. I understand studying is your priority but you said you'd be in Connecticut. You were still in Maine. You invited me to Connecticut. You invited me on Spring break. You invited me skiing in January.

I guess I tried too hard to speak to you. You started it. You undid it. It's not like you to be a dick and not call me. I guess Karen is pregnant or causing you grief. I only wanted to spend a nice night together, just the two us to see if... I only wanted to have dinner.

I hate you now. Two times is enough to be hurt by you.
-r

ps. You said you may come to my brother's wedding in Vermont

Pining. Wishing. Wanting. Dreaming. Can you blame me? The things he said to me. I couldn't help but falling for him, but why was he always so indecisive about his feelings for me? Help! You always want what you can't have...

12/16
The wedding was beautiful- too intimate for you to be there. [9] I hate you and can't stop thinking about how you hurt me AGAIN! Merry Christmas. Happy New Year you shithead.
-R

12/30
You were in NYC. You left me a message saying you wanted to meet for a drink. I got obsessive. I was at a party uptown and you were midtown. 3 CALLS! The first time, I spoke to you and then got cut off. I called back- the last thing you said before we got cut off was you didn't know where to meet. HELLO! Hello! Hello!! I called back three times and left three messages. One wasn't nice!

Tonight I called you in Maine. I went for margherita's with Cristina, Michelle, and Kiki. Yes, we were all fucked up. Terry said: "Is this Gina?" I replied: "No! It's the other one. Tell him it's the one he wants to go skiing with." Terry said: "I know he wants to go skiing still...." Well- it's not Karen! It's not Gina! You fucked up, Terry! Hey Marcus- keep getting laid-you ass. I hate you. I love you
-R
Ps when did you become such a dick??

---

[9] My brother married his Boston girlfriend.

I should have just forgotten about him. I believed in second chances. I remembered how he was, those few times we were together. Compassionate. Affectionate. I believed in the truth. I believed the things he kept saying to me. I believed in love. True love. Was I so naïve as to not have seen the truth? Is love really blind? I had 20/20 vision.

1/28

Marcus-

You told me you loved me, matter-of-factly. The conversation proceeded and I said "...and you know I love you. We have that special bond." You responded "me too". Later on, you told me you loved me. I'm beginning to believe you do. You told me you missed me. We have plans for Valentine's weekend. We have plans for Mexico. Cristina bet me $100 you don't show up Valentine's.

-R

PS You called me three times this week.

Was I blinded by love? Were my senses so dulled that I only listened to what I wanted to hear? Did I hear? Did he say what I had been waiting so long for? AGAIN?

I'm not crazy. My mind keeps talking to me...

7.
The Meaning of Vice
Marcus
(continued)

My mind keeps talking to me. I am not crazy, I keep reminding myself, just a little bit quirky. It's just that my mind moves so quickly and my actions are a close second behind. On the first eve, he said the words I love you (or so my subconscious heard). By the second eve, he wanted to get the hell out of there but a blizzard prevented him from leaving. The third day, we cut it short. I threw the teddy out the window as I drove away...

I THREW THE teddy out the window. Teddies... Once again, I guess I came up with the ultimate fantasy- our dream weekend, Valentine's weekend. It was really going to happen. We were finally going to get together this weekend. A weekend which was suppose to be a romantic adventure of love, lust, food (and sex) set in Vermont's pristine surroundings. The barn: a converted structure with cathedral ceilings, post and beam style (8*8's throughout that Bob Villa would be amazed by), a huge fireplace that extended the thirty foot height, a big bay window overlooking the brook below, two lofts, and a minor constant issue with flies and ladybugs. It was too planned- everything I did was planned. I wanted to... to emulate my sister's actions. Rich fell in love with her (Kiki). Why couldn't Marcus fall truly in love with me?

Doomed from the start...

2/8/97

m-

I spoke to you to again- I knew what you would say "Vermont is over eight and one half!" We fought. You asked me "would you drive that distance?" I answered yes. We continued to fight but you wouldn't let me hang up. I told you I couldn't keep defending you with my family. (You always promised to show up.) I made the mistake of telling them. You said that no matter what, we'd see each other. You wanted me to go to Portland - too far for me- I have to work Saturday and it would be too far to drive. I called you back later to say I'm sorry. Please don't disappoint me. I'll meet you anywhere as long as you make the plans (I love a man who takes control)- it's a Holiday weekend so I really don't think you'll find a hotel- a bungalow- anything. I want to see you and its only six more days. I love you. I hope its our beginning again.

-r

ps. I turned down a date with Peter this weekend. It's only you I want!!!

2/11
m-
I spoke to you today. You called me and apologized for not getting back to me yesterday. You're spending Friday with your roommate in Mass. Or somewhere. I'm so glad you're coming but I'm so scared about our weekend. It's the first time we're going to be alone. I hope you don't end up hating me. Here's to a great weekend and our future.
I love you,
-r

Doomed from the start...

I left the city later than expected because I was afraid to tell the little white lie (that my sister had gotten into a car accident) to my staff. (The little white lie proved to come true when two weeks later, Diana's (my seven months pregnant older sister) car flipped on an icy road with her two toddlers in the back seat. Everyone was okay but it was my first and last little white lie). From that day forward I went by my Mom's motto: "Always tell the truth. No one will believe you."

Doomed from the start... I didn't pack correctly- where were my long johns, turtlenecks (I didn't own), snow jacket, hats, gloves? Suitcase? I had everything (what little I didn't bring) stuffed into a shopping bag. What was I thinking (probably that I wouldn't need any clothes)?

I arrived in a micro-mini suit (short, short wrap skirt), fishnet hose (all the women in Italy wore them!), and high heeled loafers. The long, wool, black coat with a fur-lined hood was the only saving grace that protected my bare ass from frost bite. I was coming from the city and dressed downtown funky as expected. I didn't want to change because I wanted him to see me as the executive I was. I chose that outfit very carefully that morning. What was I thinking?- I was going to Vermont. Snow. Ice. Cold.

I got into town and drove around. I went looking for him in the only bar- a micro brewery. He wasn't there. I drove around for another 15 minutes... Maybe this was just my way of prolonging the inevitable.

The house was dark. The roads were dark. Quiet. Too quiet after leaving the hustle and bustle of Manhattan. The setting eerie, at least from this city girl's perspective. Where was he? My insecure self wondered if he had changed his mind? Did I owe Cristina $100? Could he be so callous and not show up? Or worse- was he in an accident somewhere between New Hampshire and here? Where was he? Our meeting time had a 30 minute allowance + or − and he was late.

I was leaning over the trunk, looking for the flashlight, when he appeared out of nowhere. "AHHHH!" I screamed. "Where the hell did you come from?" (As usual, off to a wrong beginning- my mouth running rampant. I imagined our greeting as a lasting hug, a soft kiss hello, the warmth of friends and soon to be lovers...) "I was waiting in my car in the driveway (100 yards away). I drank half the bottle of vodka waiting for you." Was he drunk? I didn't think so- he was in college - high tolerance - he could handle his liquor.

Doomed from the start... the house was filthy. Left in a disparaging state by the tenants- I knew my Dad shouldn't rent to college kids. The ladybugs decided to be a nuisance- buzzing about. Weren't lady bugs a sign of good luck? Why were these dropping dead by the handful??

I told him to sit and make drinks while I went (immediately) downstairs to get wood from the basement. I trudged the heavy logs up the steep stairs still in heels. I made the fire in my fishnet hose. Role reversal. I was so stupid. If I could only have separated myself from the manager I was and be the femme fatale I could be, I may have won him. I was still in that delegation mode. I was still in that NYC city mode. I was still

being the type A personality against his laid back self. Relax??
I didn't know what those words meant.

The only thing I wanted to do was be in his arms. Have him
kiss me... Doomed from the start as we became intimate. He
said that sex should be fun. Fun? What did that mean? I
thought sex was supposed to be passionate. I couldn't imagine
laughing at him as he entered me. We had already slept
together. More than once. Why was he springing this on me
now? (Oh yeah... my book. I wanted to write a book on "what
makes a woman good in bed" from a male perspective. I was
interviewing all the male friends I knew. I was good at asking
questions, making them feel comfortable, making them open
up. Hell- it was research and they were intrigued. Hell- they
were so egotistical as to think they'd make it into my book.
They started telling me about their best sexual experience but
I turned it around. I wanted to know what makes a woman
good in bed.)... Anyway, someone made the first move.

Too planned. I was trying too hard instead of just letting
things be. I wanted the ambiance to be conducive to us falling
in love, to be perfect. And I was like a nervous little girl,
awaiting that first kiss... giggly... saying stupid little things...
rushing to get this weekend going... Doomed from the start...
The heart shaped homemade cake had too much rum, like
biting into a sweet tart. The teddies were too sexy and
provocative- think Frederick's of Hollywood over Victoria's
Secrets... The gift I bought (silk boxers with hearts) made him
uncomfortable- a short ride. The lasagna I cooked- let's just
say that, once again, a way to a man's heart isn't through his
intestinal tract, especially if he is lactose intolerant. He was
still very polite considering the circumstances of my failed
aphrodisiacs. I didn't need them. Just the fact that he was
alone with me should have been enough.

Doomed from the start... Maybe, REM's "*Everybody Hurts*"
playing all night long (I had hit replay, accidentally) had
something to do with it.

2/17
m-

It hurts a lot knowing you gave me up in one day. I guess we're not compatible. I was only looking for conversation, for me to make you brunch and dinner... I whispered in your ear (I think I did) I love you because I felt it was right. You gave up on me. Only the night before you spoke about moving to Thailand and having me there for you to take care of. Were you leading me on? When will I meet your parents?

Somehow we got on the subject of children. Amalia-my child's name. "Amalia A -," you said. I wanted you to make love to me. I believe you did. You even bought me a valentine gift so I believe your expectations were as high as mine. Was it the lasagna? The cake?

On that second eve, what led you to say that we're nothing alike... I called you into the bathroom not to show you (my body) or invite you in but to talk to you. That's when you stated we should be friends, amidst the candles, the wine you declined, the steam from the hot bath... It hurts because I love you and I know you care about me. You distanced yourself again.

Why did you agree to meet me? Would Portland have been better? It hurts so.... The pillow in between, the pulling away, the sleeping opposite. Why were you so repulsed by me... I hate you. I love you. Its best we try to be friends. You should have let things be.
-r

It was on that second day that I understood the meaning of his nickname, Sloth[10], when he didn't want to do anything except watch Nascar, his passion. Passion that should have been directed at me, with me. I convinced him, by whining and yes, nagging him with a smile, to get up, get dressed, to go to the expensive (money wasn't an issue) brunch at The Equinox Hotel. He didn't want to be there, evident in his scowl. The polite self forgetting his manners and embarrassing me by pointing at a stain on my pants as we waited to be seated. He was clean in a crisp woven shirt, creased khakis as if he had just had them pressed, short neat hair. I was disheveled-swollen eyes from the dust and ash, the wild bedroom hair, stained pants (toothpaste?), a vintage beaded sweater (only on the cuffs). Mr. Preppy and Ms. Downtown. Different as evident in our style of dress... Different as evident in his reserved personality (sans alcohol) and my upbeat attitude. Different as slovenly is to lively! They say opposites attract, don't they?????

We didn't wait to be seated. We went back to the barn. He watched television. All day. I tried to find things to do, like clean up dead ladybugs. He didn't want to eat though I heated up the lasagna, placed chips and dip before him... He didn't want to play games though the table was set with a 3'*3' backgammon board, the toboggan begging us to take a ride down the snowy embankment. He didn't want to have sex or snuggle or be affectionate even though his erection sprouted the moment I cuddled up against him. He only wanted to watch Nascar... He didn't want to be there- with me.

What happened? Did I snore that first eve? The Doctor prescribed a new asthma drug that I was taking daily. The little white pill was supposed to help me breathe not hinder it. Did I snore because of the dust and ash? Did I snore because of the dirt left behind by those collegiates?? Wait! that shouldn't have mattered- we were drinking and everyone knows that alcohol relaxes your throat muscles and tongue-causing the snoring.

---

[10] Sloth: one of the seven deadly sins, a vice; the avoidance of physical or spiritual work, lazy.

Maybe he couldn't imagine being with someone like me- heavy breather for the rest of his life. What he didn't realize was that the heavy breathing may have been an unconscious reflex related to our lust... Farfetched, but my imagination was powerful...

I wanted it to be perfect, our weekend. Why was my body not behaving the way the prescribed medication was supposed to make it? Why wasn't I perfect this weekend, our weekend?? And we had agreed to meet in Cozumel in March...

8.

THE CASA DEL SOL di... something or another. The name doesn't matter. He thought we were at different resorts. Did he purposely book himself elsewhere? Or did he mistake the name since they both had "del sol" in them. Little did he know that in January, I had changed my reservation. I found out there were, indeed, two different resorts and mine was five miles away, in a desolated strip, too far even from the town. I wanted us to be at the same place since we had planned this vacation together when things were looking bright in our future.

The Casa del Sol di... Strange coincidences. Kiki and I were originally on the same floor, in a room next door to them. We then moved due to some issue, probably the view. Strange coincidences. On that first night, Kiki and I went into a local bar. It was empty so we continued on down the strip to find something hopping. Marcus had been drinking, alone, in that bar all night long. Two ships passing in the night... Why couldn't fate have let us meet?

After the cab dropped us off, I needed to know if he had arrived. I had felt his presence and so I asked at the front desk. They even gave me his room number. I wasn't being the stalker- I just needed to know. Anyway, my sister Kiki was there to protect me. Should I knock on his door? Should I break the ice? Kiki emphatically wouldn't let me. She said: "If he's here, he'll find us." I should have knocked and thrown propriety out the window.

What a disaster from the beginning. Kiki said some guy stared at her as she passed him near the elevator. We thought we saw Marcus and that same guy as we passed the pool on our way to the beach. Marcus was sleeping but his roommate kind of stared, again, the same way he had at Kiki that morning. They were far away. Was that really him? "Lets go over," I said. "No," she replied. "He'll find you." My mind was preoccupied on finding him and making right our horrible weekend, putting behind me what is probably the most embarrassing moment of my life.

One hour later, he came down to the beach, stopped, looked at the water, turned right, up the three steps, meandered over to the bar. (We were off to the left.) Was he looking for me? Or just getting a drink? Wait- they had two pool bars... "Should I go over?" I had to use the bathroom anyway. Should I go over? I would have to pass him. Damn it. I was wearing my new zebra bikini but I felt fat 'cause I wasn't tan yet. (Tan fat looks so much more appealing than white fat.) I hope the bathroom had a mirror. His back was to me. Maybe he didn't see me. Courage. Where was the "80 proof" boost I needed to break the ice? Just at the moment as I came out of the bathroom, doing a two step on the hot white sand, he turned around and said hello. (Did he have eyes in the back of his head?) He kissed me, a friendly peck followed by a hug. How nice. The ice broken... at least temporarily. He walked with me to where my sister sat, dropping casually next to her on the sand, catching up, being fun, being the Marcus I knew. I was a "nervous nelly" but somehow began to relax. (It was an all inclusive resort so Kiki and I were imbibing on Coco Loco's and Rum Punches as we tanned.) And then she came down..."the little girl" as I dubbed her. She, with her cute pubescent upright breasts, her long, lean torso. She, who plopped herself right next to Marcus, practically on his lap! She, who was so stupid. What was going on? The tropical heat had suddenly gotten a chill. He wasn't receptive; in fact, he was uncomfortable. The sunny day turned dark and sullen as the clouds rolled in...

Two women. Or I should say, one woman, one child. I couldn't compete with that. I couldn't compete with... what was she? 16? 17? 21??

It was my own fault I lost him. I think he really tried to make amends. On that third day, during happy hour at the beach bar (by now Kiki and I had made lots of friends, a mixed crowd of eight single/married, exciting people)... he came up to me as I sat with my new friend, Sara. I had to make that one (okay, two) comment- "Marcus' robbing the cradle- he likes them young. Remember 15 will get you 20..." We laughed at my obnoxious, un-called for statement. I couldn't help myself. I had the green disease- I was jealous. I admit it. I was jealous and couldn't stop being so. He got mad at me, pulled me aside, and asked why I embarrassed him. Once again, my mouth running rampant... I was witty and wise or so I thought, the big smile hiding my hurt, insecure self. The one liners just kept coming... or was it the LI iced tea talking? Too bad. I was jealous. How dare he throw another woman, child! in my face!!

3/15/97

Marcus -

I gave you your space this trip. So much- too much. Kiki kept me away. I wanted to go to dinner with you all (when your roommate called) Tuesday but Kiki and I were too far gone (too many rum punches). You did show up late that night where I said we'd be.

You had lust in your eyes on your birthday but it wasn't for me— only Kiki. I had to put a stop to it.

I LOVE YOU and tried to show you I can relax. I can party- I can let you just be...Leigha really hurt-18!, seeing you hold her hand in the Plaza- a hand which should have been with mine, seeing her kiss you on the beach. I should have put my foot down. I only laughed at you as you told her to leave you alone.

You didn't want her but I know she had you for at least two nights. Did you sleep with her? Did you make love to her?

That 1ˢᵗ day when she sat next to you with her arms, around your shoulder "Marcus. Do I have pretty eyes?" she said after Kiki (stupidly) gave her a compliment. Were you embarrassed? What were you thinking with me sitting next to you? It hurts. It hurt. But I was lucky to have met some great friends. They kept me away from you.

I hope you got my note. It was meant to let you know I want to be friends.

Yes- I'm jealous. Yes. I'm not you. Yes. It can work.

Goodbye my sweet.
May we meet...
R-

And that was the end of him. Two years to the day. (But as you will be made aware- it was raining that year. They were falling in my lap. So many men. So many coexisting emotions.)

9.

I THINK OF him. I can't help it. He seemed sincere. I know when I first met him, it was only a vacation blunder– a week of relaxation that can cloud your judgment, a week of fun, carefreeness, being someone other than the true you. My problem was, is... I always show the true me. I am real. I speak my mind and then I let it go. He's a sweet guy, a boys-boy. I think that from frat house to military school, being an only child (sort of), he didn't know how to act or let his emotions follow their natural course. Boys-boy. More comfortable in his masculine role, masculine environment. Boys-boy. My teddy bear.

Anyway- he was too young for me. They were always younger than me- four years! I would have to wait for him to grow up. Do men ever grow up?

Chapter
iv.
The
Man of the Month Club

He whose name escapes me... and of course Marcus...One of many that so easily fell into my lap- no pun intended. That's when The Man of the Month Club started. This became a private family joke though my ever so Christian Mom did not approve. The Man of the Month Club, similar to the Book of the Month Club; however, instead of reading and living from the outside in, I was creating and re-writing the scenes, with one common denominator in my life- sex, well... kissing... but you know by now what that does to them: One kiss and I could get them going...

THE YEAR OF my 30th Birthday. What a year! 1995. Peak had
just begun...

I met them. They pursued me. I let myself be pursued though I
was still afraid. It became a scrimmage game of emotions- the
outcome irrelevant as practice makes perfect... My heart-the
ball: back and forth it went, kicked, cuddled, thrown, caught,
coveted, fumbled... I gave them 110% and the relationshipS
turned because, as usual, they took me in, I felt secure, they
made me feel secure, I thought they cared... and I wanted
more. The relationship flat-lined... It suddenly rained that day
(after a long drought)! You know- *its raining, its pouring, the
old man is snoring* except in this case it rained, the old man
woke up with a hard-on, and brought with him another to
cultivate my waxing desire, a deluge of continual boy-toys at
my disposal (but remember, temporary adornment- me!). The
Man of the Month Club just began one cold January (and I
never sent in the membership dues).

The first to be given the title was James. Mr. January. I met
him on a last minute vacation. I say last minute because my
Mom asked me if I wanted to go with the Alumni group trip.
She had a cancellation. I called up the District Manager, with
whom I had developed a trustworthy relationship. "I have an
opportunity to go to Paris." "When?" "I leave the day after
tomorrow." "Okay." Okay? It was January. It was retail. I was
surprised at her answer. Nevertheless, I had just finished a
sixty hour/seven week season of crying children, chaos, and
your usual Christmas madness. She added: "Go! You deserve
it."

It was the St. John's College Alumni trip that my mother
organized. James was there with his some of his family: Mom,
Dad, two younger sisters. I was very quiet during the first two
days, reading my book, not really socializing, being a lady,
dressing well. I could get dressed up again, especially after
wearing the GAP uniform of jeans and wovens for so many
months! I could get dressed up again! Suits. Scarves. Vintage
Jewelry. Dresses with fishnets. A very European look. This
was Paris- the center of the "fashion haute" and I wanted to be
a part of it, to become a fashion leader, a bit of the avante

guard. Okay, I was dreaming since I didn't have the discretionary income; nevertheless, I made sure that every day I was well coifed.

James... cute in an Italian (stereotypical) big nose way. He would make the perfect husband: same heritage, one of six children (two boys, four girls), same economic status. So many similarities. Okay– so I called him an asshole- but he was acting like one, bossing his sisters around, his mistake was trying to do the same to me. I was a boss. I was a manager by inclination. I was a leader. He was the same. He was such a domineering man... This is why I liked him. He was definitely one man that could tame the shrew (the shrew really only needed to be kissed)... This is why I felt he'd make the perfect husband. He was just like me in so many ways, the middle child, one who could stir up trouble, say the sort of thing to incite a family riot instantaneously, one who spoke his mind. I felt something stir inside of me- just a twinge but something and I wanted it to get stronger. He irked me. He got under my skin. When I returned to NYC, I told everyone I had met the man I was going to marry...

On one of the final nights, as he was getting off the elevator after an evening of the usual Parisian highlights, probably the Moulin Rouge or some other very French place, French wine... As he was getting off the elevator, he turned, pointed his fingers and beckoned me to follow him...

After a few pecks- he didn't like to kiss due to a former trench-mouthed girlfriend- ouch- that must have hurt! Anyway- he didn't like to kiss- this should have been a red flag, the small distant voice "warning. warning." Man who doesn't like to kiss=intimacy problem... WARNING! WARNING! in a best "Lost in Space" robot voice. After-all, I got wet with one tonsil-hockey play-in-action. WARNING. Warning. warning (fading)...

I gave him a in the bedroom.(I know... unorthodox behavior befitting a woman brought up in a strict catholic household.) I hated giving "head" but James was so controlling. He was the type of man (bastard) that would push your head where you didn't wish it to go. I hate men when they do that. Yuck! I say yuck 'cause it was yuck! After this eve, he wanted nothing more to do with me, the cold shoulder evident as we continued our vacation. Bastard. He never replied nor showed up to my "Ladies in Red/Men in Black Tie" party. I got even.

I got even. I am evil- well, just a little bit devious. I sent him a Valentine's Day card mailed from some address in the Midwest that postmarks it with Cupid's arrow. He'd never know it originated in Queens. The card was a sort of play on words- it was signed a secret admirer. If he ever found out what I did, his contempt would know no bounds. Nevertheless, if he had been smart enough, coy enough, or put his legal-minded thoughts back into his pants, he would have seen my name highlighted throughout the body. A legal-mind would have realized that the answer is usually simple, right before your eyes... Wonder if he ever it figured it out?

The cold winds of January brought a much brighter February with cupids arrow, aimed clearly at me. Mr. February: David, of the "Mr. Dating Book of Etiquette" status. David was a nice boy- Cristina's boyfriend's best friend. I was not supposed to meet him. To transgress- hooking up with David, took place on a blizzard night when the roads were closed (even in NY) and we walked the 11+ blocks to the local bar, Sly Fox for law school night. We being Cristina, her boyfriend, Bobbie (of the T-cubed plus one fame) and myself. Cristina was attending St. John's Law (in this age when everyone wanted to go to law school). This weekly meeting of friends at Sly Fox was a ritual that Cristina and her friends never failed to miss- to meet, drink, and discuss life outside of legalese. It's a shame that this groups' existence conversed in nothing but law, torts, contracts, and what not. Anyway, on this crisp winter midweek night, David just happened to be there. A non law-student- he knew how to speak of things in real terms- the real world at real speed. He made his move on the dance floor and well... he kissed phenomenally. I can't go into detail because it would be incestuous since David is now my brother-in-law. Cristina wasn't happy. She would continue to say: "I didn't want you to be with him. I wanted you to meet Arthur."

We were mutually compatible- the best friends' friends. When I returned from my Cayman extravaganza, I felt it was my duty to see him (though my mind was preoccupied with Marcus), give him another chance. I expected David to grab me, kiss me passionately since I was so tan and sexy and hadn't seen him in two weeks. As I straddled him on the rocking chair and kissed his neck, he was more preoccupied with the NCAA finals! I ended up kicking him out: "You should leave, now!" (Needless to say David and I didn't work out when I smacked him across the face at my 30th Ladies in Red Party for hitting on another woman (another Rosanna). A righteous indignation! Okay, I was out of line. I was drunk- two sheets, really three, to the wind... Anyway, I had been waiting for Marcus to show up... disappointed he hadn't shown up... Couldn't my fairy tale come true just this one time? After-all, it was my birthday...)

As you already know... the blustery winds of March had brought Marcus into my life. Mr. March: Marcus, my lonely merchant marine from Maine. He received his own chapter and deserved it since he transgressed multiple months and years. I pined for him through April's misty climate, hoping, expecting, wanting, waiting...

With May came the sunshine and a time of renewal... I was still pining, wanting, waiting, hoping...

Summer's onset brought me Stephen- Stephen #8 who literally picked me up off my feet at Casey's Pub to the tune of Blue's Traveler- "Run Around". You know..."*What's yours and mine the fishing's fine and it doesn't have to rhyme so don't you feed me a line. But You, why you wanna give me a run- around. Is it a sure fire way to speed things up when all it does is slow me down*". I always thought of this song as our song, our wedding song since he told me in his husky, scotch-happy voice I was his soul mate. No one ever said that to me (drunk or sober). Anyway, I thought the words to the song harmonized: "*what's your is mine, mine is yours...*" I thought he wanted to share his life with me. My musical ear was lacking (or maybe the one beer had gotten to my head).

On this Sunday eve, my sister, Kiki, and I went out for a casual beer on a weekend that began the onset of New York's summer invasion east. A casual beer. A casual night of ponytails and sneakers. A casual dance. Just the two of us, And, well, Mr. June with his red hair, red face, strong workman's arms, and a last name that was more Italian than my own. (June began a relationship that to this day we still play with.)

July. Stephen was still around in July. He came to the parties we held (I was a guest of) when he wasn't complaining about driving West in the summer traffic. Stephen, a landscaper, who owned his own business. Stephen, who never told me his age but I guessed at being seven years younger than me- accounts for his maturity (lack of). Stephen "8"- wants to be my soul-mate... but I had met another...

August. I was flirting with Peter (the same Peter of the Westhampton house). Not flirting (though a few may have perceived it as such since my innate personality was upbeat). Just talking. His mother had cancer. He knew he needed to prepare. He was great conversationalist. We'd sit for long hours and talk about life, family, death. We sit on the roof and look at the star clusters, the constellation groupings we couldn't name. He was such a nice guy. A big, adorable, vulnerable, stuffed animal. A plush. My plush?

With September, I can't recall... I think I'll call him Ron. He was Cristina's client, the plaintiff in some Admiralty Law case. Out of the blue, he asked her if she knew any single women and lo and behold my name came up. "She's nice." "She's a lot of fun." "She's Italian."... Our date ended before we even got to the appetizers. He called me the next day letting me know he went home, after our date, to find his jealous ex waiting for him. They got into a fight. Huhhh? One day, his ex-girlfriend stalked me at work; caused a scene. With all the wacky girlfriends I've met, what was one more added to my list?

Autumn begat a steady stream of nocturnal dalliances but I had reclaimed my title. Virgin was being bestowed on me, an exemplary title based on non- performance. Just kissing. Let's just call him... uhmn? Well, names don't matter at this point in time. Just kissing. The compliance factor remained steady at 95%. The compliance factor was high because I wanted it that way. Until...

The holiday cheer brought forth the holiday horns. Mr. December: Arthur. At my infamous Christmas bash, a party in which my hostess skills lacked since he monopolized my time, followed me around, upstairs, downstairs, into the kitchen, the bedroom. He finally cornered me under the mistletoe, between the office doors. Back and forth. Back and forth. A tennis game. Love 40. My friends got a view through the nurse's station window, that little window where payments are slid through (it was my Dad's former office). The waiting room (presently my sister's living room) was intended as a romantic nook, not the seating arena of a great match being played. Back and forth. Back and forth. Arthur and I went as I tried to get him off me. As I tried to get away. He went after me like a bitch in heat. He kissed me. I melted. Match! Game! Point!: mine. I took the winning swing. I kissed him back. One kiss and I got him going... under the mistletoe in Santa's workshop.

Turo- the Latin Lover, with his Cubano machismo. My bullfighter who hid behind his crimson cloak, ready to entice, torment, take me in... My "latin lover" who resembled Desi Arnaz, with his jet black hair, dark veering eyes, a strong karate-trained physique, and who could put on an accent that made you melt. My latin lover who made his move and I loved it. I love a man who takes control. He made his move and threw everything into the game. FAST! Fast! fast!! He swept me off my feet. Three weeks of hot! Hot! Mucho caliente! My body temperature would soar just sleeping next to him. He told me I tasted good. I wasn't yet comfortable with "69". I was intimidated by his gentle forcefulness. He made me feel secure, telling me I tasted good. He explained to me in a very scientific manner that the body responds to the foods that we eat. Therefore, a spicy dinner consumed by her doesn't always add up to a delicious dessert for him. Makes you want to think about your next meal!

Wet. Wild. Slippery. Powerful. He taught me how to defend myself against an attacker then pinned me down, kissed me, and let me go just as quickly. I wanted more. Take me, I'm yours! my body screamed. I wanted to succumb. Rape 101 and I was failing the course. One eve, we picnicked "Chinese" on a blanket in my bedroom, with the sconces casting a warm glow on our radiated faces. I fell asleep on the floor as he caressed me...

On one date, he took me to dinner and it wasn't awkward. There was nothing awkward about the moments we spent together. Carmine's. I wish he had picked a more romantic place. I hated tourist traps, tourist Italian family-style restaurants. The noise was so loud that we couldn't hold a conversation as I sat across from him. I couldn't hear a word so I took the initiative and moved beside him as he yelled into my ear. It wasn't awkward- he had this way of taking control. I knew he would pick up the check. His machismo called for it, demanded it. He was such a strong manly-man with charm. My Latin Lover. He really was the great pretender. He swept me off my feet. I thought he cared, picking me up at the subway, waiting on the platform with flowers, a full bouquet of roses (thank goodness they weren't red!). He didn't sit in his car or leave it idling on that busy, hazardous Queens Boulevard. He parked the car (miraculously finding a spot) and waited for me under the city streets. Romance wasn't dead. It was alive- in temporary mode, temporary passions, passionate temperaments, momentary adornments. Hot. Hot. Hot. Good girl/bad girl. I had been fighting it for years. I lost my crown, the exemplary title snatched away as the thermometer reached record breaking heights that holiday..."I'm dreaming of a hot, explosive Christmas..."

It ended Christmas Day. It ended just as soon as it began, as soon as I felt he cared. I gave myself to him, relinquishing my "virgin" crown. We made love in a bloody mess. We ended up in a fight, probably because he was being an ass the night before, not paying me attention, hanging out with the boys in the other room, smoking cigars, playing pool, drinking beer. I was dressed in my red satin mini with my Grandma's vintage beaded sweater over it. The great pretender. He always did this to the women he dated. Fast. Fast. For once, it wasn't just me. Christmas. What is it with the holidays?? My gift was one of those well-thought out personal items. Thoughtful, but I didn't want it. He made me open it. I never gave him his gift, the leather jacket that sat in my closet for three years before my cousin finally bought it from me. Return on Investment: 20%. Return on Self Esteem: -50%.

I spent New Year's alone. I liked being alone. I would continue to be alone for the next seven months, no dates, no dalliances, no broken heart. Besides, I wanted my title back...

Only one problem. I was in peak!

Chapter v.
Lean on Me...

Being on crutches helped me meet a man even though I was indisposed...

1996. THE SUMMER OF Fun except for the fact that Princess
Diana and Prince Charles agreed to a divorce. It was the
summer of fun for us. On one occasion, Kiki and I drove, a
last-minute, spur-of-the-moment decision, seventy-five miles
east. We ended up on the dance floor of one of that summer's
hotspots, a hotspot that would disappear before the next
invasion. Just the two of us, minding our own business as we
swayed and gyrated to the reggae beat. One by one, the men
came to us. I guess it was because of our apparent aloofness.
As I said, we were minding our own business. One by one, we
danced with them and said "thank you. Next!" They kept
coming. They kept watching, encircling us from above (the
dance floor). The women really hated us that night. We were
pegged, quite frankly, as those women you just hate: self-
assured, confident, with the "our shit don't stink" charm, an
attitude of knowing who we were. We were the type of girls you
look at and you just don't understand. You're consumed with
watching us. You ask yourself: "What do they have that I don't
got?" We mesmerized all. We didn't care. It could have been
our smiles that read approachable-unapproachable. Or maybe
it was our sisterly support system (iron-clad). One by one, we
danced with the men and then said goodbye. As I said, they
kept coming as if Kiki and I were a treasure, the prize to be
won. A little competition, a little testosterone play in action.

We eventually met someone that night, just dancing. Two men
who didn't like the "thank you, goodbye" attitude we had
shrouded ourselves with. I think his name was Kirby. Kiki got
matched with his friend, Treat. I had to pull him off of her
because he got too close, the dancing too sexual. I needed to
protect my little sister from his perverse advances! Kirby
interjected our fight, a fight that almost got ugly... He asked
for my number but I didn't like giving it out so I took his.
Advantage: mine. I never called him.

The summer continued as Kiki and I would jump in the car
and just drive (east), not knowing or caring where our
impulsiveness would take us... just drive (east), once (or twice)
stopping by our friend Toni's house... Toni's house was
occupied by her boyfriend and ten of his friends, ten men...
eight of which were single and good looking, single with "six

pack"-taught stomachs, single with full heads of hair, bulging bi-ceps... single and very young... Let's just say we got ourselves in a bit of a situation (or two) that Angie had heard about. She told us to stop embarrassing both Toni and herself. I can't imagine what she meant...

That summer continued even though I became indisposed. Being on crutches helped me meet a man. It was an amazing night- how each one approached and asked "what happened?" I fell off a mountain while repelling. I was skydiving and landed badly. I was water-skiing, took a jump, and hit the water incorrectly. Yes! Superwoman! Too bad I didn't have a great story to tell them. I couldn't lie. I didn't like making up stories.

Once again, Kiki and I took a drive to the Hamptons- that Summer of Fun when we did a lot of spontaneous adventures. I think we went to a club in Quogue- it had a big outdoor bar. The name escapes me, possibly the China Club (if the China Club still existed under that name). This was the summer of the attitude of "You, over here, now!" I looked good. I felt good. The shy, demure me was hidden behind a smile that demanded attention, a gaze that captured your undivided look, a body that looked great in a mini dress, a micro mini that is. (I had to lose weight for my current position as a General Manager in a Soho fashion boutique. The clothes were tight, form fitting. The clothes were designed for skinny, tall people. I was just the opposite. Thank goodness for low slung pants- they fit my new petite body.)

Anyway, she wanted to get me out since I had been in bed for two weeks, been hobbling around for three. It was the Summer of Fun and she was getting restless. What happened? I had the bones removed from my pinky toes. Too many corns. Too much pain. I worked on my feet. I was running around for a minimal of ten hours a day on marble floors in stilettos. What happened? "I hurt myself," I replied. Men. I met a lot that night. The adventure story would have kept them intrigued. Oh well.

This one was younger (not too much), in a band, and just lost his job. He approached me with a friendly smile, the type of smile you know is harmless. He looked harmless. He possessed that rock-n- roll kind of messy appearance. Hey- he wasn't a pretty boy but he did have a musician's appeal. In fact, he looked a little like Richie Zambora (Bon Jovi fame) except he wasn't as handsome. He played the drums. He lived in Queens, in a so-so area. It would never have worked. I would have been stuck in a grungy apartment with nightly gourmet dinners of Chef Boyardee and Ball Park franks served with the finest Schlitz beer vintage. Socializing would consist only in perusing acrid local bars. My once olive complexion would become sallow, beautifully enhanced by the smoke-filled pool halls I would patiently wait in as he played on and on, night after night, gig to gig. Get my drift. I had too much class for him. Bitch! I guess I deserve to be called that. I apologize for being blunt, but the differences were evident in the way he spoke, the clothes he wore, the car he drove. Bitch! Is that what you're thinking? That's what I would be thinking.

I gave it a chance. He liked me. He called me often. He came over frequently. And he kissed me back with the same passion, kissed me in places I had never been kissed. Anyway- I was lonely. My sister just wanted me to be happy and made sure I was courteous to him. So... I gave him a chance. He continued into the fall when the city started to wake up again, when the city was the place to be seen....

Okay- so it wasn't right when I went to see his band play in some bar on the Upper East Side... when I asked Simon to join us. Band boy was happy I showed up, though a little surprised that I had brought an entourage with me. Simon- he's another one. We met in Newport, Rhode Island.[11] He had a lot of plaque in his mouth from smoking too many cigars. Simon worked in the movie business. A grip. He wanted to become a Director and was working his way up the artistic scale. He spoke like Jack Nicholson. He kind of looked like Jack Nicholson- the grin!, those mischievous eyes, that certain

---

[11] Kiki had rented a place for August in Rhode Island. I went up quite often, partied with her new friends and eventually hooked up with Simon (or should I say Simon hooked up with me since he made the move!)

twinkle. He had a little bit of class that comes from a former up-breeding. I say former because his parents are divorced and he was forced to move elsewhere. His Dad is in the oil business- Oklahoma born and bred. His mother... that's where the class ended... Anyway- as the band played and the music continued, I kept going back and forth from the bar in the front to the band in the back. Luckily, Kiki, her date, and Cristina kept Simon busy. Simon didn't care anyway. He was astute enough to understand he was there as a back-up (my back-burner friend)... We finally left. I told the band boy that my sister's friends were taking us out to dinner. Somehow, band boy ended; however, like a good song- the tune (his tune) still remains sung in my head...

I went from the culturally illiterate (Band-boy) to the literate uncultured (Simon). Simon didn't want to go to dinner so we split from the group and went for drinks. What a jerk. He didn't want to pick up a check, let alone a check for five. Jerk. Miser. Cheapskate. Voluntarily opening his wallet was as significant as someone cracking the security code at Fort Knox. That's how tight he was. I should have made him go to dinner. I hated dates for this reason. That awkwardness when the check comes- who's going to pay? What is it they say- at least offer? It was so much easier in the past when priority dictated that a man pick up the check without second thought. Today, it's anyone's game. We went for fresh lime-squeezed marguerita's just because I didn't want to be put on the spot. How insecure am I? I should have insisted we go to dinner with the group and let him deal...

The sex is inconsequential. We were always drunk anyway. After a night out in some happening bar, usually the 14th Street Lounge, I would call Simon up and just tell him I was coming over (or Simon would be out with me). That gross apartment in the East Village. A five floor walk up. Got me in shape. It could have had charm but the bachelors lived like poor college boys. I never could get used to brushing my teeth in the kitchen sink amidst a weeks worth of dishes. A good girlfriend would have washed the dishes. I wasn't his girlfriend. She lived in Atlanta and he made sure that every woman he dated (or fucked) knew about her. He began. He ended.

On my last "booty call", I was wearing an evening gown, my "Ladies in Red" gown, a long-sleeved lace gown with a red satin criss-cross woven through the sleeve, a satin bow on each wrist, and a satin criss-cross through the mid-line. Quite frankly, I looked hot! With the perfect amount of décolletage, the perfect hourglass figure. Kiki and I, with our usual (growing) social circle, had gone to the fundraiser on the Intrepid- over 1000 people. You think I would have met a man that night? Boredom soon set in and so I left Kiki and my friends, telling Simon I had lost them and had no way to get home. Poor stranded me. He paid for my cab. Imagine that. Booty call on the agenda, my agenda...

It would have been nice if Simon had a little gentlemanly charm and complimented me on my look, at least the sexy bra and panties I was wearing underneath. A simple compliment- that's all I was looking for, that's all I wanted... to know I appealed to him. Who cares- the booty call was mine!... The next morning's subway ride (I had to jump on three trains), uptown to the west side, reminded me of college, THE WALK OF SHAME: leaving the boys campus in an early morn's dew and trudging across to the girls campus. Coed school. Single sex dorms and single sex campus' split by a lake. The walk of shame... The subway ride of shame... me in my red dress...

Simon began. Simon ended. I should have warned Dawn that next summer: "Don't get involved with him. His charm is short-lived (and his teeth are green, anyway. Yuck!)."

<u>SEQUEY</u>

MAYBE I'M JUST a great pretender, reinventing myself again and again, using clothes as my driving determining factor in the character I will be....

- The 1940's elegant debutante,
- The 1950's martini-and-cigarettes vixen
- The 1960's super-cala-fragil-ist-ic-ex-pe-ali-do-cious...

My quirky personality... I'm not afraid to be the center of attention when I walk in a room but only when my confidence level is high (which usually means I'm petite and a comfortable size 4). In turn... this creates that sensual aura. It's why women hate me until they meet me, speak to me and realize I'm funny. I'm nice. I'm thoughtful. I'm giving. I choose to be happy. I have an appetite for life, a voracious appetite. No drugs. No therapists. By being happy with myself... well, this helps me remain faithful to life.

I should tell you that I grew up in a loving, chaotic, large family. Hell- we're as dysfunctional as any other. Besides the two dogs, cat (we had five once), and Italian relatives visiting/living with us.... the house was (and still is) always full. My sisters and brother live conventional lifestyles, a lifestyle that I always thought I wanted, belonged in, dreamed of... The eldest (Daddy's princess) married her grammar school friend, has three daughters, and lives in a country-colonial in the suburbs of Stamford, Ct. The next in line (heir to the family name and tradition) remarried, made his millions as a tribute to his ex's snootiness, retired before he was 38, and lives in an affluent Manhasset, LI gated community with his wife and two sons. The younger two, "irish twins", formed a union defying parental authority (and got away with it- somewhat): Kiki, married David (Mr. February). They live on a mountain in Upper Westchester and have one angelic, chunky monkey beautiful daughter (my Goddaughter). Her "twin", Angie, was another who married her grammar school boyfriend, has one son, a second on the way and lives on an estate in New Jersey. The baby of the family, JoJo, was adored and adulated by all in his handicapped being. JoJo... well, he's special and you'll learn more about him. Close family ties. Close family. But we fight, yell and love as any of you do.

And then there is me... that middle child. I almost died at birth (it seems the umbilical cord wrapped itself around my neck). Me- the creative mind... So- where do I fit in??

I grew up taking dancing lessons (jazz, tap, and ballet), piano lessons, banjo lessons, art lessons. Part of the Art League. Winning awards for my creative talents. Girl Scouts was an important part of my everyday life (until I was kicked out for supposedly smoking in the lower Church and starting a fire). I took classes at the American Academy of Dramatic Arts in NYC because I wanted to pursue acting. I played sports... basketball, swimming, softball, cheer-leading... always excelling, always getting placed on the varsity squad. And my greatest accomplishment, to this day, is being the only girl on the boys baseball team- something that was not common back in the 70's. I obtained my nickname: Rocky. With my Dorothy Hamil haircut, I always created a controversy: "Is that a girl or a boy?" they would ask considering that I was flat as a board. I was a precocious child with a voracious appetite. An appetite for...

I received straight A's throughout, competing in The Math League. I was bright. I was smart. I had a big mouth. I was a leader. I got accepted into all four of the top catholic high schools. In addition, I made the three top public schools: Bronx School of Science, Brooklyn Tech, and Hunter High. I also received an acceptance letter to Art and Design. How can I forget the scholarship to Marymount High School? I thought the white-glove graduation ceremony they mentioned was a tad upper-class for me.

In High School, things skewed a little bit as I was introduced to... Let's just say that my hunger for knowledge (which exceeded far beyond the bell shaped norm) escalated into a thirst for boys. The change would quench my appetite as I explored my sexuality within Catholic school corridors, swinging from the scripture pendulum between good and bad.

Maybe it was that middle child syndrome? The trying to get noticed by either bad or good behavior? I spoke my mind to get heard. I needed attention and would do anything to get it. I didn't (and couldn't) focus on my studies (anymore). During one parent/teacher conference, my Biology teacher told my mother to make me break up with my boyfriend: "Your daughter got an 85 on her test. She has a B average. She should be getting 100's. No diversions!" Good teacher but butting in where she didn't belong.

I was popular. I embraced puberty. I accepted my sexual being... Good girl/bad girl came into play.

I went to a Southern Baptist College so unlike me that I made it my personal goal to graduate. I showed up in my Freshmen year (with 20 applied credits from AP classes) in miniskirts, high heels, three contrasting colors of eye shadow (the Chanel look), tank tops, and gold chains. No wonder, I was called "Hosanna" behind my back by the pretty in pink (and green), knee socks, plaid-skirted, Berkshire-footed Preppy Prisses. Those Buffy's and Brooks. Oops. Can't forget their add-a-beads. Trial and error as I conformed to oxford shirts and plaid vests for a few months, got my long hair mistakenly cut into a fashion five years behind the times, stopped wearing make-up... Tried to conform. Not! I was being pulled and pushed as I went home to NYC and got "what are you wearing?" Returned to Richmond and heard... "too much make-up!" Help!! I was trying to conform, trying to fit in, trying to be someone other than myself. No more...

After graduation, I lived on the beach in San Diego, "crystal alley". We didn't realize that this particular street was inhabited by Crystal Meth addicts. What's crystal? We stayed clean and enjoyed the beach life. It was during this year that I embarrassed my family by appearing on a racy, NC-17 episode of *The Love Connection*. I got to choose.

A year and a half later, I was summoned back to New York City by my parents. I had no choice since this California city didn't offer career opportunities for college-educated women. I left the surfer dudes, plastic women (and men), easy lifestyle to get a job, start a career in the hustle and bustle of New York City. I've been in New York ever since.

Chapter vi.
Let's Just Call Him Thomas
Bargain Bin in the Bargain Basement

There is no moment so real as that dreamed then remembered so clearly as if it happened … It must have been at that moment, at my sister's wedding in Rome, that I lost him forever. Was it a dream? Or did I whisper in his ear as we danced: "You're right. This is what I want." It was an unconditional love - pure in thought and mind and reason.. (Not since "him" had I felt this way.) Too bad it was one-sided from the start…

I DON'T RECALL how it started or why it started. I wasn't
interested in any of them. I was pining for another- Marcus. I
was still pursuing, waiting, wanting, questioning... I became
their friend because not one of them spurned my interest. It
was because of this disinterest that I became comfortable. I
didn't have to be someone else, watch what I said and did,
because I wasn't trying to impress. I could be me- quirky,
funny, full of energy!

After-all, we had met as strangers and became fast friends.
Five eligible bachelors on a trip I was invited as a "fill in" by
my cousin because someone had canceled out.- Seven
days/six nights in Vermont- Killington. Five bachelors:

- The chubby "separated" moping child, moping like a
    little boy as if a toy had just been taken away from him,
    his face never changed from toddlerhood (Micky
    Rooney)
- Bozo the clown, with a big grin, his overbite evident, a
    button nose, large ears, with his thinning red hair
    parted down the middle
- the typical-stereotypical Jew, as New York as you get-
    large nose, rounded glasses covering squinty eyes,
    nasal voice that whined... whineddddd!!!
- the long-haired, much-too-young-to-be-gray, salt and
    peppered MIT professor. Didn't anyone tell him that
    long hair was out, hippies were a thing of the past?
- the all-American boy with his blue, blue eyes and short
    blonde hair, tall athletic swimmer's body. You'd never
    guess he was a pot-head??

The motley mix of intellectual, engineered-minded geeks. The
only thing missing was a calculator protruding from their top
pockets. "My brain (and mind) is the only organ that
continually gives me pleasure."- their motto, as they conversed
in a mathematical jargon composed of binary numbers... A
diction that only this group of genius' could decipher. I didn't
even try to chime in. I changed the subject. "So- what bar
would you guys like to go dancing at tonight??? How about
The Wobbly-barn. I hear its phat..."

..."and girls just want to have fun!... My bo-dy!... just wants to have f-u-nn-nn!" Cindi Lauper. She was a Queen's girl and so was I. *Girls just want to have fun* and slam dance! Or at least Pogo. I started it. It was bad enough I convinced everyone to go out since the women wanted to cook a "nice dinner at home" (no wonder I wasn't invited back the next year.). I started it. Little 5 foot me. Up and down. "Come on guys", I coaxed. It was an alternative beat, perfect for the POGO. Up and down. "Oops, sorry. I didn't mean to bump into you (or did I?)." I got the group going. I got the club going. Up and down. Down and up. Everyone was up or down!! Sideways. Oh-oh. It was starting, so much, that the bouncers kicked out the few who really got into it. "No slam dancing allowed!" the sign said, posted just above the dance floor. As if that would stop me from pogo-ing. Up. Down. Up. Down, breast to chest. (In actuality, breast to protruding belly, a soft cushion that wouldn't hurt my somewhat-still-standing-upright-thirty-one-year-old- breasts.) Up! Down! UP/DOWN! *"And girls just want to have fun..."*

He asked me to ski with him as he snowboarded, a separation into teams based on skill level. We had been alone on the ski lift as it rode the 20 plus minutes to the summit- talking, just talking about his life, his wife, his divorce. Talking casual- at ease- because I wasn't interested. I didn't care and I could be me- just me. Just me and him for the day because we had lost everyone else through a blizzard-like whiteout. Different trails. We went east, the rest west. We had lost everyone but he kept waiting for me as I skied cautiously over the ice. I kept waiting for him since he was a novice snowboarder- a novice 33 year-old snowboarder. He had bought me lunch. I didn't want him to. I tried to hand him money. No complications. This wasn't a date. Help!! We spent the day together- casual, full of life, laughter, a happy moment in a transitional time in his life.

On the last night of the trip, I recall we were all in the hot-tub-relaxing, drinking, laughing, enjoying ourselves and the carefreeness of the eve. I didn't have a bathing suit so I borrowed a t-shirt and shorts. Whose? They were all gentlemen so it could have been any one of five. Everyone left and Thomas and I were suddenly alone... Strange...

Unintentional... Just something that happened. Thomas, the rolly-polly, "separated", moping little boy. I don't remember how it began. I only know he blacked-out? Did I kill him with one kiss??? I could get them going but I never killed anyone. I remember that someone came down and interrupted us-surprise! I know that it continued in his bedroom, we were wet (from the hot tub!), me getting up and running away when he tried to fuck me. I only remember it continued. It was in his first letter that I knew I had made an impression. Maybe, I thought, someone likes me for me. Or maybe he was questioning his own intentions...

1/20/97

Hi Rossana

I have most likely spoken to you at this point but I thought I should write anyway. If only to have thought about things before I talk (ed) to you. How was your drive back? Mine seemed really long because I couldn't stay awake. Hope ours was better. Got home and the cat started screaming at me- she was out of food and wanted to get out of the house too. Also the water pipes had frozen at my place for a couple of hours.

I must say I had a wonderful time last night when I wasn't nearly blackened out- actually that was often at the best parts. It was truly an experience for your book. Although I am not sure I can identify the source or cause of the excitement to the level of detail you seem to be looking for, Clearly there was you, and my experiences with you up to that point.

In particular, the evening before, when everyone else had gone to bed- a moment when, as you described later, you were afraid of me. I too felt an anxiety or excitement, a fear of not being sure what to do next. I think we both concluded that going to bed was the best thing to do at that point. For me, I remember that going to bed was full of relief and regrets. The relief stems from the fact that I don't feel totally free to pursue new relationships yet, not to mention other anxieties associated with the first new intimacy in six or seven years. The regrets were well supported by the actions of the following evening.(at this point I will have enough detail to satisfy your curiosity. Or at least better direct it). I don't remember all the details of how the next evenings actions began- you and I alone in the hot tub, I massaging your shoulders, you nearly drowning in relaxation. Then I put you on top of my knees to keep your head above water and something in that moment- probably you reaching down and gently caressing my thighs... things seemed to build very quickly like a soft warm tidal wave coming over me. First, I'm standing knee deep- just enjoying the view and the experience of you. Then, boom... tumble, gasp, grab, and hold on, I'm fully engulfed in you, being spun around and gasping for air, but never wanting it to end- even to take the breath. I just wanted in... intimacy- the end of year of solitude.

MAYBE I HAD TOO MUCH TO DRINK, OR STAYED IN THE HOT WATER TOO LONG, but I think the cause of the lightheadedness was the excitement of being with you. There was the tension from the night before. The energy you have is very enticing too. Certainly the possibility of someone catching us kissing and caressing. Then there was the way you climbed on top of me and kissed me. The critical kiss. I loved it, you pushed your tongue into my mouth, you sucked on my lips and you sucked on my tongue (that one in *particular gets me going), I pushed my tongue in to your mouth. I had not had much experience with a good kisser in the last several years. The kissing alone excited me so much I trembled I didn't believe it until we started kissing again this morning and again I trembled.*

....which leads us to the obvious- what are we? What kind of relation are we going to develop? Friends? Intimate friends? Lovers? The long distance love is very hard to maintain, yet alone build... its hard to discuss things in a letter. No matter how many or how well you pose questions to the screen, it never answers. Yours truly, gratefully, and phenomenally tiredely, THOMAS

Ps I know the typed letter doesn't seem very personal... I think the letter is ultimately more enjoyable when it can be read and thus understood. And besides, right now, I m really tired- it's hard to sleep in a wet bed despite how much fun it was wetting it.

1/22/97

blah, blah, drivel, drivel, prattle, prattle. Youll have to excuse the ramblings of a lunatic. I don't get to express myself very often so I do it very well...thank you for your call last night... I'll have to call you again. I really enjoyed the weekend.

(Maybe this is when I began to love him.) We were casual acquaintances, then friends, then in a moment that you can't understand, and can't predict, we became lovers... or soon-to-be lovers. I don't know why. I should have never let myself. I had my choice. I chose the wrong man. But him? Why did he go for it? Go for me? Was he lonely? Horny? Was I an attractive female? Was it the kiss that reminded him of intimate moments he once shared? What was it about me that made him want me so- just want me? Just lust for me? Just...

These are questions I keep asking myself... One kiss and I get them going- short lived. Why couldn't they want me for me? Why couldn't he want me for me??

2.

IT SEEMS HE did want me for me but not in the way I would have hoped for...I should never have gotten involved with him. I chose the wrong man. During that Vermont weekend, they had all been sweet, massaging my aching feet, having deep intense conversations. There were five eligible bachelors who paid me attention- each giving me something to remember them by: the lollipop, the t-shirt from the Wobbly Barn, another t-shirt from the other bar, a baseball cap from God knows where. What did he give me? Oh yeah- orgasms-intense ones... I chose the wrong man. I always choose the wrong man. He made it so easy though. He paid attention to me in every way-my thoughts, my profession, my other boyfriends (offering advice on my failures), and my feelings. He really cared. He tried to guide me; psychoanalyzing the actions of the others to make me feel better. More than anything, I fell in love with his mind. I know I keep repeating myself! But ohhh... his ability to communicate. We never fought (except once) because we always talked through it, talked in soft voices, caring voices, friendly voices, "inside voices". He did not live by the motto "football is my life", nor "Go Red Sox!", "Go Celtics!" He enjoyed partaking in sports and was very athletic considering his portly build: jogging, biking, snowboarding...BUT... sports did not consume his life. The time he spent with me wasn't wasted on watching the boob tube. He never said "wait until this play is over" if I stood before him and asked a question. I was lucky to have known him, to have experienced him, to have loved him. This one Vermont week was only the beginning... The letters continued to come. He continued to visit... But...

It was timing. I should have stuck to my standards. My standards were high and the criteria should have stood. I should have stuck to never dating divorced men. I didn't want to be a "Carrie". Carrie was my brother's third girlfriend post wife. (The first: Maria Angela Constantina Lucia something or other...the saintly "guidette" from Queens, spiked hair, long red fingernails. She worshipped my brother. Her mistake was that she kept talking about their wedding and the five children they'd have! The second:- what was he thinking?! Prudence Priss, with her floral dress, straw hat, and waspy mannerisms, the go-back-to-Connecticut Prep... And that she did... on the night he met Carrie, the night he snuck out of his bedroom and met Carrie on the beach, while Prudence Priss slept (poor girl). Carrie. They lived together for three years. He upgraded Carrie from farm-girl to NYC Valentino sheik. He never loved her though she thought he did. She wanted to marry him but he found another...) Carrie- the re-bound (rebounds in my brother's case). I didn't want to be his "Carrie"...

No divorced men. No fat men. No bald men. I had an aversion to bald men even though my Dad was bald. Thomas was two of the three, of average height, the spare tire in the middle like the Michelin man, and an ass that was gouged-in (due to some unforeseen accident). He had a dented ass! I fell in love with him anyway. I fell in love with his mind. I didn't need to search- it just happened. I felt it deep, deep inside. I knew it was right for me- he was right for me. I fell in love with his mind, his genius cause that's what he was- a genius. Every conversation was a learning experience, every visit was fulfilling, engaging, incisive discussions about life, things, objects, people, anything and everything... Timing! At what point are you meeting him. At what point is he meeting you? At what point in time is he ready?

I wish he would have decided that he wasn't ready... He came to visit. He spent the weekend, a weekend with me and the great city as our backdrop... It was our most romantic moment, unplanned, relaxed, enjoyable- ice skating in Central Park, a walk across the Great Lawn, window shopping along Fifth Avenue... He sent me flowers, a mixed bouquet (thank God they weren't roses!). It surprised me. Was he courting me? Were his intentions genuine? I was still unsure. My heart was committed to another. Maybe this is why I was so comfortable with Thomas. We were friends... good friends, in a short amount of time. The flowers though? And his next letter... I re-read it four times! Hold on... Its get heated...

Feb 10, 1997

Rossana,
How's it going? Friday night and I'm here sitting typing a letter. I really need to make a more exciting life. I'm a bit depressed, actually lonely. I made plans, fall back plans and they all fell apart... and the cat doesn't cut it. I think I'm going to have to start driving in to Boston to go out. Yeah, yeah. I know. I should move into the city to get a life. I like living someplace I don't have to lock the car or front door. I like having a yard and a grade, to be able to go for a walk in the woods. But its hard to meet single people out in suburbia. But this isn't what the letter is supposed to be about.

It was supposed to be about the great time I had visiting you and your sister. I really enjoyed spending time with you. You're a great person and a sensual voyage. I wish we had more time together, but I know we shouldn't. I was so... frustrated by the time I got home I didn't realize until later that I was truly exhausted. That's the problem with being frustrated- I don't sleep very well, but I really didn't notice because it was just too good to be with you. I do hope we can remain friends. But it takes time to make a friendship and spending time with you is so tempting its dangerous.

A sensual voyage of Rossana- the valleys and hills, contiguous curves. The small of your back changing, leading, beckoning on to the hips and buttocks. The response to the touches, kisses, caresses. The motion, sound, the scent, taste and feel of your body consuming all the attention I could give. I wish we could have felt more comfortable with the whole situation. You seem to be overtaken with guilt sometimes and I had my own ghosts hampering my ability to fully enjoy the experiences. I wanted to take you- I wanted you on your knees so that your hips could gyrate over mine. You're really a very sexy woman. Some woman are just pretty, but they are not sexy. While pretty is good, sexy is wonderful. I've got too many thoughts running through my mind for this letter to make sense.

I'd love for you to come visit here; however, I don't trust myself to behave. It would be so nice to have you here with me right now. To feel your skin against mine, to stroke your face and kiss your neck and then...my mind wanders off into lurid details it probably should not.[12]

I need to get to sleep before I get too worked up... as I review, thoughts, images, desires from the weekend all come back... I just wanted to thank you again for ... everything- the dinners, the skating, the time. I don't know whether to hope to see you again or to wish you luck in finding someone better for you, so I'll hope for both.

---

[12] As I write this, "I will always love you" by Whitney Houston is playing, some oldies station... *"bittersweet... all I am taking with me.... So goodbye... please don't cry.. we don't know.... and I— W-i-l-l Al—ways Lo—ve Y-ou!!!!.... I hope life treats you fine and I hope you have what you've dreamed of... I wish you happiness and at this moment I wish you love.... And I——— will always lo-ve you———-!!"* Is this a sign?

Saturday
Hi- guess who. How did you know it was me? You could tell by the typing. So how are your flowers doing? I'd like to send you more but the flowers that get ordered over the phone are lousy, at least compared to what you get when you walk in and pick out the flowers to create a bouquet.

I wanted to mention one other thing about our weekend- ok, I'd love to talk about a lot of other things from our weekend. But there was this striking thing about it for me and that was how quickly I felt comfortable there, Sitting around talking to your sister, making dinners together with you, picking you up at work, running to the store for groceries. It was frighteningly domestic. And I really miss it. Of course it was only for a few days and it may have gotten old after awhile. Well, just call me the lost suburb husband. How revoltingly average. At times like this I want to buy a boat and sail to the Greek islands. Or something unequally unlikely to happen.

Sunday-
Its very hard writing a letter that has any kind of direction when there are so many conflicting feeling trying to direct it. I wish I could have been there t o see you in your bed in those alluring flannel pj's- I would brush your hair back with my fingers before running them down the sides of your face to rub your neck. Your moans of appreciation would encourage me to continue rubbing your neck and shoulders. For your sighs of enjoyment, I would kiss you, starting on your forehead, then your cheeks, holding your head between my hands I would kiss your lips, then your

whole mouth. I would see the subtle protrusion of your erect nipples on top of your breasts and feel your hips start to squirm. I would continue kissing you and pushing the tension out of your shoulders and neck. You would continue moaning, squirming, moistening. You would start removing my shirt as I undo the large buttons on your pajama top. At the last button I would start moving my lips down on to your neck and around to your ears, and my hands move down to cup your bosoms and feel your large nipples between my fingers.

Ok, that's all I can take. This kind of thing is likely to drive me nuts. I can't do this ghostwriting- besides what am I going to do for inspiration? I do hope your reality allows you to finish this story with someone else.
Yours anytime,
THOMAS

Ps I'm looking forward to licking the envelope!

(on the back of the envelop he wrote: *"ohhh. That was fun!"*

Woooo! My heart was with another but my body... Are you as wet as I am? Oops- sorry to be so crude. It was February. Each weekend, I somehow managed to be the social butterfly. It was raining, heavily, this month. Four men at once. Suddenly in my life. Four men. Not only a concurrent demand on my ego, but of my heart. Marcus was soon to end. Peter was just around the corner. Stephen #8 was still playing games. And Thomas... his letters will reveal all...

February 14, 1997
Rossana,
Hi. How ya doin? It's about quarter to five, Sal and Geo won't be here for another hour... you're probably just getting on the road to go to Vermont. I should be doing something, but cant remember what. Obviously not that important. Maybe I'll take a nap.

Monday Feb 17
Just got back from Waterville valley. Sharon (soon to be ex-wife) and I and one of her co-workers.... I boarded all day. I did pretty well...Sal and Geo got here yesterday about six. We went to the liquor store for whiskey and beer. Sam brought the tequila... We drank ourselves adolescent...

Tuesday Feb 18
I'm sorry you didn't enjoy your weekend. I hope you have a better week. I was trying to think when we might get together again before March 16 but I couldn't come up with anything. It's tough getting together when your opportunity is on the weekends and you need at least two days...

I spoke to Sharon about our Okemo trip and she wants to go. She wants to get together and try to get over the awkwardness our divorce has put on friendships.... I need to tell her about you soon too. I need to feel comfortable with seeing you- I guess I need her to say it's okay or something. or maybe for closure of that relation. Maybe I need to let her know I'm moving on and she should too. Anyway- I want to do that before you get up here so hopefully all of that can be worked through ahead of time. I don't feel like I'm sneaking

around. But mostly I want to enjoy your visit here
with as little outside thoughts distractions. I hope I
can make it up then. I know you're coming back from
Mexico so you may not want to travel...

By the way you are formally and cordially invited to
visit my humble hovel I call home...

Wednesday Feb 19
Just got off the phone with you. Again, thanks for the
card- its nice to read what you're feeling. And the
card was funny too. Sorry I woke you. I want to go to
the morning step class- nothing wakes a guy up like a
room full of women bouncing around in bodysuits,
but Ill never understand the thong thing- that has to
be distracting if not uncomfortable... I was out with
Sharon... she asked me about having coffee so late in
the day... but I swear it hasn't been affecting me
lately. I think it was getting your card that got my
mind turning. It sure won't stop. I really liked your
card. Did I say that already. I'm not sure why I like it
but I do...

I told Sharon I want to see other people. You think it's
not a big deal considering we are getting divorced.
She's having a hard time accepting this. I am too but
after we got separate apartments I didn't think things
looked good... six months later her brother moved in...
it was clear things weren't improving...then filing
divorce papers... that's when it really started sinking
in that's its over. Over lunch, she asked when we are
going to start doing things again.. that's when I told
her I said I wanted to start dating again....

(we now return you to our regularly scheduled letter...)

Hi,
Me again. So you don't think you can make it up for the weekend next month. And you want me to come down there because you will have been on vacation for a week. Oh yeah "I've had a rough vacation of lying on the beach and making the tanned towel guys run and get me drinks from the bar. You just have to come down here." Oh yeah, that's a convincing argument. ...well, okay. But I can't come down until Saturday... I have theatre tickets. I was hoping you'd make it up for the show, but I know that would be really pushing it. You let me know - I'm sure we can work out something.

That is it if you're still interested in this BORING letter...And to think, this was supposed to be a letter you're going to respond to... Did I tell you I've been cuddling up with a pillow at night sometimes pretending it was you... I know I didn't put directions in here, but since I'm going down there you don't need directions. See you soon I hope.
Later Babe,

THOMAS

Three letters. I had known him a little over one month. Three letters. Each letter was written over the course of several days as his thoughts ventured into an unknown territory, as his thoughts brought him to me. Love letters?? Friendship letters? Lust letters? The letters... and they continued...

Don't panic (smiley face) written at the top
March 8
Hey Rossana,
How was your voyage, your grand adventure, ok, would you believe your vacation in Mexico. You can tell me about it when I get there...I hope this trip was better for you than your trip to Vermont. I don't really know much about what your situation is/was with "the other guy", but clearly you expected some level of commitment that he was only talking about. This is the danger with long distance romances. It becomes difficult to gauge what the other person is thinking or feeling without continuous contact. Face-to-face contact with the other person is so seldom that it puts a lot of pressure on the short visit to catch up. This is something we will have to be careful of. I guess that is why you want to be celibate for awhile. That's all right. I understand that. You had a few disappointments between that and your birthday and its probably a good idea to step back and give yourself some time and space to figure out where you want to go from there. Maybe cultivating a relationship isn't what you need, maybe you need to turn the soil and let it lay fallow so that the next seeds of love have a rejuvenated place in which to grow... I'll see you in a few hours.

Your friend and compadre,

THOMAS

Was he offering me advice? Or preparing me for our eventual long distance downfall? He knew where my heart had been. He knew I wanted to stay away from a relationship. He knew I didn't want to be his "Carrie". He began to get confused also...

March 18, 1997
Hi Rosssana,

How is your week going? I hope your adjustment back isn't too shocking. I was pretty depressed... I felt better after a nap and a work out. And even better after a little frustration relief.

I don't know if I'm as ready for a relationship as I thought. Maybe I'm the one who needs to lay fallow for awhile. We did discuss it, at least as it applied to sex. Thank you for the weekend. I did enjoy it. Please thank your mom for dinner. But I came away feeling I did something wrong. Or that something bad occurred that I can't figure out what it might be. Sure there's the sexual frustration thing, but I really don't think that's that bad... Then again, I have a cold and don't feel good and this has nothing to do with the weekend. Maybe its the rebound thing or just not getting enough sleep.

March 19
I hope you're getting over your cough... I was thinking about what might be bothering me. I think I'm looking for something that doesn't exist. I cant tell you what I'm looking for because I don't know. Which is why it doesn't exist-its not been defined yet. Circular reasoning can be so helpful. No really, I think I'm looking for something in our relation which I'm not finding. Until I figure out what I'm looking for I won't be able to find it. That, is not fair to you. But this is just pure conjecture at this point. It may not be what's depressing me at all. Maybe it's the realization that I'm truly divorced and I'm on my own again. But I felt on my own for some time now.
Yours truly,
THOMAS

Handwritten on the back of the above letter...

Monday
Hi Rossana,

This is why I hate talking on the phone. Now I feel I've upset you and I don't believe there is much reason for it... I need to be able to talk to you about how I'm feeling. Not that I'm looking to you to necessarily fix the problem or cheer me up, I just need to talk to someone about it and your the logical victim of my emotional dumping... I also want it to be clear that you do mean something to me.

You're a good person and friend and certainly attractive. I don't think you should feel insecure in your personal relations. I know you've had some bad times lately but I know you'll come through it. We have a good time and there is a mutual respect and it's a good relation even if it's a bit undefined. I hope you are enjoying it too. I wish you could come visit me sooner than later...

THOMAS

In the same envelope as the above letter..

Saturday 3/22/97
Hi,
How are you feeling?.... I met a woman about a month ago and we've been exchanging e-mails and went on a date last night...It was okay...and then this morning I felt depressed... We had a pretty good time... but no real connection. I'm not sure how you

feel about me dating other people. I hope it doesn't upset you too much - or at least not as much as it seems to upset me... I talked to someone and his reaction as "Yeah, I always hating dating." I guess that's part of it.... In the past, I've always been a friend before being a lover. But even so, I've not been upset after dating someone new...

Hi- its 2am and I just got back from Boston and got pulled over for speeding...

Good morning-
How are you feeling today? I wish you were here right now laying in bed with me. There are some mornings I can lay in bed- but I need something to do-like caressing your body. Or in this case, just writing about it. Huhm... I'd really like to kiss you right now. Okay, fine. Go brush your teeth first. Then we'll kiss and I'll undress you so I can feel your naked body against mine. Then I'll roll you on top of me so I can have both hands free to roam your body while we kiss. I'll hold your face between my hands and then drag them gently down to your shoulders, down your back, and cup to your wonderful ass in my hands. Now I'll roll us over. I'm on top of you so I can expose your naked body for further enjoyment/exploration. Start kissing your ears and neck while my hands move strongly up your sides to caress your breasts and feel your nipples stiffen. Now I really want to taste your moist pussy so I start backing down your body stopping to kiss your neck, your breasts... your little brown belly...kiss your sides, bite gently into your hips, your thighs, the inside of your thighs. Then my hands move under your butt to caress, squeeze, and lift you into my mouth... hmmmm. Hey, where'd this other

naked woman come from? Oh boy! (it was your idea) written in red pen.

I'm going to take a cold shower... One letter. Written over a few days. A range of emotions. Confused? Yes- he was. How do you think I felt (besides aroused)? We had yet to consummate (in the fullest extent of the word!) our relationship. Confused? I had yet to visit him up North. Confused... He hadn't defined us yet...

3.

HE COULD NOT define who we were yet. Friends? Just friends? Lovers? Boyfriend/girlfriend? I didn't think a definition was needed. He did. He thought too much- too much about "us" or what constituted "us", too much about what he was feeling or trying to feel. I think this was the problem, the issue. He thought too much instead of just being...

When I arrived at his palatial estate, a five room, wooden house at the base of ski mountain, the first thing he did was massage me. He kneaded the aches out of my neck, caressed my skin, started to kiss me, first softly, on my ears, then passionately as he spun me around. He continued to run his fingers through my hair. He continued to stroke and push the anxiety away, far away. I stopped him and asked him why? "I know how tense it is to drive in the mountains, at night, not knowing where you are going, how far, or even why you were going- if the destination was a place you really wanted to be..." He spoke in a concerned manner, never stopping, continuing to touch me. My coat finally off, drink in hand, we talked as he cooked dinner for me.

Late that eve- I couldn't breathe. I was wheezing, really wheezing as if the air had suddenly tightened its grips around me. I couldn't tell if it was his down comforter or the dander from his cat. "I tried to keep her out of here." he said. "I even vacuumed, knowing you were coming." He was always so considerate. I was scared. I was embarrassed. I didn't know how to act. I couldn't breathe. I was used to shortness of breathe (s.o.b.), the continuous yawning, induced by an allergic environment but this was far worse. An asthma attack? I didn't have asthma just s.o.b. I couldn't breathe and I started to cry, which of course had a detrimental effect and worsened the condition. I had stopped him from making love to me. I was torn between letting him have me and something else. Someone else? I don't know what caused this sudden downturn. In an angst-driven moment, I got up, abruptly, left him, and moved to the front room to sleep on the couch. I needed to escape. I was overwhelmed- with the inability to breathe, with desire, with just being with him. Was I indecisive about coming here? You bet!

He came in and covered me with a blanket. He didn't leave me alone as I sobbed, and sniffled, and yawned trying to draw the air into my lungs. He sat beside me and stroked my hair- so tender, so caring, so sweet. He was so considerate, always considerate. He stayed with me until I could regulate my breathing. He stayed sitting beside me, watching me, planting one kiss on my cheek as I closed my eyes and the tears subsided and I wandered off into never, never land... At some point in the late, late night, I got the courage and went back to him, crawling under the sheets beside his naked body. He held me from behind, side by side we lay, two spoons sleeping perfectly together.

We awoke that morning, our bodies moving slowly, in unison, the heat rising between us as he rubbed my back, kissed my neck, caressed my shoulders, cupped my breasts. Somehow I knew it was just right as he slowly, carefully, pulled off my bottoms, as he withdrew his cold fingers warmed by my insides, as he entered me, touching me, never letting me go, heavenly, pure, gentle.

We snuggled into the wee hours of dawn as it changed to daylight. The sun may have risen but it was clouded by the icy downpour, a rainy cold day, a day just above the freezing point. A day when the trees take on a glasslike appearance, the twinkling of icicle capped branches as the sun peaked through. The comfort level of just being. as sweet and harmonious as Enya's melodic voice, a voice that echoed through our lovemaking, singing softly. The environment, our love shack, as simple as the four walls of plywood that held up the structure he called home. The winter bliss, a sign of our happiness. We were content.

I was content as the 33 year-old man nestled peacefully against my chest that afternoon, heartbeat to heartbeat, beating in perfect unison, we were one. We were one, at peace, for these short-lived few days... Hour upon hour of lovemaking as he bent over me and devoured me, slurped, licked, kissed, tasting me in ways I had not been comfortable to allow- "sucked me dry"... A repetitious interaction and reaction. At this time, I realized that I was a woman. He convinced me that orgasms were good, let it flow, let go. Made me experience- great! for my mind was not to get into the way of my body's responses and reflexes. "Don't think," he whispered in my ear, "Enjoy!" as I relaxed and the uncontrollable urge took over again and again. He took me to plateaus I had never been. Hour after hour he continued to please me. Every part of me had a heightened awareness, the nerves and electrons pulsing, exploding, my blood boiling. I was at a continual vortex of ecstasy- the point of no return. Aaahhhh! Who knows when we finally got dressed. That eve? The next day?

I would do anything to bring us back to this day, these few days. As miserable as the weather was, the stormy winter day outside- we were protected, warm, content in our impenetrable cocoon. No money. No materialistic issues. No outside elements could touch us. We were ..."just us".

4.Isoceles Triangle

IT WAS APRIL. The letters continued. April 9, 16, 17, 19, 21 all sent together as one special package...

Hi Rossana...
I'm sorry I didn't explain why I chose to stay in Greenwich when we first discussed it. I would rather

stay with you, but I'm very attracted to you and I don't want to go through the torture of denial. It's easier to not just be tempted... it's just so much fun getting you excited and naked. See- just the thought and images of you... ah never mind....

...You shouldn't worry too much about not having e-mail.. e-mail letters are not good- they are generally a few lines long... You shouldn't feel I don't want to settle for you. Settling had nothing to do with what we have as a relation. We are both busy and confused right now. And we live three hrs away. Its been awhile since you've had a relation with someone who lives close by, but it is really helpful to the relationship if those involved can actually see each other more than once a month. (HINT: to the downturn) This is probably one of the bigger difficulties we face in trying to have a relationship that goes further than just friendship. Well that and the fact that I just want to rip off your clothes off and eat you up. So what do you think of this new orgasm pill for women? Sounds ridiculous to me- you haven't had much trouble that I can find...

April 16
...so when can you come up again?... so how's your life going? Are you torn between hating work and being afraid to give up the income?... I don't want to keep doing this kind of work.. but when this job is over I'll start contracting again and I can make well over $100k/yr and the idea of giving that up to go back to school to do something I enjoy... maybe if I knew what I wanted to do. But I don't.... if only I had no morals and could feel good about taking advantage of others people's stupidity so I could make a quick

million and just retire There's only a thousand legitimate ways to do it...

April 17
... so I'm all set for our weekend...
April 21
...Take care and I'll see you this weekend
April 22
...Have a good day...
Thomas

It was April. Chiara and I were sitting on the board of the upcoming fundraiser We were in peak. Fifty of our friends were attending. At the pre-cocktail bash, fifteen of them joined us. Thirteen men, two attached women and us. That's the way we liked it, surrounded by men. We had enticed them with "you'll meet our friends, single women..." (The women had yet to show up.) Anyway, I was still trying to figure out how I'd manage, manage between two men, manage between dancing with Thomas and playing Black Jack with Peter. Manage between keeping Thomas in one room and scurrying across to meet Peter. They were both coming. Thomas was here now. Peter said- let's see. I was torn between the two of them.

It had been three months of "in the back door, out the front door", a constant Dobbler... Thomas would frequent, leave by four, Peter would be ringing the doorbell by seven. Crossing paths. Different directions. Same goal. Me. I wondered how many times they had been at the same street light, concurrently. *In the back door, out the front.* The revolving door. Triangles. How I hated them but this time it was different. This time I was the one with the better angle. After-all, everyone should have two. (*Nasty, so you think I'm a nasty girl.. Nasty!*)[13] The boyfriend. The lover. I should have kept my heart out of the second. I should have just let it be for sex but Thomas made it difficult. The letters. The love letters...

---

[13] Janet Jackson's song.

I was confused and the letters made it more difficult. Peter was here, now, his thoughts elsewhere. Thomas was 250 miles north but seemed to always be right next to me in bed. Peter didn't like to kiss. He told me I always had sex on the brain. Thomas... I couldn't get enough!. Peter had told me I was it but... Thomas had warned me that I could never be ... Confused... I was torn between two men. Was I breaking a commandment, committing adultery since Thomas was still technically married? Would I be banished to hell, into eternal damnation? It wasn't my fault, these perverse pleasures of the flesh... I couldn't be held accountable for my actions, could I? After-all, I was in peak! I just wanted someone to love me. What was I to do?

I went to Church. I had not embraced God in six years. It was Lent. "Bless me Father for I have sinned... It's been five years? Ten? Oh, God! Sorry, God! (another commandment broken- I used the Lord's name in vain). I can't recall how long it's been since my last confession... I've lied. I've stolen. (What other sin could I conjure up from my youth?) I aahhh... (How could I tell the priest?) I ahhhh (I'm fucking two men)... I... ahhh... I've-been-having-relations-with-two-men." (There, I said it!) My absolution, a few Hail Mary's, a couple Our Father's and I was healed. I had been forgiven for my sins. A fresh start... I turned my attention to Peter (but I still dreamed about Thomas).

And I still received Thomas's letters...

May 8, 1997
Hi Rossana,

...I've been thinking about you and us a lot too...It occurred to me that we did very little kissing this past weekend and I feel jipped. Then of course there was the usual frustration (which was discussed during the drive home). I've been trying to come up with ways that we both could get satisfaction from our trysts. But I think that's probably not going to happen and

not a good thing to pursue. I guess. I don't know. I should be trying to find someone else to date. Probably in the same state....

May 5th, 1997
...I took off from work early. We are running out of work to do. I'm not complaining...You should know that I think about you more often than I write in these letters. As you know, my thoughts often wander to less than proper thoughts and then I get distracted. So I end up doing something other than writing to you. But I am thinking about you....

May 8th
... so when do you think you will be able to come up and rearrange my house? I don't think you should bother- I want to get a new place to live...but I want you to come up anyway...

Thomas.

I called Thomas. "I can't talk. I'll have to get back to you." He would have to get back to me. Strange? He always talked to me. Couldn't talk? What could he be doing? Alone. In our love shack? He explained later that he had gone out on a date with someone and well... The thought of him with another woman. It was devastating. The thought of him going down on another. It was excruciating. Had I called him while he was in bed? With her? In our love shack? (Strange coincidence.) I was jealous. I had no right to be but I was. I was so confused...

May 1997
Hi Rossana,

...It took me awhile to realize why I was upset. First, I realized I had trivialized our relationship. And

second, I figured I thought our relationship wasn't what I thought it was...
I'm really sorry I trivialized us- there's no excuse except that I'm a butthead sometimes falling back on the insensitive guy role. This was part on focusing more on the "friend" part of our intimate relationship because of this I felt not only I should tell you and that I could tell you. I'm sorry. I was wrong. I really had such a nice time during our last visit. I felt like we were really good friends...

Love,
Thomas

Things remained quiet that summer with Thomas, the incident had caused a sudden breach in our trust. For two months, I left Thomas alone to find himself. I took the time to focus in on what was before me, what was tangible. My focus was work and Peter. I am going to interject Peter in here. So many co-existing events. I would keep him separate but well... It's best he arrives now!

5. MPS

PETER. THE SUMMER of 1997. He had made so many promises, empty promises. He had paid for a double share, in the usual house in the Hamptons... we had the room to ourselves. He invited me to come out each weekend. Empty promises about our summer together. Promises, I dreamed about. Promises, I wanted to come true. Promises, I tried to facilitate...

It's best he arrives now! You met him once before... The Summer of Fun. This should have been The Summer of Fun 2. This is how I imagined it to be. Empty promises....

Peter is a good man. I'll start with that. He asked me to go to our friend's wedding. This is how it began. I asked him to accompany me (an innocuous date) to "Beauty and the Beast". That is how it continued. Peter seemed to really care. Peter seemed to want to pursue "us". His priority was his dying mom. Originally he wanted to keep us separate. I guess he thought he could... but I wanted attention. She needed his attention. I understood the parameters getting into the relationship. I understood them and tried to work within them. He wouldn't let me. He couldn't let me. That thick-headed Italian macho attitude. And he only had brothers. I hated men who came from single sex homes. They just didn't understand the needs of a woman. I was breaking all my rules. Dating a divorced man. Dating a man who only had brothers. I should have stuck to my standards! Peter and his petulant glances. The man with MPS.

I know you probably think I transposed the letters accidentally. PMS- a state of mind you're constantly in, sometimes in, or never in (because you're in PEAK!). PMS- a state of mind that your husband keeps rubbing in your face. MPS- a disease that only the female gender really understand the ramifications of its meaning and a man would never admit to!! The next time he rudely asks you "Is it that time of the month, honey?" Ignore.

MPS- male penile syndrome. Your boyfriends have it. Your lovers have it. Your husbands most certainly have it! Symptons (and there are many!): Grumpy. Moody. Irritable. Huffy and Puffy (and I'll blowww your house down). Ill-tempered. The constant frown. Does he have a permanent stick up his ass? Has he suddenly become a tight wad, questioning your spending habits? Is he picking on you because you've put on a few pounds. He's one to talk! Is he gassy! Does he belch and burp constantly and then tries to blame it on your cooking NOT the chili-dog he devoured at lunch. Does he whine in a childhood voice: "Honey... my tummy hurts!" but he's too lazy to get up and go to the bathroom for some Maalox as he sits in front of the TV viewing an endless marathon of sports extravaganzas. Getting him to take out the garbage (let alone put up that new light you bought) is like pulling teeth... Is every word out of his mouth: "No!" "Later!" "Maybe." "No!!" Get even!

Get even. Retort. Reclaim. Respond in your sweetest motherly voice: "Honey, are you experiencing MPS?" "WHAT?!!!!" Then hand him two Midols. That will shut him up!

Peter. He was in a constant state of MPS. And who could blame him. Triangles. Two. Me. His Mom. Himself. Me. His Grandma. Himself. In a constant state of "agita", those women in his life never gave him a free breath. He couldn't be everything to all of them even though I tried to help him with this. I was a master at writing to-do lists, assigning tasks, follow up. We would treat his life like a never ending list of things to get done. It was the only way he could manage his time, to learn how to multi-task. It was the only way he could find time to be with me... I tried repeatedly to help him manage his career, his studies (CPA), his time with me, his time with his Mom and his Grandma. I suggested a weekly schedule, even included the day he would leave work one hour earlier so he could shop for food. I really tried so that he could manage it all and still give me the attention I needed. I tried. Shit. I left French Connection and went to work for Victoria's Secrets[14] in Long Island. Closer to him. Better hours. We could plan our time together more efficiently! I gave up my flourishing career for him!! Timing. It was the wrong time...

It should have been the Summer of Fun 2, a summer filled with laughter and jokes, and ease of manner that left the city's chaos behind, the comfort zone. A continuation of last year's hot season, a summer that we had all experienced. Summers in the Hamptons. Summer in Westhampton Beach.

There were extraneous factors: the newlyweds, our friends. The girls would not let their husbands be the men they fell in love with: obnoxious, witty, flirtatious, carefree. They had to conform to the role model. The men became serious, attentive only to their wives, put up with the nagging "Change your shirt!" "Honey, I want ice scream." "Honey, I want. I want. I want." The men. With marriage, they became suddenly

---

[14] I knew that was a career calamity when each day I had to remind myself to check that my skirts fell three inches below the bottom of my fingertips. A company that sells sex; yet, we had to imply conservatism.

castrated! They'd be right there to cater to their wives every whim rather than face the rrrrrrowlllllllll. The wives- they were content with devouring... devouring various chips, dips, fatty fried foods, chicken wings, nachos supreme, cheese, sour cream, hot dogs. And these were just the late afternoon appetizers. They were sublimating food for sex. The ring on their fingers gave them power, the sense of security. Bitch. Bitch. Bitch. No one was safe from their abuse and mockery. They weren't nice! Every word out of their mouths was "FUCK! this, fuck that!!" It wasn't a slip of the tongue but a daily part of their every day jargon. "FUCK!!!" "She's fuckin so anorexic, fuck!" (Maybe because you've become a cow.) "She fuckin' smokes so much fuckin pot." (Uhmm... I can recall you lighting up a joint!) What happened? They got married. What happened to the wild-I-have-to-go-jogging, I-can't-eat-that, let's-get-a-drink, smiling, funny women of the summer before? They got married. Extraneous factors that added to Peter and myself becoming a part of oblivion...

I was always crying. It was an abusive relationship, not in the physical sense, but in the mental anguish. I was stressed enough from a taxing work week. I only wanted a little affection. I only wanted him to put his arms around and hold me (the way Thomas did). I needed him to hold me. I only wanted him to accept my affection, to kiss my hand when I threw my arms around his neck, to hold me when I came up to him (the way Thomas did). I told him that too. I knew communication was important since I was always crying. I told him that when I acted up, when I became hormonally imbalanced (usually alcohol induced), when I became irate (hey- the whole house was), when I had those few moments of irrationality, I needed him to hold me. Simple. Nothing more. A hug, a bear hug! Just put his big burly arms around me and hold me. Instead, we were always fighting, one-sided with me crying. Me yelling. Me crying- real tears. Me running to the beach, tripping over the hills and valleys being forged from the land-fill, hiding behind sand dunes, crying, sleeping, crying until I got hold of my senses, until I realized he wasn't coming. He wasn't coming to look for me. He didn't care enough about my well-being. I was crying late at night, alone on the beach, the sand- my blanket. Nothing around but the sea, sand, myself staring at the stars on a beach he promised- "I can't wait until the summer so we can take walks on the beach." "Peter, lets go for a walk – it's a starry filled eve." "NO! I'm tired." "Peter, the ocean is clear. You can see your toes in it. Lets go for a swim." "No!" "Lets go skinny dipping." "NO! I have to study." It was always NO! to every question I asked. I wouldn't have asked them if he hadn't put the thoughts in my head, if he hadn't said these were the things he wished for. He promised. I asked. He was always saying NO! I cried.

I only needed to be held, to show me that he cared. I wanted us to be safe. I took a home AIDS test. As the waves quietly broke on the shoreline... I whispered in his ear and revealed my troubled self. I whispered as those early morning pleasures, as the sound of silence muffled his reaction... He didn't share in my joy. He said nothing. He only looked at me with disappointed eyes as if my confession was a betrayal of my virtue, a betrayal of "us". It was a burden I had carried, thought about, for the last five years. He didn't share in my joy of having it lifted, my shoulders free from the weight I bore these years. He didn't share in my joy as the dawn's light snuck its way in, beyond the window shade... his stocky build throwing a disproportionate shadow over my petite frame. The sound of silence- an escalating pitch, a far greater noise...

When I first met him, I liked him for his authoritative tone. I liked him for his manly-self. I needed to be rejuvenated, to unwind, de-stress but I didn't know how. I was managing THE Flagship and as usual the demands to run the stores like a museum, to maintain my impeccable standards, to never let my guard down... took its toll. This store, one of eleven stores, did 25% of the company's business. (You do the math.) I was good at what I did; however, I put the demands on myself to succeed... He picked me up from work one day. He looked at me and said, "You're going to walk it off. Leave work behind you... the tone, the manager mentality, the drill sergeant. Leave it behind." Huhh?? What did I look like?? How had I sounded? "It's me. It's you. It's your friends for dinner and drinks." It was a short six block walk from Soho to the West Village... but he made me walk around the block a few times. "Leave it behind you!" he demanded. And I did.

As for the sex. He thought I was over-sexed but there were a few times he initiated... A few times...I fell asleep in his bed as he read. He woke me up as he turned me over and entered me, carefully. He whispered to me that he looked at me, so peaceful, so gentle, so relaxed... it stirred his loins and he couldn't help himself.

A few tender moments... At 6'2" and 325 lbs, Peter was a big boy, like a star of the WWF! The extra weight we could overlook. (After-all, he had a lot of other issues to deal with.) He was a big boy... He didn't like me on top. He said I bent his penis backwards into an excruciating arc!! He was a BIG BOY! Think of an 800lb gorilla making love to an adorable chimpanzee. A few tender moments... He looked at me as he lay on top of me, his 12 inch penis, hardening on my tummy. "Where does it go?" he laughed. "I don't know," I giggled. I couldn't figure it out. Was it like an accordion, retracts upon impact? His penis was sitting on my belly, from pubis to breast line. Where does it go? How did it fit into my petite five-foot frame? I wondered. We laughed.

A few tender moments when I aroused him... On one beautiful, sunny afternoon, we got out of the car and were walking up to the stoop of my parents house. He stopped. "Come on," I said. "I can't," he flushed a deep red. "Why?" "You know," he said again, lowering his head, criss-crossing his hands in front of himself. He told me later that he looked at my ass in its tight, beige polyester pants and up it went!

A few tender moments... At someone's wedding (he only knew the groom), he told me I looked beautiful. I was wearing my mom's 1960's gold lame jumpsuit, plunging neckline, bell bottom legs. He looked at me and told me I was beautiful.

I was always kissing him, always saying I love you freely, always trying to hold his hand, sit on his lap. He was cold. I only wanted to bring joy into his life. He was cold. I was consistently crying.... It was the wrong time.

Maybe it was the pot he smoked with his mother, his brothers, his friends. Homegrown, if he needed a quick fix, the plant so well cared for, in a landscaped yard, overlooked, overgrown. His mom had cancer. Breast cancer that had metastasized. The marijuana was legal. Maybe smoking pot took away his libido? Maybe it was other things. I was over-sexed in his eyes. I was in peak. I guess I just wanted from Peter what Thomas had given me.

In September, I wanted Peter to go away with me, up to Newport, Rhode Island, only for a few days. I had been asking him for the last two months. To plan our vacation. I had a one week vacation that I needed to take. "No! I can't go away right now." "It's not far," I cried. "You can drive home in four hours if its calls for it." "No!" He was always saying NO!

I was no longer absolved from my sins... Peter drove me back to Thomas. He forced me once again into Thomas's arms, an uncontrollable involuntary reflex. I only needed to be held. I spent a few days in Boston with Thomas and then the two of us went to meet Chiara in Rhode Island. This vacation changed things... It was a strange occurrence. Peter stopped touching me, seven weeks of no sex, no affection, no comfort. Peter must have known. There was no way he could have known. He stopped being my boyfriend. He stopped being my lover. He kept his distance as if looking through a shop window at an object (myself) he coveted but could not fully possess (at this time). He kept his distance and detached himself from me little by little. I continued to try. I still kept trying to keep "us" alive as a couple, even though Thomas was my lover. By now, I accepted things as such. Everyone should have two.

In October, Peter continued to pull away, not wanting to come to my sister's engagement party. I pleaded with him, suggesting he study in the early morning and drive with his friends from Long Island to New Jersey. "I have to study." "But I don't want to be alone," I whined, "besides, Angela and you have been friends for years." "I have to study." Good excuse. It was a justified excuse. I tried. I tried to help him manage his time. I really wanted him there. I didn't want to be alone. I was always alone. I was always crying. "Please," I whimpered. He came to the party but only after his friends convinced him to.

On this freezing, damp, rainy evening, underneath the tent, 100 yards away from the house, when we were finally alone, it dawned on me. I was always telling Peter I loved him. In my own way, I did. "I love you Peter," I said as I kissed him. "I want us to get engaged." "You're it, Rossana. You're the one," he said with a slight twinkle in his eyes. "You're definitely it but I can't right now." He was always telling me I was the one but only <u>after</u> I said (and I said it frequently), "I love you, Peter". He had been telling me I was the one since we first began dating... but I wanted to get engaged. I wanted the ring. I wanted to feel secure, to know he really cared. "I just want to get engaged. A long engagement, two plus years..." "My mother is dying," he said, so stoic. "She might die today. She might die in ten years. Why should we wait? She can join in our happiness," I said upbeat, happy, encouraging. "She's jealous of the time I spend with you." "I just want to get engaged," I coaxed. "You're it but I can't right now," he said even more serious. "Then you're going to lose me," I replied in a flat, emotionless, matter-of-fact tone.

That wasn't the end of us. I continued to keep two as one, trying to help. I was always trying to bring some pleasure into his life. Since it wasn't sex he wanted, since it wasn't compassion he wanted, maybe I could help him manage his time. Maybe he wanted friendship... He didn't want me though he kept saying..."You're it, Rossana." I'm it except for your Harley-riding, white-trash, truck-driver mouth, dying mother!!! She had never left her spandex, Long Island biker existence. It wasn't that I didn't like her. I tried to get to know her. I even bought her a birthday gift. She wasn't a pleasant person. I knew she didn't want me around. It was so obvious by her tone. She was jealous of me, jealous of the time I spent with her son. Maybe it was the medication, the poisons that kept her alive, yet made her bitter. She didn't want her son to spend anytime with me. "You're it," he said over and over again.

I'm it ...and so I dreamed about our wedding[15]. It was a simple irreducible fact that she didn't like me. The wedding would have to wait but at least we could get engaged.

I was still experiencing lascivious thoughts about Thomas. But... I was still trying to keep "us" alive because I knew that Peter had issues, real issues that monopolized his thoughts and that would eventually dissipate. I loved him in my own way. Even though the relationship was a volatile one... In November, I planned a surprise birthday dinner for Peter, starting out with four growing to a party of sixteen! I invited his childhood friends, the friends he never got to see anymore. I just wanted to do something nice for him. He had sacrificed so much of his youth for his Mom. He needed to be with his friends, to enjoy life again. He was young, only thirty, though he acted like an old man. He told me this. His youth had vanished. I wanted to make him feel young again, no worries, no stresses, no thoughts, except for being with his friends... Ever the party planner, I outlined a four course dinner, the type of pasta, the racks of lamb, the wine I would serve, the champagne toast... Two days before the scheduled event, he called me and curtly said: "I understand you're throwing a party for me. I told you I didn't want one!" "It's only a dinner, with your friends. How did you find out?" I was still positive. I didn't want to cause a fight... "Rob told me. I'm going fishing this weekend. Cancel it!!" "You made your choice," I said. CLICK!!! And that was the end...

Maybe he just needed to be alone? Why did he reject my selfless act of kindness? They were his friends. I only wanted him to have a good time. It's Peter's fault I turned to another. I only needed a hug from him. I only wanted to make him smile. I only needed attention, just a little bit from him. Why is it we always want what we can't have??

---

[15] I knew I didn't want to pay for a wedding- it would happen at zero cost. Everything donated from the ridiculous fee the church charged to the outrageous catering demands. I designed my dress and would find a costume designer to comp it. In lieu of gifts, I wanted a donation to be made in Peter's mother's name to the Baldwin Breast Cancer fund. Why have a wedding to pay for a wedding? This was one thing I knew he might say yes to.

He got to spend the time with his Mom, with no one else vying for his attention and affection.. His redeeming quality is that he sacrificed his youth for her, a mother who had left her three boys when they were children. I told you she wasn't a nice lady but she deserved a second chance with her children. Peter gave her this chance... to be loved before she died. I stopped crying. I gave Peter up for love. I needed something he couldn't give me and I couldn't be the person he wanted me to be... for love. Peter never told me he loved me just "You're the one. You're it." I'm what????[16]

In trying to stimulate him emotionally, I sometimes think I pushed him too far. It was an abusive relationship, psychologically, and came very close to crossing the line physically. It we had married, our tempers would have intensified into domestic-violent proportions. I remember thinking about how angry he could get, that Sicilian temper escalating- face red, eyes fiery, arms flailing, shouting matches, myself crying, always crying. I kept thinking he's going to hurt me. At 300+ lbs., it would take only one smack to knock me out and maybe I deserved that smack, for my garrulous tongue always got me into trouble, saying first, thinking later. He's going to shoot me because I pissed him off. (Did he own a gun?) Then... he's going to shoot his mother, like the lame dog, to put her out of her misery, realize his mistake, kill grandma because she witnessed it all and then turn the gun on himself since he had just killed the three (two?) most important women in his life. What a lovely ending except I would still be alive- crippled, a paraplegic, mute... It was a volatile relationship, the ups and downs, hairpin turns taken too fast, twisted involvement... The best thing that ever happened to me is that I let him go. I don't think he really wanted me anyway though he spoke those words-"you're the one". The one what?

---

[16] Peter's mother died 9 months later. He never called me. His friends never called me. I went to the funeral. I didn't think I belonged there but I went. During the processional, I turned away. I couldn't look at him. He bent over and told my sister, "Thank you for coming." During communion, as I passed him, he looked at me, with those big sorrowful sad eyes as if to say "See... you should have just waited..." I wanted to put my arms around him. I wanted to hug him because he was so alone in his grief. (Even his drug addict brother had someone). He was so alone... something I understood, something we had once talked about. I ...

It was his fault I turned and gave 100% of myself to Thomas. One week later, I was crying once again. Thanksgiving. I gave my heart to Thomas... What began as a tumultuous affair of the body, all wrapped up into a single recognizable fact that I belonged to another, grew into an affair of the heart and mind. I realized that I wanted him (Thomas), and only him (Thomas), when Peter had rejected my selfless actions, and at the inopportune time Thomas had made his decision to move West... When I realized that Thomas was the one for me...

6. If I had A Million $$$$

THOMAS WAS THE one for me. I felt it, deep inside. We were always doing things, keeping busy, making love... We went one rainy day to see the Bug movie. I can't remember its name but the bugs take over the world... Pretty stupid. Pretty "what a waste of an afternoon" until... we stopped by his office. He needed to check on something. He showed me hid project, the project that left him a lot of time to play... with me. I couldn't comprehend how I was viewing a three dimensional image. I didn't understand the simple mechanisms. He'd turn it one way. Showed me another perspective. I was impressed. I was astounded. It was fascinating.

There was no one in the building on this icy, Sunday afternoon. No one around as he hugged me while I sat on his lap and compiled a fake love-letter (e-mail) to his friend, as we started to kiss, as I held onto the side of his desk as he devoured me. God. I was in heaven as he entered me and I held on, gripping the desk, holding on as I lay back, holding on as we... There was no one around and we could (I could!) make all the noise we wanted as my screams (he always got me to scream!) echoed down the empty corridors.... Oops- the corner office recently became occupied. When? Who cares when he arrived... he intruded and eavesdropped on our party... Or were we the uninvited guests disturbing an environment reserved for "computing" not fornicating? A little office gossip never hurt anyone... Anyway, this office needed some stimulation. Thomas said he could never look at his desk in the same manner. He could never sit without thinking about me. Thomas said he could still smell me on him for days. He may have been exaggerating; however, my orgasms were so powerful...

December 6, 1997
Hi Contessa Rossana,

I was driving back from seeing Sharon tonight and Bare Naked Ladies "If I had a Million Dollars" was on the radio and I became depressed/lonely. I've been thinking about aspects of our relationship- mostly reflecting on how I felt or more accurately what I wasn't feeling.

The song made me think about how inadequate I've been feeling since my separation. I really felt like I need to be able to give on a grand scale. That's partially due to my upbringing and in part due to the tremendous monetary needs of Sharon's family and in part the break up making me feel that I failed, just adding to my sense of inadequacy. What's does this have to do with you?...not a whole lot. However, it obviously does affect how I relate to you.

And I have to stress "try" because I am trying, despite my less than stellar performance. I realize how little I've been able to feel over the last few years and our relationship is just another example. That is not to say that I'm not feeling but that I believe I should be feeling more. Maybe I shouldn't, maybe I just would never fall in love with you. But I'm not sure this is the case. You're a great person- considerate, attractive, intelligent, sensual, and humorous (one of the things I like most about you). And self- sufficient (this had taken on a growing importance in the last few years) so from rationalizations and what little intuitive insight I can actualize/accept, I think I'm too unconfident- feeling inadequate. No matter how good things are when we were together, I never really feel like I'm there. And sometimes... I'm really somewhere else. I have good times and enjoy your company immensely but I'm just realizing that I never feel like I'm worthy-like I can never take on my half of a relationship.

That's why I'm into the weekend warrior type activities- snow boarding, mountain biking, flying- to try to compensate for or prove that I am capable. But I haven't convinced myself- I don't feel that I have the necessary control, skills, and abilities. But of course these are the wrong adjectives to be striving for in a relationship anyway. So clearly I'm not even looking in the right places yet. But the point is I miss you and I like being around you. But I don't know if I feel more or if I can feel more. It's kind of odd- I'm really worried about the fact that I just don't seem to feel anything that strongly. Not because I just don't seem to feel anything too strongly I can't even get that upset over not feeling. Anyway, I've been feeling more comfortable around you lately and feeling more involved, more alive. But I'm very afraid that you're going to hurt in this. And I really don't want that to happen. This morning in bed... you were asking me about the caressing I do and whether it's innate/something I would do with anyone or something special to you... Well... both. To a degree- anyone I care deeply about I will caress, but the way I touch you- where, when, how- is something that I do for you.

Sunday 12/7/97
Well, clearly finding all your notes this morning has gone on to prove me wrong about being able to feel. Maybe just afraid to feel. I wish you could come with me cross country. But now I'm afraid it would just make the goodbye more painful. I know I need to do this but I've been having serious doubts about it over the last 24 hrs. Thanks again for the notes- I've only found three of them.

Monday 12/8
I really miss you. I hope you can come visit me before May. I'm having a great time with you now - hope you don't hate me too much.

Love, Thomas

9pm-
I found another note- this one was in my sock drawer.

Yes- he confused me. All in one letter- telling me he didn't feel, couldn't feel for me and then in the next paragraph changing his mind. HELP!! It was too late. I loved him and he was leaving me.

I spent as much time as I could with him this last month. I quit my job with Victoria's Secrets. Guess had recruited me three months earlier (but I needed to be closer to Peter). I followed up with them. Guess made me an offer with a lot more money, a chance to be back in Soho, a chance to be back in NYC.

Thomas called me every day as he drove across the nation. I flew out to see him for New Years. Just the two of us bringing in the New Year at some upscale, San Francisco bar in Pacific Heights. Just the two of us in this lonely city of men, straight and gay. It didn't matter. It was "just us".

7.Do You Know the Way to San Jose?

JUST US. OUR sexual excursion continued even though he had moved West, a job opportunity he needed to take. I wasn't going to lose him. He was confused but he would find himself in a land where he'd be mentally challenged, continually stimulated, work would become exciting and passionate. He would find meaning in his life...

Our sexual excursion... he couldn't keep his hands off me as soon as I arrived. He always had flowers. Thank God he knew of my aversion to red roses! He always was waiting right at the gate, carrying a card, always happy to see me. Somehow I found a way to go West almost each and every month. It was difficult not being with him; however, work kept me busy. I was happy at this time, no matter how fierce "bridal bliss" had indoctrinated my life, had saturated my competitive career, I was happy, happy to have him. He was 3500 miles away but still sitting beside me, lending support and guidance. I was happy. We were happy. Do you know the way to San Jose???

Jan 25th, 1998
I'm still at work... I found an apartment but its pretty expensive. $1400 for a 2br/2ba... It gives you another room to decorate. And another room for us to fool around in. And another bathroom which I can lather your legs and shave you smooth....

Later, Thomas

Okay- I left out the page and half of lust, sex, sex, sex!!! His letters were so explicit but so sensual. I didn't need to be there. I could imagine and be taken there...

8.Tiffany's

HE CAME EAST this February. We spent the weekend in
Vermont...

He handed it to me, so small it fit into the palm of my hand. A
present. Oh, how sweet. After all, it was my birthday but he
knew I hated celebrating it. He was so sweet. And wrapped
just so, in the blue signature box, a white ribbon. He was
always so considerate. A little box!? My Mom always said that
the best presents came in little boxes. My heart was
palpitating... Was this what I had been waiting for? The little
box.

Upon closer inspection, I realized its shape was a little too big,
a little too rectangular, not cubed as it should be. I felt like the
little boy, Ralphie, in *A Christmas Story*, you know, Red Ryder
bb gun, and he's so disappointed that he didn't get what he
wanted, always wanted... Dad says look behind the couch,
he's so excited... That was me... disappointment soon
changing as he urges me to open it, the little box. Me? Okay-
he knew the routine. Why wasn't he kneeling? I was on cloud
nine, still dreaming, still hoping even though the box wasn't
the right shape. Excitement I couldn't hide, excitement I
couldn't control as I ripped it open.

The dolphin was blue. So miniscule with a string attached.
What in God's name was this? A toy? Some sexy lingerie? A
blue dolphin. My bewilderment evident as I looked at him
perplexed, disgusted, wide-eyed. "Try it on," he smiled. Try it
on? I didn't understand. "Like this?" "No- like this," as he
adjusted the... beak? No- birds had beaks. Spout? Mouth? He
adjusted it so (one size fits all, and the straps were elastic so I
had nothing to worry about). He turned it on and the dolphin
started to dance? swim? rock back and forth? The sensation-
uhmn, ahhh, so-so. It was electric, well... battery operated.
Nothing could substitute for him except my own nimble
fingers. Why did he buy me this? Yuck! The pulsing was doing
nothing for me. Mind over matter? Probably. I was a sexual
person but this... Yuck! I didn't like it. I didn't like this little

sex game. We didn't need props. I didn't need a prop. I kissed him as if I enjoyed this toy. He had turned on my libido so much I didn't need a prop. Was he afraid I'd turn to another back in NY? Was the gift his token way of trying to keep me chaste? I loved him. I would never turn to another. I would never consider it.

So considerate. He was always thinking about me!

I put it away, deep inside my closet. I forgot about it until one day... my nieces were playing dress up. The dolphin was hidden with the bag of the costumes. "What's this?" the six year old asked. "It's a toy." I said as I grabbed it. "It doesn't work!" I threw it in the garbage, first concealing it in a paper bag!!

Blue dolphins. I prefer blue boxes... little blue boxes.

9. Sugar and Spice and Everything Not Nice

MARCH. A WOMAN'S body is often compared to fruit, her form and flavor one to be savored...
A banana waiting to be eaten, like a woman undressing, peeling away layer upon layer of insecurity...
The sweetness of an orange, succulence of a peach...
The first bite squirting juices, sticky, over one's chin and lips.

Screeeeeech! Like the roadrunner before a calamity! Was my life imitating art or vice versa? Were these borrowed words, phrases overheard? A scenario out of *"Like Water for Chocolate"* or *"9 1/2 weeks"*? The poetry of my actions just a simulated event. (Uhmm, I mean stimulated!!!!) Who cares. It happened!!

Our adventure with fruit began one lazy, rainy afternoon. After arduous lovemaking, time for a snack- a prelude to a much better adventure. How it began is irrelevant to the turn of events, one innocent drop of a grape on my belly, a kiss, a lick, his head moving south, coming up for air, a kiss on my lips(north) yuck! The saltiness of an unknown taste. A finger pushing melon into my mouth to sweeten my palate, sweeten my changing temperament, and to diminish the displeasure shown on my face... And that's when those hands whose fingers knew me so well began a gentle probing, taking the coolness of an iced strawberry inside the hot pulsing walls of my dark, empty corridor. The feeling is indescribable- an orifice filled with sticky... soft... hard...the pliability and roundness of what was entering me... lips once again- in and out, circling slowly about my clit, a pause, a grasp for one more grape, once again sharing the pleasure of a kiss... I became his "juicy bit of June", the luscious crimson cherries, red, ripe, and purely delicious, strawberry's savory appeal... the tart pleasure of a kiwi making me his delectable dessert. I became his culinary delight... our lovemaking, its unique flavor, a function of mood and appetite, ravenous...

AND THEN THE MINT... Icy hot. ICY HOT. ICY HOTTTTTT!!! The coolness of a breeze on a sun-baked ocean and sand, as it melted slowly from the rising Fahrenheit of my insides... Icy-hot as he blew. Icy-hot as he sucked. Icy-hot as he teased, the mint on his tongue, inside me, round and round, icy-hot. STOP!!! I screamed. Too much. I couldn't handle it. I wasn't comfortable with it. I was afraid that I might have an allergic reaction to the aspertane or whatever else made up the mint.

Get real! The pleasure mounted but my mind raced. I got paranoid. He got angry. Enjoy!! He said. I was a mess, a sticky wet mess... the fruit? or from my own explosion?

Delicious... delectable... desirable... that's how he made me feel. That's how he always made me feel.

10
Can you Swim?

APRIL. ON THIS trip west, he gave me permission... I took advantage of the time he was at work and the time I was left alone in his apartment. He knew what I was up to. Decorating was my passion... I made his apartment into a home, moving furniture, moving that heavy bed, unpacking his 18 boxes, hanging photos and prints, creating a bar with the antique, sterling-silver pieces, situating the sculptures of his mother (crafted by his mother) around so that they told a story... story of a woman longing, a story of a woman in repose, a story of a woman desiring... They were beautiful sculptures and looked even more resplendent merchandised as a vignette. I met his Mom on this trip as we drank Martinis and got drunk and laughed. (And I thought I was a little bit eccentric!)

April was the month I think that he became content and grounded. I think this is when he realized that California was his home. Maybe this is when he finally saw "her" as a woman. After-all, I wasn't there all the time. "Her" -the one who forced "us" into forming a triangle, scalene, all sides different, not one equal with the other (at this time).

Nevertheless, "we" (him and I) were always doing things, going places (like the trip to the Russian River Valley to taste the wines or across the mountains to the beach), making love. It didn't matter where. We could never get enough of each other. On this trip west, when we were saying goodbye... of all places... the San Francisco Airport. (This salacious action could have gotten us into a lot of trouble. It didn't matter. When you're in love, you'll do anything, anywhere. Passions take control of your otherwise rational pragmatic being. Or maybe it just was the excitement of possibly getting caught, embraced with the terrifying reality "that this wasn't kosher".) We had to move the car twice but we were never alone. An empty spot soon became occupied. Occupied spots became vacant. I kept climbing off his lap, as if I was reaching into the back seat, dangerous and naughty as I rode him. Oops. Here comes a family. Reach. Reach. My coat covering our naked bottoms. Oops. Here comes a man, right into the car next to

us. Reach. Reach. What am I trying to retrieve from your
hatch back? Oops. I put a stop to it. Too many people. Too
many children walking by. The airport- its own little city,
never private. We were on display to an audience of
insurmountable proportions. He was mad. He was frustrated.
He took so long. There were too many people around. I was
uncomfortable. Too many children. We couldn't do that to the
children. They were still innocent. It would not be fair to have
them ask questions about something they should know
nothing about. He was mad. I stopped him. Too bad. I was
equally frustrated.

..."Are you swimming yet?" I asked in one of our many late
night, long distance conversations. "What?" he said, dazed and
confused. He was still at work. "By now, you're half way to
Hawaii," with girlish laugher, I joked. "Huhh?" he said (He was
probably thinking- what drug is she on?) "You're still
swimming! Hit the Philippines? China?" I screeched, my
speech incoherent, as I laughed and giggled. Needless to say,
he didn't understand. He wasn't supposed to understand. The
moment I put on that wedding dress, he started swimming
west, far, and far away from me. He continued to swim as I
completed the ensemble from gaudy headpiece to sexy
undergarments (ouch! wires-but what an hour-glass figure
and that cleavage!) to matt-satin shoes (Dyeables. They'd fall
apart in the first puddle!)... I wonder if this one wedding gown,
this one role-play, this one make-believe experience had
decided my future, determined my fate as one of perpetual
spinsterhood. Urban legend or plain old sibling rivalry? Seven
years earlier, my sister Diana warned me...

She couldn't find a dress, in all of New York, in all of Long
Island, in every boutique that existed. Kleinfeld's. Bridal
Boutique. Bridal Couture. Peggy Sue's. She tried them all on,
every size, every color, every style. And so we went to Rome,
Italy, my mother's birthplace, the land of romance. We were
guests of all the best Bridal Salons and Houses. Couture. At
one place, we could look but couldn't touch. At another, we
were seated to view the private fashion show. We then could
inquire. Of course, my sister inquired about more than a few.
On the third day, finalmente! One gown! She finally found it.

One gown, white (who was she kidding), silk organza, with a thin, cathedral length train, hand embroidered, hand beaded, the crystals sparkling in a beautiful contemporary mosique. "Quanto Costa?" my mother inquired. "Quaranta millioni lire." "Grazie." my mother replied and continued to converse with the owner. We found out later she had told her she needed to discuss it with her husband. "How much?" we asked. "We need to discuss it with your father," my mother teased. "How much?!" my sister demanded. After all, the gown cost a mere $25,000 and the dollar was double the local currency. "Hey, Diana, you want a wedding or a wedding dress?" I added in my best "you wish" voice. Anyway, as her maid of honor, I was caught up in the experience and dreaming of my own wedding (though Prince Charming was probably still in diapers since. I always dated them young.) I wanted to try on a gown, to play dress up like her. "NO!" Diana said. "It's bad luck to try on a wedding gown unless you're engaged!"

I should have heeded her advice.

I had always wanted to work in the Bridal business, to design Special Occasions gowns. I had a knack for designing elegance, for designing the right style for the right bride, a passion I never pursued.[17] As luck (or fate) would have it, I was recruited heavily to manage a bridal superstore. I always wanted to be in Bridal- such a nice experience (yeah- right!) Those damn recruiters. The offer was too good to turn down (25% increase in salary). I took it.

During the training, in order to understand how to sell a dress, you had to understand the emotions of being a bride-to-be, you had to partake in the ritual of selecting a gown, the overwhelming feeling, the pressure, good, bad, hormones on a roller coaster ride. After-all, this is the most important day of your life, a day you have been dreaming about since you were a little girl, a day when all your fantasies could come true. I'm

---

[17] A passion I would have pursued except I got disgusted by what was said to me by two, not one!, Professors at FIT. "You need to draw your croques thinner. The fashion world dictates that they be drawn this way- thin, long legs..." What happened to thinking out of the box? developing a personal style? drawing a real woman the way a real woman looks (curves, all curves)?

sure you remember that day. (Thomas once told me that the difference between a man and a woman is that the woman views the dress as the most important thing because that is what he'll see, she thinks. Thomas said that when he got married, he saw his wife and his future walking down the aisle, not a dress!) Selling skills 101. An in-depth role play. I got to be the bride first.

I was happy and ecstatic as I put on the dress and looked at myself, a grin from ear-to-ear, a vision before me. Was that me? The bride. A short walk down a long aisle. A quick glimpse of him kissing me. I do. His wife! The honeymoon (oops! too x-rated for this day dream)... The dress. An ivory (I knew better) matt Duchess-satin off-the-shoulder A-line with blush border. Two tone. Tiny, yellow (there was a dye lot issue) rosettes throughout the bodice... and the train- an in-laid organza Cathedral train. I couldn't stop staring at myself in the mirror. I couldn't control my giddiness. I was overwhelmed (me! of all people- overwhelmed! and this was make believe). When they put the veil on, added long gloves, I started to get teary eyed. I was a bride... finally!

Selling skills 101. I made the mistake of telling him about this. I knew he went swimming, west. He didn't think it was funny. Maybe this is when it changed. He had said he missed me. He had said the apartment was mine as much as it was his. He had said he couldn't wait to see me. He had asked about my training. I made the mistake of telling him. April 1998. This is when it changed. It was no longer just us.

April. May. Five weeks. I found his apartment, his life, still in cardboard boxes. I had turned his apartment into a home. I transformed his "bed and box" boudoir into a peaceful enclave. Uncovering, moving, hanging, changing. I left him happy. Five weeks. I had left him alone. Something changed. He missed me and it would be five weeks before I would see him again. But the letters kept coming, those love letters...

April 20, 1998
Dear Rossana,

I was just looking through the pictures- **BOING**, *schwing*, hhhhh, hhhhh, hhhhh- yeah baby! Show me what you got! I probably shouldn't be working on this letter at 9am- it'll just get me all worked up and frustrated. I've been that quite enough for the last week. Ever since someone left me in a parking garage all worked up and no place to go. I had to relive my frustration twice yesterday. All I kept thinking on my way home was I really wished you enjoyed giving head as much as I do. That's kind of a general desire anyway, but it could have been appropriately employed then., Oops, yeah, here I go, getting all worked up and have to be in a meeting soon. I enjoy oral stimulation too much but I do enjoy receiving it too. Oh boy- I did want some then- I was ready to pop, explode, fill you with my desire... (trip plans)

Tuesday morning
It's not fair, I think women should get all sexually frustrated and know that relief is only a dolphin away but real relief is much further. Ok- I'm still frustrated. I was kind of mad at you on Saturday because you weren't here and it was a really nice day out and I did some work on my place and it kind of feels like its your place too but you weren't here to enjoy it and I'm really just rambling on right now but its all your fault- so there! Hold on- need my coffee...

So where was I- ahhh, sexual frustration, nice day, you weren't her- yeah, so I was thinking how you should be here... I keep thinking how juicy you are, I can almost taste that silky, slippery, almost syrupy sexual secretion- next time I pick you up at the airport, I hope you're not wearing pantyhose, maybe not even underpants. I'm trying to get work done and I'm getting all worked up. And you wonder why I don't write you letters- look what it does to me.... (trip plans)... I hope your training went well. I'll talk to you between now and...Only four weeks 'til I see ya! I guess I should get the suit fitted?...

Frustratedly yours,

Thomas

11.

MAYBE IT WAS the weather, the Nor'easter refused to let up, mother nature at her fiercest, day after day of rain, day after day of gloominess, day after day of... Human beings need warmth. Maybe he sought it out in the body heat of "her"?

May. He was so confused. I was more confused. His last letter stated he missed me and that his home was ours; yet, it was a cold shoulder that greeted me at the business class lounge of Alitalia. Maybe it just was a bad flight? Maybe he was mad I hadn't met him at the gate as planned. I tried. I hopped on the shuttle bus but it broke down. I couldn't walk across Kennedy Airport- he was at the other end, another terminal far, far, away. I tried. He would just have to believe me. I was mad at him for not dressing better. Didn't he want to get upgraded? Stuck in coach, it was a long flight to Rome. It didn't matter. He was here with me. I was so happy. For once, no disappointment. We had made plans before he left, over seven months ago and he had kept the commitment. I would not have to go to a wedding alone (the story of my life). I would not have to be at my sister Angie's wedding alone. I was with him.

Rome...land of romance. It was a hectic few days. Family commitments. Friends galore. Over 75 people had come from the States. The rehearsal dinner set in Medieval Rome. If I had one more Limoncella shot? Afterwards, we hit a small local pub, pubs were becoming popular in Rome...10 of us. My crazy brother-in- law-to- be, David, decided to get up on the bar and dance with the young lady, half dressed in a croptop, black hot pants, fishnets, and leather boots, hired to draw attention. An empty bar soon became packed as one after another curious Roman sauntered in to view the crazy American gyrating, dancing, swinging, swaying... with the half naked woman beside him! A night of drinking that would give us all a nasty hangover the next day.

The wedding was like no other... the ceremony was held at Il Quirinale, a small, circular Church perfect for the intimacy of the event. Thomas looked so elegant in the trendy Guess suit I had purchased for him. The goatee I had begged him to grow transformed his boyish appearance into a charming scholarly look. Why was he wearing a yellow shirt? Where was the black one I had purchased? "The yellow one was a gift." "From who?" It didn't matter...he was here with me. The reception was set on a grand estate, Villa Il Borgo at Grotta Ferrata, one hour outside Rome. Too bad the charter bus got lost. We rode around in circles before he finally got us to the estate at sunset. Thank goodness, I had purchased some local vintage wine and the festivities commenced as we passed the bottles from lips to lips, the party continuing as we circled the mountain for a second time. As the wine dimmed our senses, we were one in the realization that the radio tower now stood to our right??

We arrived late... We could not enjoy the gardens; however, Thomas and I made sure we christened the boxwood hedge while the statues kept watch. Thomas appreciated me like a beautiful piece of art, every curve (of my body), every color (that I wore), the texture of my skin (that I made sure remained silky). Sold! To the highest bidder... He appreciated me and taught me how to be a woman! We snuck out shortly before the main course was served. I came back glowing... g-l-o-w-i-n-g... I loved him. He was here with me.

Rome was chaotic. My aunt kept coming up to the penthouse apartment where Thomas and I were staying... "Rossana, Rossana"- knock, knock, knock... as Thomas and I were... doing what we usual did when no one was around. "Rossana, Rossana."- a second time..."Your sister is on the phone..." I stopped him. We continued. "Rossana, Rossana."- a third time... "Your mama is on the phone...". He became frustrated. My aunt had interrupted us... as we were about to... as we were in full action. Luckily, she was a lady but I could see the embarrassment on her face. She knew what we were doing... The curse of that penthouse as my next door neighbor would point out that eve: "Be careful, any couple who stays in the penthouse... usually breaks up. Chiara (my sister) and Sal, Jimmy (her brother) and Jill. Sorry- I didn't mean to jinx you but it's a known curse..." The curse of the Monte Mario hospitality. The hex had been cast...

12.

OUR VACATION TO Greece didn't happen as I planned, a journey into the past where Thomas would declare his love for me, once and for all. It started out in a happy familiar atmosphere. In Athens, we had dinner with his grandparents, a cute couple in their 90's who still managed on their own, a wonderful couple married for over 70 years... Nevertheless... on this first night, he sprung it on me once again. Like his December letter... he was confused. He didn't know if he should feel more. He didn't understand why he didn't feel more. He wasn't sure if he could ever love me. Once again, I was subject to his doubts... He loves me. He loves me not. He loves me. He loves me not... Doubting Thomas at his best... Once again, I felt insecure, inadequate. What more could I do? He knew I loved him. "I'm going back to Rome, with my family." "No!" he cried, the tears falling, "please don't leave me." "I need to go back to Rome- its useless for me to continue with you..." "No..."

I went to the window, looking for answers, looking for guidance, hoping that the view would give me a sign... As I looked outside and turned my head west, I saw the Acropolis standing alone, dark and sullen. I pondered? Where were the lights whose reflection cast a glow on the Doric columns of an ancient civilization, a world long, long gone? Why was this monument, a landmark, clothed in a shroud of black? Was the blackness a foreshadowing of a void soon to be? The Parthenon- an inspiration to the Mediterranean world- why couldn't it inspire us? It stood as a tribute to Athena and represented the beginning of western civilization, its changing façade reflective of its changing uses: temple, church, mosque. Was its lost brilliance our lost love?

Rome! Oh Rome! That's where I should be... He convinced me to stay with him, amidst his tears, his ramblings, his weak demeanor, his sensitivity. Why didn't I see the signs...love IS blind. I was blind. I loved him so. And he COULD feel....

I stayed with him as if nothing had changed. We went to the Greek Islands, the Island of Paros and stayed in Parikia, the main town. We had the island to ourselves since the tourist

season was still three months away. We had the island to
ourselves and explored, a sensual voyage of sex and food, our
cries echoing down dark, quiet hallways, the power of our
lovemaking reverberating through thin "American" walls, our
sighs escaping outside open balcony doors whose neighbors lie
carelessly eavesdropping, our happiness, momentary, being
carried by the wind over the glistening Mediterranean.

We had the island to ourselves but Thomas had been pick-
pocketed in the Athens flea market. No license. I didn't have
mine. A little dilemma. We would not be able to explore... Until
he convinced the local shopkeeper (possibly his grandfather's
influence) to rent us a scooter. We had the island to ourselves,
no one else... as we explored Naoussa to the North, Aliki to the
South, Dhrios to the East... the island to ourselves... It was
just us.

13.

JUST US... After one and a half hours on a scooter and a meal
of grilled fish, a traditional Greek salad with goat cheese that
melted in your mouth, tzatziki (my favorite), and a bottle of the
local Retsina wine, I told him I wanted to walk, explore the
road that elevated behind us, especially since my thighs were
rubbing after only four days on the island. What would my
body look by day eight? He rode on to see what, if anything,
was at the top- a top that never ended from this sea level view.
So there I was walking, jogging, tripping, sweating up the
never- ending dirt road... up, up, up as it got steeper, turned
left, sharply right, zig-zagged its way getting dryer and
sparse... up, up, up- behind water, above me the rocky cliffs.
Just as I stopped, bent over, catching my breath, trying to
regain my composure, he came zooming down. To save me?
Rescue me from impending heat stroke?? So considerate-
always thinking of me (or just not wanting me to yell at him
for leaving me for so long!). We rode to the what appeared to
be the pinnacle.

One lonely, deserted lighthouse loomed a half mile above. Was
it an optical illusion caused by the desert-like conditions?

After all, I was tired, dirty, perspiring from my trek. Or was the structure, reality, a representation of the power of the island, once guiding the ships into the safe harbor? Its ghostlike walls showed no signs of life from within-too quiet, too complacent, undisturbed. From this height, we could barely make out the taverna and sea below, behind us from whence we came. In front, the cliffs dropped precariously down to an ocean of magnificent proportions, one small boat bobbing on the horizon. We were perched on a rising land mass, two sides surrounded by water- one, calm, the blinding reflection of light from its glasslike plain; the other turbulent as the waves rose and fell, their crests a white contrast to the azure temperamental surface. We were alone on this rocky, barren mountain. Alone in paradise. Outside. In touch with nature, the heat of the sun could not compete with the rising temperature of our lust compounded by the beauty of this domain...

...And so we made love, in heaven, above the earth, spinning on an axis of desire, flying as we swooped and glided, windswept over the sea below... weightless as I was lifted, arching my back, a much too blue sky encircling me ... I felt I could reach out, touch the stars, outer space was within my grasp... Heaven- in our Garden of Eden- just the two of us. The sun, moon, earth, water- four elements circumferencing and enveloping our naked bodies.

It was me. It was him and nothing else mattered... Not even when we left and saw the abandoned scooter very near, discarded in a haphazard way. Two other lovers, perhaps? Or a voyeur? Our act, a captivating educational forum.

It was me. It was him. Nothing else mattered... As we drove away into the twilight eve, the sun setting into a cascade of colors, an artists palette of hot, explosive, fading light.

14.

IN JUNE, THE weather prevented us from being together. I cried the whole ten hours as I waited at the airport. I tried to get on a plane, any plane. I needed to get to him. I cried as I begged the airline agent to place me anywhere. I cried as I returned home ten hours later, still in NY, no scheduled flight west... A stupid conversation which I initiated when I couldn't get a flight. A stupid conversation in which I said it was difficult and I couldn't handle being apart. He agreed. It was difficult. "Maybe we should start seeing others..." "No," I cried. It was difficult but I would find a way to make it work. Someday... he'd ask me to move west!

6/6/98
Rossana,

How are you doing? Not that great I guess. Between work and this past weekend, things have been better. Though physically nothing has changed, the apartment feels emptier, photos of you/us vary between piercing and hollow depending on my mood and work has suddenly become overwhelming.

Why am I writing? This may the last thing you'll read from me. But mostly to let you know that you are a significant person and influence in my life.... I will always think of you as a close friend... not to mention I will never look at apples or grapes in quite the same way- how many people can say they get turned on by fruit? ...I'm glad we went to Paros- for me it ranks as one of the best of our shared experiences

Love, Thomas

15.
"I Left My Heart in San Francisco"

JULY... I needed to see him. I needed to look into his eyes. I
needed the closure. I didn't want the closure... He sent a limo
to San Francisco when my plane got detained, I missed the
connection, the next leg re-routed. I arrived at three am. The
futon was waiting for me with open arms. I was a little
flabbergasted. Why would he want me to sleep elsewhere? If
that wasn't a red light. Why was he making it so obvious that
he didn't want to be with me? I went into the bathroom,
keeping quiet, trying not to awake him. God I loved him. I bent
down, watching him sleep, looking at him with adoring eyes. I
bent down to kiss him goodnight, on the cheek. He awoke,
deliberately. He kissed me back. We kissed for long hours, our
bodies wanting, wishing, but never... I slept in his arms that
night. He held me tightly. ...The next day he called and said he
was detained at the office. I spent the day exploring the
vintage stores in the seedy part of town. I loved vintage, so
much a part of my quirky personality. Vintage made me feel so
feminine... I picked him up late, very late.... We went directly
to the pool, swimming, playing, laughing. He held me in his
arms and kissed me. He picked me up, threw me over his
head. He caught me and grabbed me from behind. Just the
two of us in the community pool. Just the two of us in this
jovial early evening game. We took a hot tub and continued to
play and tease. As if nothing had changed... Just the two of
us. I think he missed me. His actions showed he did. His
expression remained stoic. I couldn't tell.

One depressing July night, only one week after my last and
final trip West, when I was sitting alone, and I felt lonely and
my decision had already been made to move back with my
Mommy and Daddy... I received the call, the dreaded call
which should never have been made for its revelation should
have happened three months earlier. He told me about her.
She was his boss. His boss? I thought it would be the cute
twenty-something girl who watered his plants. His boss? She's
Asian. Why would he ever? Duhh... she was exotic, what every
white male is currently in pursuit of and I was the minority,
your average anglo female. His boss- the comptroller of a

successful, internet company. I was stuck in a mid-management level, working in middle-class retail, always the bridesmaid, never the bride (though I got to deal with them daily). His boss! She was the incumbent. She wasn't supposed to win. His boss. Successful, wealthy, educated... How could I compete with her? My self-esteem just plummeted... like a bird whose wings had been suddenly clipped. His boss!

It was enough that he had found another, but why did he have to cleanse himself of his developing, escalating, guilt-ridden anxiety by explaining and giving me more information than I cared to hear, to choose <u>this</u> moment to put me in my place. He could have simply said "it's over.. there's someone else." Instead he had to insult me further, rub salt in the wounds just beginning to scar, by stating that "one thing led to another..." in this wimpy, childish, it-wasn't-my-fault voice!

"You prick! You didn't need to tell me you were sleeping with her!" I yelled as I got a visual of the two of them, post-coitus, naked bodies (was she skinny?), flushed faces, his lips dripping, slick... "You prick! I didn't need to know!"

"Well, I just wanted you to know how it happened. She had a boyfriend. They broke up. We broke up. You know..." On and on he went ... "You prick!" I cried and slammed down the phone, sending it flying off the kitchen table, breaking it into a thousand pieces... That night he had to add one more thing to my plate of increasing, unresolved issues.

A few days later, I received the statue in the mail, the Greek mythological statue, the Greek with the large penis, the prick! It made me laugh, the comedic relief needed in this never-ending horror story of "when good things turn bad!" The statue that caused the airport alarm to set off as he ran through the x-ray catching his post Rome connection west. The statue that I had thrown and hid in his carry-on. The statue that he was unaware of... the statue that he unwrapped in front of a tough NYC airport security team. A statue that would turn his cheeks from an exhausted pink to a crimson red, spreading rapidly like a bad rash to his face and neck... The statue which I now hold, usually hidden and tucked away in my bedroom. A statue which he sent back as a reminder of who he was in my eyes. A statue that reminds me of him, always ready (willing) to please, always in a state of arousal, always (trying to be) prone, always...

She had not quite won him over, I thought! I knew he would be back east in five weeks for his cousin's wedding. "Can't you just stay and escort me to my sister's wedding?" I asked. "Too much time away from work," he said. "Can't you fly back?" "Too costly," he added. As if $375 was going to bankrupt him. It was always about money with him. "I can't," he reiterated.

I knew I would see him. I knew he would want to see me and when he did, he would realize his longing and desire for me... I refused to fight for him but convinced of my purpose and value, I would surge forward and obliterate the competition. I wanted him to come back to me... I just wanted what was once mine and so rightfully belonged to me again... He would come to me. I had a few weeks to plot and scheme, put together my masterpiece, plan the ultimate coup d'etat! I would win him back...

16.
One night stand, two nights bliss...

SEPTEMBER. THE $10 black knit dress (I think I bought it at Mandies) was draped with the $250 Ferragamo scarf he had given me for Christmas. It was an understated elegance- the classic line of black (to make me look thin) with a sharp contrast of color (red, hot!). It was designer cheap and chic all dressed as one. The perfect blend of feminine charm, style, and seduction suited for our reunion. I made sure I looked good! I would not grovel, nor beg him to take me back. I would win him back...

He brought me a gift- a brocade vintage suit. I had asked him to go to the seedy part of downtown San Jose and purchase something, anything vintage. I had found the store on my last visit but had run out of money so I couldn't shop, shop, shop.

He remembered. So considerate. He was always so considerate. And it was perfect.

That night. Dinner with his friends- Churascuria. The Brazilian restaurant where skewer after skewer is brought before you, sliced before you to taste, devour, gluttonize. A little circle on the table indicating yes (green) or no (red) not that the waiters paid any attention to that. Lamb. Filet mignon. Pork. Veal. Steak. Prime rib, etc, etc.. Kept coming round and round. It was like old times, very recent times. Fun. He was so attentive. We were relaxed though his friends seemed a little apprehensive. They couldn't figure out why we were together, if we had gotten back together, if we were... What were we?

Drinks at the Irish bar around the corner, just the three of us: Thomas, his best friend, and me. I shouldn't have had that last vodka. I purposely had that last vodka. I didn't want to drive home- alone. Good trick. It wasn't a trick. I just wanted to extend the evening... I just wanted to remain in his company.

My house. I didn't want it to be that "wonder-what's-going-to-happen" kind of night so I curled myself up into a quilt on the floor, next to the antique brass twin bed. He came out of the bathroom into the room. He bent down and picked me up, cradling me in his arms, my protests smothered by his kisses. He laid me gently on the bed. He kissed me slowly, sweetly, caringly, the way he always did. We made love that night, late, late into the evening, into the early morning. (Luckily my parents slept on the other side of the house!)

After an embarrassing cup of coffee with Mom, I drove him back to Connecticut but a bottle- neck prevented us from going past exit 13 on the Hutchinson. It was Saturday morning. Only in NY is there always traffic.... He drove me to work with a promise to return my car later. At some point in the afternoon, he came into the store. I wanted him to stay but I didn't say this. I only thought it. His brother was waiting for him and so I went out to say hello and what I thought was goodbye, forever... or until we meet again. I knew that the night before was special but isolated. He called me two hours later. He surprised me by his actions. He wanted to see me that night. He asked to see me that night. He had a family function but would meet me later, after. Of course I said yes...

I went home. Took a nap. Took a shower. I got dressed. The clock struck ten. I hadn't heard from him. I wasn't worried because I knew he wouldn't stand me up but it was getting late and I had to work the next morning. I left him a voicemail and drove to Connecticut with the hope of getting there about the hour he was due home... Perfect timing..

We sat in his sister's apartment (an apartment which you had to access through a three story fire escape behind a travel agency in one of the commercial houses set off a side street of the Greenwich strip). We sat in the small crowded living room with his dad, sister and her fiancé making idle conversation. The company seemed "incohesive" as if being together was the last thing they wanted. I needed to get out of there. It was an awkward setting and I didn't feel like I could add anything positive to this "stiff" environment. I needed to get out of there because I wanted to be alone with him.

We took a walk in the cool September night, amidst the large Greenwich estates. We ended up on Main Street in a local bar-The Dome- but it was crowded, three deep, with single people, a night out, ready to meet, mingle, etc... I just wanted to be in his arms, alone. We found a quiet restaurant, sat outside, and talked. Just being there with him was enough. I was happy. He seemed... I can not quite peg it. His job was going well. He told me he had yet to take the stock options (His company was on the verge of an IPO, as most tech companies were, in that time of escalated wealth.); however, his boss kept coaxing him to. His boss. (Little did I know that "his boss" was now officially "his girlfriend".) I had been telling him the same thing for months. It was something about money. He was always concerned about money even though he made a base salary over $85,000, even though he lived simply. He was always talking about money. I asked him once why? "Sharon (his Tennessee two-stepping ex- wife) and I never had any money because she was always sending it to her family."

He did something, the something that I can never forget, the something that will always bother me. He took his ring off his finger, the crest (his family crest) that I had always admired. He placed it on my left hand, next to my pinky. I looked at him and said quickly: "I'm a size 6 ½." Quickly. Too quickly- a flash thought of him kneeling, asking... as my heart raced. It was gone in an instant, erased from my mind as if it never existed when I looked at him. It was weird. He was acting weird but there was an apparent lack of anything as his calm, stoic stance remained so. That calm stoic stance that seemed so much a part of his waspy upbringing. He was just sitting there although his eyes revealed his troubled being...

I was confused, bewildered by his actions. Near miss? What was he doing? What was he thinking? Did he think he loved me? Did he think he wanted to marry me? I say think because he once told me he wasn't sure if he knew how to love. He thought too much. (I was astounded when he once said to me that he thought he had been in love with only one woman. She was not his wife.) What was he thinking this eve?

Was he asking me to marry him? It was so weird!!! He was so weird, all weekend. He wanted me. He pretended to want me. He pretended...

As they always do- temporary adornment, momentary passions... I spent the night. An isolated event turned into a weekend of passion, our weekend of passion. I was with him again! I had won him back, I hoped. I dreamed. I wanted. No one could foresee the events to come that would change things forever...

17.
Judas
(Thomas continued)

For one week, POG emanated. POG (post orgasmic glow) had me dancing, singing, smiling. I dreamed of us. I knew "us" could still be. I never would have thought that a tragedy would disrupt my happiness...

MY SISTER GOT married one week later, a ten-hour reception held at Amagansett's Gansett Green, a beautiful ten-hour, sunshine-filled afternoon, sunset, evening. Ten hours with friends and family. Kiki married my ex-boyfriend. I wanted Thomas there but he didn't want to spend the money to fly east. He couldn't take off work. He missed out on this perfect, happy day. The only negative occurrence was a little uneasiness the morning of... JoJo, my sweet little brother, had a bad attitude. He turned against my best friend of 27 years, Cristina, and yelled at her during breakfast: "This is for the T———'s only. Get out!!" What was wrong with him? "She's a part of the family", I yelled back!!! Something wasn't right with him. He wasn't his usual friendly self...

Three days later, a Tuesday, I left work early. I knew he was going to die. I kept thinking as I drove along the Clearview Expressway..... He's going to die and I'm going to see Steve(#1) at the wake... I thought about his death. Why was I thinking about death in lieu of POG, in lieu of the happiness I was feeling. A premonition??

This feeling of uncertainty grew stronger as I knew my mother was feeling the same uneasiness. We, my mother and I, are both witches. We share that same sixth sense. My mother and I share the same dream- a dream whose outcome left us, together as one, with a sense of emptiness, guilt, and longing for someone we may have saved. The reality is we couldn't have saved him... His body could not fight the magnitude of this last impediment...

We both heard that scream around 5 am, the beginning of a beautiful autumn morning. I remember thinking "Mommy-JoJo's calling you." I remember even speaking these words-spoken in a quiet tone? a somewhat audible tone? or just not at all? My mind was a little restless, falling half way between the subconscious state and the fully aroused one. My body was too tired with not enough strength in me to discover the source. My Mom also heard the scream but couldn't distinguish in her fog-like, half awake state what it was or where it was coming from... She would be checking on JoJo shortly, when she got up, anyway.

I remember waking up and looking at the clock – 6:00am – too early. Okay, I could sleep in this morning because I didn't need to be at work until 11:00. This meant I could roll out of bed at 10, leave by 10:30. My thoughts were interrupted... Next thing I knew, I remember my mother calling from the bottom of the stairs in a gentle tone, devoid of emotion: "Rossana-get-up, get-dressed, come downstairs- JoJo has fallen." Fallen??

My Dad was leaning over him- the stethoscope hanging loosely around his neck. JoJo was on the floor- the froth seeping from his lips. THE FROTH- the insignia of death. I had known it- experienced it- seen it all before... déjà vu? Had I awoken yet? Why was I being subject to this nightmare again?? JoJo was laying on the floor, barely breathing- (was he breathing?) though he was still alive. JoJo- gasping, wheezing, the spittle coming out of his mouth, spittle that was still white, a sign that his lungs had not yet filled with blood. A sign that he was still alive- barely... maybe... please, God. Young men just don't drop and die.

JoJo – my sweet little brother, who only three days prior had danced with my sister, Kiki, at her wedding. (It was if this wedding was the final culmination, his last hurrah. Could he have known?) JoJo, who only that week played golf with the boys, watching his brother-in-law snag a hole-in-one. JoJo, who just last week, ran up behind me, threw his arms around my neck (so unexpectedly) and planted slobbering kisses on my cheek, exclaiming "that's 'cause no one else will..." JoJo, only that Sunday, had handed me a Diet Coke stating: "I bought this for you because I know you're thirsty and I don't want you asking me for some of mine". JoJo. His speech impediment was strong; however, if you listened carefully with fine-tuned ears (instead of rudely asking: "what did he say?"), you could understand every word as if clearly spoken, the syllable count as it should be. His disjointed gait was evident; yet he managed to run and keep up with the best of us. JoJo- our temperamental, energetic, loving, disabled brother. What he lacked for in physical ability and mental intellect, he made up for with his looks. He was the handsomest of all the T's with a tiny pug nose, midnight eyes, voluminous dark hair and a magnanimous smile, always a smile. In many ways, he looked most like my eldest sister, Diana.

I was told to wait for the paramedics, to escort them to the basement- JoJo's bachelor pad. His swinging apartment was designed with leather couches, a sound system that could blow the roof off any rockin' house, two tv's, two vcr's, cable, a room with a vast inventory of cd's/videos that anyone would be jealous of...

The paramedics arrived within five minutes, five very long grueling minutes. Prior to becoming national heroes, they were my heroes. The Fire Department paramedics- who handled this incident with professionalism and poise. The Fire Department paramedics- who couldn't revive my little brother even after injecting him with Valium, with Ativan, with another anti-seizure drug. No response. Calm and professional- they tried. No response. The paramedics- who exclaimed they had never seen someone not respond to all the drugs. They didn't understand why his lungs had so much fluid. (They were talking calmly to each other.) The paramedics - who did not let pride get in the way, who called for back up, whose only personal goals were to save this young man (not yet 26). Still... no response. My heroes, who stayed with us in the emergency room, until a diagnosis could be made. The paramedics- whose names I never knew... If in need of help, call the Fire Department - professional, prompt, with poise...

My mother rode with JoJo... As she was getting into the truck... she saw something- his legs flying, up and down! A response? One last fight? One last spasm of pain? Could he even feel??? Did he know what was happening? (Was the cry this morning, a cry of anguish? A cry for help? Or just a cry to let us know?)

My father drove himself to the hospital- he didn't want me with him. I drove myself. Did we need these few moments to collect our thoughts and realize the calamity of the event taking place? Did we need this time to regain our composure before facing the truth? We were three unified in our pain yet we needed to be alone for just these few minutes, a short drive that transcended over an immeasurable fraction of time... A short drive to the hospital. A short drive that somehow made us all strong and supportive. Until he was stabilized? Until we had some tangible proof that he would live? Until he was dead?

We were all calm in the chaotic events taking place before us. We were all calm with a formidable grip on our faculties. My mother, my father, and myself.

The head of ER informed us that JoJo had suffered a cerebral hemorrhage. He would be subject to additional tests in order to evaluate and determine the extent of the damage to his brain. I didn't understand. Dilantin had kept JoJo's seizures under control for the last eighteen years. Why had he suffered something so severe now? Young men don't just drop.

I called Thomas. I needed his advice, his quiet calm to keep me focused. He listened and then told me to keep him informed. He knew I was upset but staying strong. Then it was time. I had to call my siblings. I was afraid. Every one of us possessed the Sicilian tempers of our heritage. I was afraid because I knew a single sentence, if not clearly stated, could throw any one of us into conniptions. It was time to call my siblings, a task that proved difficult due to extraneous factors, not only the message that was to be delivered... Kiki had just changed jobs. I didn't have her number. Angela was somewhere in the city working for? The name of the company escaping me. I couldn't find her number. What was I to do? Who was I to call first? Remain calm, I kept telling myself. Remain calm. Birth order became the determining factor. Birth order...

"Hi Diana? What are you doing? Give the baby to Rob. We are at the hospital. JoJo had a seizure. You need to come here now." I was calm, flat. I had no emotion in my voice but was determined to make her realize she needed to get here now! I took a deep breath as I knew what was to come, what was to be said. "What??? How?!" she screamed. I knew this wasn't going to be easy. "I don't understand?" the small child questioning. I could tell she was losing it. "Explain to me what is happening"... as if at this moment I could go into a full recounting of events. "Just get here now!!!!" I said in my best "you're pissing me off" sisterly voice. "Okay- but I need to call Albert..." Diana taking charge in the only way she could. Diana, the eldest, our role model, the one I emulated and aspired to be like ...once an Assistant to the Governor, now mother of three. Diana, who now needed her Daddy at this moment.

Two down- two plus more to go. Kiki? She was a newlywed, still basking in the glory of that milestone she had reached. How could I tell her? I didn't even know how to find her. I called my best friend. "Can you call your husband and get David's number and have him call Kiki, please. Tell her she needs to come now to Long Island Jewish. Tell her..." Angie- she wasn't at her desk. Should I leave a message?... Jessica (my sister-in-law) lived nearby but she was pregnant. Should I call her?? How was I was going to get in touch with all of them? Remain calm. This was probably the most difficult moment in my life. I had to tell my sisters and brother about JoJo. Remain calm. I realized that the news would have a detrimental effect on all of them...

We were all calm as we waited for the family to arrive. I knew that Diana would be out of control and I warned the ER nurse that a dark haired, irrational women would soon arrive. We were waiting at the paramedics desk...We were all calm as Diana came running, crying, demanding to know what had happened... as Diana crumbled into my Daddy's arms. We were all calm in the face of the hysterical... as they arrived ... my family... one by one.

We sat. We waited. We wondered. We contemplated privately.

The diagnosis: JoJo had suffered a grand-mal seizure caused by a massive brain hemorrhage- too extensive, too deep. "If he comes out of the coma, he'll be one third of the person you once knew. I can't operate. I won't – it's invasive surgery." God (the neurosurgeon) wouldn't operate. To my father: "Doctor. If you want me to operate, I will, but... Doctor to Doctor..." This cocky, son-of- a-bitch Doctor was being direct- too damn direct in lieu of the crisis we were facing. I didn't like him very much. God. Who did he think he was?

In the first few moments of the family gathering, as we sat at the paramedics desk, we decided unanimously, to pull the life support- JoJo wouldn't want to live that way. JoJo, so full of energy in his limited capabilities would not want to live as a cripple, as a mute, in a paraplegic state. JoJo- so full of life...We would donate his organs. We were unanimous in our decision- it seems cruel but we simultaneously thought the same thing. Except MOM- She alone held on to hope. She alone believed in miracles and life. She alone stated: "NO! I will not make that decision. Joseph's going to give us a gift. Joseph will come out of this or he's going to go quietly on his own so we won't have to make a decision." Mom. So strong. So alone in what she believed.

One hour? Two? We sat, united in our decision. We had resolved it in our own minds. THEN ... The other Doctor, the neurologist, came by to give us an evaluation of the cat scan: "There is brain activity." We asked the questions, questions that are difficult in light of the new circumstances, circumstances which should have made us happy and filled us with hope... however, we had already resolved certain things in our own minds. "I can't make the decision for you to pull life support. There is activity," he said in a concerned way. He seemed afraid of us, as if we were a rogue mob set lose to destroy, burn, and pillage. We were just 11 (well, 10) concerned (scared) individuals who thought as one...

What do we do now? He's dead? He's alive? Two opposing points of view... One Doctor- clear, concise, to the point- his brain imploded. The other Doctor- he's still alive....

This was happening to another family- not ours! Our family-how we yelled, we fought, we laughed, but most of all, we loved. Our family- the 12 of us no more.... To understand us is to know that Joseph, the youngest of six, was the glue. Our family- as dysfunctional as any other normal family. Our family, who only a few days prior, celebrated. Our family...

Tick tock. My Dad went home. A small book lay open in his study. The open page said: *Believe in miracles. They happen every day...* Every day was the same as we stayed with him as he slept. *JoJo- can you hear me?* (from The Who's "Tommy")...

as we prayed, as we spoke to him, as we prayed for a miracle. In the beginning, we knew he heard us as there was some movement, some idle twitching of his limbs. We wanted to believe this was more than an involuntary reflex... Each night, Mommy and I slept with him, one on the chair next to his bed holding his hand, the other in the corner, touching his feet. Each day, we stayed, taking turns, blasting Andrea Bocelli's "Ti Parturo" (Angela's wedding song and JoJo's favorite), singing, laughing, talking to him. Each day. We believed in miracles. We wanted a miracle. We needed a miracle.

Tick tock. I had not spoken to Thomas though I had left him several messages. He wanted to be informed.

Tick tock. Just the family. Just JoJo. Mommy wanted it that way- no relatives, no friends. Just us. As JoJo slept. Tick tock...

His body shut down while Angela, her husband, Stephen, and I went to dinner...just down the road to the local restaurant, *Nick and Maggie's*. Stephen had insisted we leave the hospital, just for a few short hours. By the time we returned... JoJo's body was cold. He was dying and there was nothing we could do. He died the next morning, Saturday, October 3rd. He died quietly as Mommy said he would.[18] He died, my sweet little brother, who only one week ago had celebrated life. His heart was kept pumping by a Dopamine drip until the organs could be harvested[19]

---

[18] We would not have to make a decision to pull the plug. We would not have to petition before the board of the hospital to carry out this wish, a process that could take many weeks to conclude.. We would not be subject to the burden of making this decision.

[19] My father and I had decided which organs- a never-ending list of body parts and organs, skin being the most needed. "You can have his heart but only if you can take it whole." I said. Three months later, we received a letter, a letter from our angel. It came a few days before JoJo's birthday. A letter from heaven, as if Joseph was talking to us. A letter from Brian...

Dear Donor Family-

My name is Brian. I am writing to, in some way, say thank you for the wonderful gift of life you have given me. I am in my late 20's and had been waiting on the liver transplant list for well over a year, Before the operation, I was unable to do much of anything but now after receiving your gift, my life has improved one hundred percent. I know this is a difficult time for your family; But I hope that knowing you have helped someone who desperately needed it will in some way ease your suffering. Thank you. Brian.

We took turns making calls, informing our friends. I was numb. Diana questioned. Angela cried. Kiki was in shock. Mommy sat, strong.

Do I blame my mother for not answering his call, for not bringing him upstairs (the night before) to sleep with them? Do I blame myself? Why didn't I just get out of bed and see what the commotion was about? We heard the same thing. We live the same night-mare. We did nothing. My brother is dead. Like Mommy said… he went quietly… after four intense days of deep coma that left him sleeping peacefully.

My brother was dead. I called Thomas but he didn't pick up the phone, at home, at work. I called him, again, in the middle of the night. He didn't pick up the phone.

I was alone when JoJo died officially Saturday, October 3rd. I was alone as we waited patiently for the surgical teams to remove his organs. The teams had gotten stuck in a Long Island Expressway traffic jam. I was alone, many hours later, when he died, legally Sunday, October 4th. I was alone when we prepared for his funeral. How ironic that the casket (no expense spared), chosen by my brother Albert, was named "The Vermont." I snuck away to have two of JoJo's photos blown up. I secretly made a photo board of his life, 25 years and he was always smiling. I was alone at the wake day one, day two. I moved Thomas' flowers to the back. I wanted to throw them out but Mommy wouldn't let me. I was alone at the funeral. Why wasn't Thomas here? Why wasn't he holding me as I cried? I was supposed to cry. It was okay to cry. I'm the strong one. No one is supposed to see me cry. I couldn't cry. I couldn't cry as I held my older sister as we walked down the church aisle during the recessional. I was numb as I held her as she cried. I never cried. After all, I was the strong one. Déjà vu…

I was alone as friends gathered, ate, drank, spoke, laughed, cried, remembered JoJo. I was alone in my room when Thomas called….

18.

I SHOULD HAVE realized in Italy, when my Dad jokingly translated his name into Italian... Prezzo Terzo: third prize. I should have known then that he wasn't worthy of my love.

His name would soon be bastardized by my friends into Third Price...Third Rate... Bargain Bin... Bargain Basement. I should have known from that first meeting. Judas Escariot had sat down beside me at dinner that January Vermont night. I thought his name was Thomas. I couldn't have known at that time. He betrayed me. He belonged to someone else... or so she thought (but he wanted me). He had been with me. He had known me and everything that I felt, I wanted, I needed. AND it was mutual.

I had not heard from him. Five days. Five days of being alone, feeling numb, no pain, not wanting or needing anything except him. I needed him. I was alone, in my childhood room. A room that held happy memories but now felt like a box, a small box in a void of blackness....the dark, gloomy feeling surrounding me with no light, no glimpse of brightness... I was in a closed box that I couldn't escape from (and I didn't know if I wanted to). I could not get out of it... not upward, not by pushing forward, forcing my arms outward, nor propelling myself backward. I was in a box that closed me in, a box I couldn't get out of... I was alone in my room, a box that did not let any light sneak through, a room that felt cold, dark, claustrophobic- yet somehow fulfilling... I was alone in my room and I needed him.

I was alone when he called me, finally. He called me, 6pm, on the day we buried JoJo. "Where have you been?" I asked. "I don't know," he started to cry. How dare he cry? "I don't want to speak to you," I said, "ever again." He started to cry, like a baby, for what he was to lose, my friendship. My love? He started to bawl, "No!!!" "I don't want to speak to you ever again," I said and hung up. It was killing me, tearing me up inside but why hadn't he called sooner? Where had he been? I needed him. He called back, crying, pleading, wanting, needing... "Please!!! ...No!! ...I can't lose you!!!..."

How dare he? I loved him. He knew that. He was crying. How dare he for he took away from me my time to grieve. I had been there for him, through his separation, through his divorce, the doubts, the reconciliation of his own self- worth. I supported his move to California. I supported him in every decision he made. I felt like one of those women... who sacrifice all for the man they love, who work and put them through Med school, Law school...and then he leaves them for another. This was more intense. I was there for him. He knew all about me. All about my past. He knew I needed him to be here for me! How dare he cry! He deprived me of my grief! My brother was dead. Unexpected. I couldn't cry. I had no shoulder to cry on. He was crying... "I never want to see you or speak to you again!" I said.

JoJo's death had too powerful a hold on me. The headlines screamed; yet, I only saw blank pages, nothing registered into the vapid look I carried. I couldn't cry. I needed Thomas; however, I couldn't go out and see him. My mom wanted me to fly west, to confront him, to fight for my love... but Thomas never loved me. Doubting Thomas. My brother's death had too powerful a hold on me. How dare Thomas cry? He deprived me of my time to grieve....

19.

MANY MONTHS LATER... Luke was done (you'll find out about him), I had no moxy and I was crippled. I was alone. I wondered about Thomas. It was May... I sent an e-mail to him... a few words... I'm coming west. Of course- he answered..."What? Why? When? Where?" I never replied. A few weeks later, I sent him another e-mail... "I'll be in California." He replied... "I'm glad you're coming though Jasmine isn't happy about it." I found out what I needed to know without asking it directly: she was still in the picture... "I'll be in California on..."

His next e-mail was surprising..."I got engaged. I haven't told anyone yet, not my family, nor my friends...." Yeah- you got engaged? You mean- she got scared and popped the question to you. You haven't told your closest friends? Where were your balls? I knew you didn't love her. I knew you! That was it- I started to put my actions into place, to plan... I was flying west, somehow I would, even with a tight retail schedule... I was just going to show up. Surprise. Scenario #1: outside the office! Scenario #2: Surprise! I'm waiting on your car! Scenario #3: Surprise! I'm sitting at your desk! What are you going to do about it, Jasmine? Make a scene at the office? Scenario #4: Surprise! Here I am! Sitting on your apartment stairs!

Surprise. Here I am. Finally... mid- July! I re-routed my ticket from Disneyland (a vacation with Diana's family) to go west. I was just going to show up... but what happened if he wasn't in town? I wanted the element of the surprise but... I sent him an e-mail that I was coming and he agreed to meet me... Chariots of Fire was playing in the background, at the piano bar. Chariots of Fire gave me the strength not to touch him, not to kiss him, not to hold his hand, not to caress him once again. The new me went to California to get the monkey off my back. The new me with a short, brunette pixie[20], wearing a very stylish silk suit. (I had cut off all my hair.) The new me. A Lady. Sophisticated. Debonair. The new me, ready. He was scared. He didn't drink. He was nervous. Was Jasmine lurking near bye, watching us?

"I am not here to try and make you break off your engagement... I love you but I will never forgive you? Why didn't you come to my brother's funeral?" I asked. "She found out about us. The night you called me, the night he died. I had to tell her. She found out about us." "It was a funeral! You were part of my family. You came to my sister's house for Thanksgiving. You came to my parents 35th anniversary party. You knew my family. You knew my brother. It was a funeral. You should have come. Why didn't you come?" I asked. "I don't know. I don't know..." he stumbled. "I love you but I will never forgive you." ...one tear trickled down my

---

[20] I cut off my long dark hair. After bleaching my hair to an orange tint, the stylist decided to cover it with a boring shade of brown.

cheek. One tear- I was not crying for "us", for his impending engagement... but the fact that he could not let me grieve.

Chariots of Fire gave me the strength... He made a circle around me as he paid the bill. He stopped, as he was about to leave, walk out the front door of the grand hotel, he stopped...He slowly turned his back, a deliberate half-turn, the hand reaching backward, intentional as if his right side needed to keep me in his line of vision. He looked back. He looked back once more as if capturing my image, to place away, a little piece of me, into his darkened heart. He had his doubts. I just looked at him, staring into his cold hardened self. I know he wanted me to run to him. I know I thought about running to him. I know I wanted to run to him. My moxy was floating around me. It was here, somewhere. I kept staring at him, holding his gaze. He finally turned away and left.

He never found the letter under his bed. The note I left him last July: *You're probably making love, to Jasmine.. or someone else... but you're thinking about me, the nights, the mornings we spent in this bed... You're thinking of me and you don't know why!*

I left my mark... *"I left my heart in San Francisco...."*

Upon returning to New York, with the weight lifted from me... I e-mailed him:

Subj: A FINAL PARTING

...Loves songs playing sweetly
...My heart shattered so deeply
...Crying not yet finished
...The sadness diminished?
Softly, softly, softly

...We say adieu
...Two lovers depart
...Moments together shared

...Now a new lonely start
...Beginnings are best
...To soon-to be friends
...Endings to those once eternally entwined
                                    not again
Goodbye, goodbye, goodbye

...I will love you no doubt
...For many years gone bye
...The heart never forgets
...That which is deep, deep inside
i love you i love you i love you forever...
rosannna
delete delete delete delete delete delete delete delete delete

That should have been the end. I couldn't help myself. I was
hurt. I was always good at shooting from the hip... She stole
my man! She deprived me of my grief.... I found her e-mail
address under the corporate directory... I wrote her. He
retaliated. I got in the last word...

Ok- it was a pissing contest but too bad. I needed to say what
I had to say. I loved him but I would never forgive him. It hurt!
I didn't have my moxy but it was around, here, somewhere...
My moxy. Someday... I would be strong again... I would always
love him but I would never forgive him...

20.
Unmentionables

HE IS A genius. I've mentioned that before. His IQ validated it.
He had gone to college at 16, never graduated from High
School though he had two bachelor degrees, and a couple of
masters. My genius. I told you I loved him for his mind! I loved
him for his mind... and for making me feel the way a woman
should- a complete state where body and mind are one.

What I didn't tell you (and shouldn't tell you) is that he
couldn't keep it —, could get it —, but couldn't —— it up. The
frustration he kept men- - - ning, kept writing about, kept

reminding me. As he pleasured me, his own hand struggled in a tether-like death grip, up and down, faster and - - - -er. I didn't have the str- - - - -, my own hand the size of a child's. I could not sat—fy him although I tr—, up and down, down and up, circular as our hands, together, formed one bond. I said it time and time again how incompetent I felt, how —— tent I —, not —— ing how to pl—— him. I had the willpo—-, not —- physical ————. His -dy became accustomed to his own ——, the force he put behind this ... this what??!!. I was so incompe—nt. I —— even —— him experience —— ecstasy, the —— pleasure. He g—— me so much pleasure-I —ly wanted to reciprocate. I tried. I really did. I tr— with the bl— jo-s that to— for-vr. He even massaged my —— as — cramp— from being — one po—tion —- so long. With the hand j—s,with my breasts- a delicate size 34. With —- sexy, —— outfits. Sexy ne—-ees. Sexy br— and pant- - s. —— the —-, unsafe sex everyw—— and anywhere. With the pummeling,ha— er and har—r. I even practiced m- Keigel maneuvers. I tried. He couldn't k—- it.

Maybe — was —- to the circumcism (at age). th— overcompensated an- took away —- foreskin so there wa—- enough friction, not enough give and play. It was two-toned, a ——— pink tip over a pure white shaft, like a Popsicle stick just been dipped in icing, pink frosted icing. Don't get me wrong, he did —— (though not as often — —). CAN YOU HEAR ME NOW?

I —— wond— if h— lack of stamina was not because of me, was not because I overwhelmed h—, was not because I ——- not please him... but a deep seated psy—o—gic— imbalance caused by his parents dysf—n—ct—- al relationship. His mother was the little girl who never grew, an heiress to some Westchester fortune. His - - -her was Greek, the progeny of the infamous, historical (NOW?) demagogue. Thomas said —— once that was —ways be the fat- - - figure, always disciplining his sib——s, taking ——— b-cause his f-th— wasn't -round, his mother didn't kn— how... how to the bills, manage the househ—-staff, how to be a mom. Thomas was ten and he was expec—d to act l—- a ——- year old! I wonder whe—-er — was abused? Se—-ally? Ment- - - -?- - -sically? Something led to his sexual in- -equac- - -. As - said, he could - - - - it up - - - he couldn't - - - - it! I- - - -ed to believe - - wasn't me. He knew - lov— —- deeply. Wholeheartedly, I lov— him. Sex w— just - small —-t of us that encompassed e—ry final moment. I loved him. —- don't let me be—-ve it me!! CAN YOU HEAR ME NOW?

It h— to b- her. I won- -red if it - - - her tight hor-z- -tal twat that won - - - over. Horizontal? I know you're won- - ring...even - - mo- -er knows what - - - - say about Asian wom- -. She - - - a horizontal hold him. Viagra had not been in- - - ted could not come to his rescue. Our rescue. The term s- xual dys- - -ction - - - not pass— before —- ears —- yours. CAN YOU HEAR ME NOW???

There is a happy ending. It just excludes me. They got married. His company went public, one of the top IPO's. The stocks stayed well above $150.00 for many months. He got his millions. He got to quit his job. He got to travel the world. I doubt he loves her. I know him. I know him well. I will always love him but I will never forgive him...

Digression

I DID NOT jump into bed with them. They led me, made me believe that they cared, that they wanted to make love to me. I only kissed them, one kiss that made them come back for more....

It was an indelible impression from my pubescent years that made me into "the champion that I confess to be"[21]. I was in the 6th grade. Danny was my first boyfriend. We kissed. He said I jammed my tongue down his throat. He told me I was a terrible kisser. It was my first kiss, my first French kiss...Two years later, he wanted to go out with me again. He asked my friend, Donna, as we walked to her house, if I had learned how to kiss. He wanted to know before he asked me out again...

---

[21] This phrase is borrowed from the Vampire Lestat in one of Anne Rice's novels.

Chapter vii.
Let's Just Call Him Luke
A Duck to Shoot, A Goose to Drink

Maybe I just needed to be fucked. Up until this time, I had been, in a million other ways; it was time to take on a more literal meaning. Maybe I just needed to be fucked!! Making love to me would be an empathetic maneuver on his part and a commitment of the heart that I wasn't able to make because everyone I loved either disappeared permanently or left me for another. Or maybe, just maybe, he took advantage of my vulnerability, an architectural veracity that built upon my weakness...

1.

AND HE WAS another one who didn't like to kiss- an intimacy he reserved for those he respected? I don't know. He told me once, that the reason that he asked for my number, after the party, was that he liked the way I kissed- the gentle nibbling on his upper and lower lip, the sensual rolling of our tongues, exploration of his mouth. He liked the way I kissed. Why didn't he like to kiss me deeply, intimately when we... we... we fucked. A few pecks here and there didn't cut it...

"Save your tears for when something bad happens. Save your tears for when you really need them." How many times had my Mother said that? I hadn't saved any. I used them all up on Peter, useless tears, worthless tears, tears that didn't mean anything. Save your tears...and I needed the release. Release- I could not. That's how Luke came into play. I used him I guess. I used him for sex. I used sex as my emotional outlet. I'm so Machiavellian. I worked through my grief by being a horn dog; thereby, the end justified the means. Sex. Just sex. That's what I have to tell myself. If he really cared, we'd still be together.

Only one time did I cry. I went into the bedroom. I cried stupid tears. Drunken tears. Uncontrollable tears. Stressful tears. Sobs that wouldn't stop, the torrential downpour, the sudden outburst of emotions I had tried to curtail, tried to keep in tact... The tears kept coming and I let them...He came in once to see if I was okay (probably because his roommate was trying to sleep). No!!! I wanted to scream! I'm not! I need you! "Yes. Leave me alone. I'll be all right" is what I said quietly. I cried myself to sleep. What I needed was for him to put his arms around me. For me to pretend to feel secure, to pretend it was going to be okay, just okay. I needed him to lend his shoulder...

He didn't come into his room until many hours later. I should have broken up with him then but I was in the state, that years later (when I was into being alone), my friends would say simultaneously... "It's better to be with someone, anyone, in some form of relationship than to be alone." I guess I knew I needed him. Someone. Anyone, even in that little, unattached physical way. Better than no one. Aaahhh, Luke... timing.

2.

AAHHH, LUKE... TIMING. It was the wrong time. It had only been three and one-half weeks since my brother's death. We were all still in that shocked-beyond-reason stage. Kiki and her husband (the newlyweds) were invited to a Halloween party. They were going as Austin Powers and his sidekick. I took them to a thrift store to help them find costumes representative of the 60's. We were having so much fun (well, as much fun you can let yourself have after such a tragedy) searching through the smelly, moth-ball clothing. We began by pulling out one ugly dress after another. $2. $4. They kept asking me to go with them. I kept saying no. Finally, after discovering a set of peel off/stick-on false eyelashes, I agreed. My mood had temporarily become upbeat (for lack of a better word). It took a lot, but I knew I needed to go out, to leave the vicinity of the four walls that held me captive (to my own emotions) for these last few weeks. I felt protected, anyway, because I was with my sister. (We were in that same state of mind.) After rummaging through the racks, I discovered that perfect blend of polyester: an orange and black mini-dress that called out "Twiggy!", resplendent in a fabric that would melt on my body if I was caught in a fire. I forgot to add, it made me look pregnant due to its empire line and pleated front... Pregnant (minimum: 25 weeks), with a jet-black wig, blue-frosted eye shadow, false eyelashes that wouldn't behave, and a grim face, I went to the party. With Austin Powers and his stylish sidekick.

..."Pumpkin, would you like to dance?" he said. A pet name? Or in reference to my orange and black costume? I was mourning. I wasn't interested. He asked me to dance, again. He followed me upstairs to the kitchen and offered me a beer. He followed me downstairs to the basement. (Why do men always like to follow me?) I was mourning. I didn't want to deal. What compelled him to speak to me, to want to get to know me? I certainly didn't look sexy. That black wig. It turned my eyes dark to match my mood. I certainly wasn't sporting a smile, my best feature. What compelled him? Who compelled him? I wasn't interested but he kept paying attention to me. And he was nice. He looked like...

Cheeto's man. You know! The actor/comedian. Chris? Chris Elliot. That is the mold Luke was cast from. He had a five foot, eight inch slim, lithe body (coming out of having sex with a portly man, this was great!-less stress on my hip abductors!), the distended tummy appeal like a starving child of Ethiopia (except his was from a six-pack a day habit), army fatigues, sporting a goatee (like another). I find goatees to be so sexy... But his comb-over, the color of straw, looked worse than if he was completely bald. G-dats! Vanity, male vanity! Shave that head! His eyes were like a mongoloid child, the Down's syndrome shape as if he had just been dropped upside down. I'm not being mean. I'm just describing him the way he really looked. This is not a character assassination! Think Chris Elliot. His deep, husky voice matched my own. And he was nice.

I can only tell you it was about sex; though I wanted more, thought I needed more... Our first date happened five days later. I wondered if he'd recognize me, sans black wig, as I waited for him at the bar, waiting in the "throes of trepidation and uncertainty". I was a honey-blonde at this time. I hated sitting in a bar alone, especially in a place dominated by those masculine Greek men. What would they think of a woman sitting alone? It simply was not done in their culture. He finally showed up. What took him so long? He lived around the corner. I hated waiting in bars and I hated dates. After one drink, I let him drive my car to my sister's for dinner. My idea. I hated dates. We ate well and drank a lot. Kiki pulled out the couch and left us alone. As Luke would say, "She wanted you to be with someone. She wanted you to feel good." I didn't have sex with him that night. However, it felt good the way he touched me. The way he caressed me. The way he held me. But... as much as my body wanted him, my mind said no. Simply no. I loved another. I was mourning. My mind was elsewhere. Then, the next afternoon, the two of us took a nap at his place, the afternoon-hangover-is-catching-up-with-you nap except... one thing led to another. It's not like it was the first date. This was the third date, that's how I justified it. Luke told me he liked women who enjoyed sex. I was still shy, uneasy, didn't think it was right; however, I became that woman within one week... Luke- it was just about sex. Sex- my outlet, my sanity. Sex- took me away from thinking about Thomas. Sex- took me away from crying about my brother. Sex- just sex. I was thrown a fastball when timing means everything. We met at the wrong time.

I went to Rome, Italy a few weeks later and sent him a postcard each day, each note lascivious in nature, playful, flirtatious. I became very creative, my hardened being softening a little; after-all, I had the backdrop of the Renaissance to stimulate my imagination. I wanted his thoughts to take him to where I was and what we could be doing if he was here with me... Imagination- mine was strong... *From the darkened Piazza of the Vatican as the Pope lay sleeping in the cover of his Christian cloak, the devil's thoughts entered his dreams that night...On a hilltop of a Medieval town called Baniorigio, near open doors antiquated with history... From a castle where horses once galloped up the stairwell to the galley above...* Postcards. From Italy. With love. I needed him. I needed this outlet. I needed to live in a fantasy. I needed to imagine a happier world. A more joyful place...

(I was still on a leave of absence from work. Luke still had a job. In a few months, it would be reversed.)

Luke and I met once, sometimes twice a week and made the most of it. We'd begin our night with a gourmet meal that he prepared: stuffed veal chops, filet mignon, baby lamb... Luke had attended one of the culinary institutes. We'd open a bottle of Chilean wine from his still-large wine collection. He introduced me to his friend, Grey Goose vodka. We'd finish eating and I'd always say I'll do the dishes later! and then the two of us would do them together. They had to be done immediately! Luke's rules. Together.

In the kitchen. In the living room. In the bedroom. Six times a night and then again in the mornings. No shit, Sherlock! We aroused each other simply just by moving an arm as we went to sleep naked, always naked. That's the way Luke wanted it as he held me. Luke's rules. We always had to have one body part touching. Luke's rules. I became a pretzel, every limb being twisted, turned, tingled... Like play-dough, he could mold me into any shape or form. I became a piece of putty in his hands. As my limbs took on a certain weightlessness, I stayed suspended in a zero-gravity realm. I let myself float higher and higher. I let myself be taken away, to escape from my own personal hell. I let myself be taken away. To an extent. If I really let go, if I really let myself I would have lost it. I cried his name out, I gasped, I told him to move faster, slower, harder but held back just a tiny bit, 1%, or I would have lost it. I would have cried. The release would have been a maelstrom of held back emotions, grief, torment, love lost. It was about sex. Great sex. And I had multiple orgasms... These rituals of the eve were my pitfall, a repetitive behavior of accrued habits.

My favorite escapade was a rooftop rendezvous: *a panorama of the Manhattan skyline, the Twin Towers mesmerized me, dominated my attention as I rode him, my knees scraping asphalt... a small maneuver and the full moon above me became my looking glass, a dreamy light on our half clothed bodies, the ecstasy and scenic beauty diminishing whatever pain I felt, my back on a concrete rooftop, the rocks piercing my skin... Just one night, an Indian summer, November night... that carnal admission of two bodies joining, separating, moving, touching, feeling...a voyeuristic, starry sky keeping her safe distance...* Rooftops. Better yet. Rooftops in Astoria, Queens. THE CITY paraded before us on this moonlit, breezy night... It's always a full moon! Brings out the best in me!

That job. My career. I had to go back that December. My boss forced me to. The ramifications of staying out meant that "someone" would jump into my shoes, had already assumed the role. I should have stayed on my leave of absence but I was too proud. I was a strong woman. I didn't want anyone replacing me. "She" had already taken advantage of the situation. I had so much to offer, so much to prove. My boss made me go back to work because she was worried, even though I was (technically) still allowed a leave (still needed to be on that leave). Something was up. She had heard things about me and needed me to go back, to pay attention, to motivate the team, to be successful.

We fired my assistant, Janet. I had written her up for not supporting me. The Vice President of the company called me. "Fire her right now!" based on an incident with one of my staff. The assistant from hell- worse than anyone beyond imagination: manipulative, destructive, egotistical, a middle-aged sycophant... The assistant from hell that I just couldn't manage, didn't know how to manage. No one could manage. She was beyond managing... She was planning a take-over because she wanted my position. Big deal- though I made $40,000 more than her. As if this was a game of union strategy, she planned and manipulated a walk out. She wasn't a nice person. She was evil. She ripped up a Mass card someone had left for me: "Traitor," she yelled at Linda. Poor Linda. She was just your loving, born-again individual. The devil (Janet) was in heat while I was gone and no one could satisfy her needs... We fired Janet and five others left that day. The walk out! It was the best thing we could have done yet...It was the beginning of Bridal Madness; a season of increased sales, increased traffic, increased chaos. Madness! And I had no assistant and half a staff... And I had lost something. I wasn't the same person. I think I lost my moxy. My brother's death had taken a toll. I think I lost my moxy. Where was it?

3.

LUKE AND I were swept up in a universal cycle of having dinner, watching TV (The X-files-Luke's rules), getting drunk (Grey Goose) and then... One day the cycle broke... One day we ventured past the cracking walls and crooked floors that bound us in his world... One day- a trip into Manhattan, on a sunny, warm winter day more conducive to Denver than to this city... I took him to Cheap Jack's on lower Broadway. I probably wanted something vintage, trying to convince him of its charm, to wear something hip. "Let's leave. This place gives me the creeps," he said only after a few minutes. And so we left. Luke's rules. Stopping at the Strand Bookstore (12th Street), Luke wanting to find the Karma Sutra books... Huhhh? I was bewildered. Perplexed? The cartoonish caricatures were more explicit than a porn magazine, position after position. He was amused. I was embarrassed (but intrigued).

There was only one other field trip: The Metropolitan Museum. Too bad Luke wanted to be alone. He didn't want to interpolate, discuss, view the artistic masterpieces before us. He wanted to be alone as we perused separate aisles, rooms, and alleyways. Even when we converged on the same object... he didn't want to share ideas. He wasn't into "us". Myself, as the ultimate object of desire, became a universal point, moot point!

Subj: Thanx
Date: 1/28/99
Fr: Rossana@aol.com
To: Bills@aol.com

Thanx for the dinner,
it was well liked.
Thanx for the drinks,
though expertly spiked.

Thanx for the show,
my mouth running wild.
To the "rise of Chaotica",
a game frequently dialed.

Thanx for the movie,
yes, repulsively porn.
I'm definitely the woman
rightfully scorned.

Thanx for the lockout,
my moment of reason gone.
Blame it on Mr. Goose.

He ain't a white swan.

Thanx for the morning
A moment to sleep.
'Til later we softly kiss
In passion's arms locked deep.

Thanx for the day
intellectual as planned,
though looking for dinosaurs
located Westside on demand.

Thanx just the same,
a day of piece, quiet calm.
Five more minutes with me,
throws your sanity into alarm.

Thanx for the nite,
as daddy watches over,
"Tell him the bills suck."
Don't worry, this poem's in deep cover.

Goodbye, again.
Hope the week's going well...
Just think of me this weekend,
Bridal madness, it's hell!!!

Moot point but we continued to... In the kitchen. In the living room. Always ending up in his bedroom. Mind-blowing sex. I didn't care. When I was with him, those few hours, nothing mattered. For one moment, for one evening each week, I was taken away... Headboard bouncing 202. Anyone wanting to join the class had a long wait list!

Luke told me I was uninhibited. It was an erotic love that fulfilled his senses, the freedom in which I moved, the reckless abandonment in which I swayed and gyrated. He said it was the varied rhythms (and contractions), the pulsating muscles around his shaft and head of his penis that drove him wild. You could hear a scream, as if in terror, but I knew it was extreme pleasure that caused <u>his</u> response... Ahhhhh. Luke.

Luke had that certain way of crooning when he was about to...
It was a sure-given sign when his body would tense, suddenly;
however, his voice boomed, a cave-man guttural chant, an
ungodly noise that reverberated into a crescendo, the cymbals
clashing to my own piano melody...

Ahhhhh. Luke.

He is one of the few lucky men who can continue it, prolong
that moment of ecstasy, twitching and shuddering as I gently
blow on his torso, up and down, the soft wind an added
tingling to his aroused nervous system... He was good. It was
good. It was just sex- incredible sex.

I sent him this poem after one such interlude, an interlude,
which began with him (me?) getting very stoned, continued in
his bedroom:

Subj: thoughts
Date: 2/16/99 5:04
Fr: Rossana@aol
To: Bills@aol

Drifting,
        Mindless
                Empty
Sweet dreams of good and plenty

Drifting
        Reckless
                Higher and higher
Mindless
        Empty
                Maybe wired??

Leaving behind
        Nowhere to go

Thoughts of stressful times,
Ultimate low.

Drifting, mindless
    Grinding now...
        Passion awakening
            Bodies aroused.

Swaying,
    Winding,
        Hair askew,
            Moments later...
Acknowledging you.

Eyes opened, fluttering so
    Screams escaped-
        Ohhhh
            Nooooo!

Bodies entwined
The movement as one
    Synchronized timing
    Soon to be done.

Minutes gone by
    Time fashions
        A moment of release
            A final passion.

Drifting, mindless, empty
Sweet dreams!!!
Mmmmmmm...
-Good and plenty.

I convinced Luke to let me rearrange his apartment, to utilize the space in a more efficient manner. It was your typical post-graduate pad with the couch that had been slept upon by more than a few drunken couples, an office chair with a broken arm-rest, one antique desk much in need of a stripping. In addition, he had more electronic gizmos than he could play with in any given day (though time was on his side). Besides his vast personal collection of wines and good (Cuban) cigars, he possessed current, state-of-the-art toys. His money (that he once had) was well spent: the Bose surround sound and Sony video monitor and components encompassed you, the Dell computer screen leapt out at you, the K-2's downhills leaned pretty, propped up on one wall, the Canondale mountain bike stood poised as the Herb O'Brien water ski sat casually on the floor- an endless inventory of grown-up toys.

Believe it or not, Luke also had a green thumb. As we were moving things, he was most concerned about his plants (violets, ferns, spider plants, prayer plants, etc...) which transformed the dingy interior into a tropical rainforest. You had to dodge the tentacles of ivy as you maneuvered through his jungle. We were careful as not to upset this natural preserve...

...He left me for an extended tour to Costa Rica. The night before he left, I gave him ten gifts, each gift pertaining to a list, his survival guide: socks because you can never have enough, lotion for his right hand (when the urge hit him), condoms (you can never be too careful), batteries for the flashlight (he would lose), a lighter to make fire (since rubbing two sticks together wasn't his idea of fun), etc... I was in a creative mood, showing him that I cared. That was me- too nice. Always nice. I wanted his photographic expedition to be a rewarding, memorable experience!

He asked me to join him. I found a flight, found the four days. After I sent him the e-mail, he replied that he was traveling, wasn't sure what country he'd be in. My man. Alone in the wilderness. Alone in the third world. How exciting! He sent me e-mails when he could, when civilization gave him the tools, something called a cyber- cafe. I sent them back.

When he finally returned four weeks later, I picked him up from the airport; however, I didn't spend the night. He said he was tired... The next week, during his photo show, the same shots kept appearing- Luke, a woman, and another. The woman stood right next to him. The man- two feet away. My inner alarm went off. "Oh, yes. I used to work with her. She likes me. Don't worry. Nothing happened." False alarm as he'd tell me the stories: "We went to see the sunrise at the temple. She got scared of the snake lying across the road- it looked like a tree had fallen. She ran all the way back and wouldn't sleep alone that night." "She was scared of the jungle noises. Don't worry. She likes me but nothing happened..." She- fat, dumpy, conservative in her Banana Republic pleated shorts, dirty-blonde blunt hair. She wasn't pretty. She had no sex appeal. Okay. I believed him.

He made a wonderful dinner that eve... venison. I had never tasted such succulent meat.

It was the light of the full moon that let my inhibitions run wild...
Thought I felt empty tonight leaving...a feeling of loneliness setting in...
Thanx for the venison and for satiating my palate.
love-r
PS I'm not your date so please don't refer to me as such...

He responded...
Glad you enjoyed the venison. By the way I think it brought out your animal instincts...mmmmm.
Is it better to say you're my muffin than date??

I wanted his return to be sparked in a romantic arena. We continued our lustful adventure... "Ahhh, ahhh" as my head bobbed near an open flame.(Hiss. Hiss.) The bed rocked in unison with our bodies. "AHHH-AHHH." (hisssss) followed shortly by a whispered "oh-my god!" "Ohh- My God." (Hiss. Hisssssss.) "OH- MY- GOD!!!" I screamed as I tried to get him off me. He continued to hold me tighter. I pushed upward, forcing my hands to push his chest away. I pushed with what little strength I had left. He finally fell to my side and looked at me bewildered. The singeing smell was strong. The smoke was billowing as I patted my head. I looked at my open hands, scared of what I would see, the strands of hair caught between my fingers. I could not believe what had just occurred. I wondered what had become of my crowning glory, my long, long hair that had been cut into perfect layers, the soft cascade of curls colored to a perfect shade of honey...[22] The tears were just about to fall when my solemn look quickly changed into a slow-forming grin as Luke exclaimed: "Pumpkin, you needed to thin out your hair anyway..." His timing just so- the perfect lending of humor to what I viewed as an irreversible situation. Histrionics curtailed. Luke's rules. No tears. Sealed with a hug (and a glop of Vaseline to heal the frayed, burned ends of what remained on my head).

...I invited Luke for Easter since his family was in Buffalo. He agreed to come. Maybe, he finally looked at me as more than someone he hugged (and fucked)? I made him wear a suit since holidays were formal in my house; however, on this day, the men decided to wear sweaters and khakis. Oh well. Luke hadn't worn a suit in six months. It was about time he showed me the sophisticated side. I was tired of looking at him in shorts, t-shirts, sneakers and jeans. As for me, my vintage wardrobe had diversified... I loved what I wore that day: a girl scout green, cap sleeve, Peter Pan-collar dress with a three-quarter sleeve bolero adorned with covered buttons. The only thing missing was the pillbox hat and gloves (don't think I didn't try to find them). I look nice in green- it set off my eyes. I felt like a lady, a lady from 1960's ala Jackie O. I thought he

---

[22] I felt like one of the young girls I read about (only at the gym) in a <u>Cosmopolitan Magazine</u>. Those stupid stories seemed so ridiculous they couldn't possibly be true, the foolish antics a mere fabrication of the truth. After all, Cosmopolitan gave every young woman step by step instructions on "How to Please Your Man", "How to Make your Orgasms Last", "How to Get Him to Please You", and so on and so forth. What happened to learning by trial and error?

would like me this way. Instead, he looked at me, as I stood proud, and exclaimed: "Pumpkin- what are you wearing?"

We've all been through it, the meeting-the-family-for-the-first-time. Imagine a big Italian one. We are an intimidating group, nice, but overwhelming! Five conversations going at once. Everyone talking, laughing, yelling at once. People coming, going, leaving, arriving at once. And of course the children (only five at this time)... Luke! No rules on this day.

Later that night, his friends picked him up and they left for Vermont. I am sure he was glad for the reprieve. As he kissed me before he left, he asked me if I wanted to come. I was surprised at his offer- the first time he extended an invite. (I believed him when he said that skiing was his passion though I always wondered if he was hooking up with another woman.) He must have missed me when he was in Costa Rica. "You didn't come to Vermont. I made up the loft for us..." He seemed to care.

4.Bridal Hell

HE SEEMED TO care. There was always a lingering, euphoric sense of contentness when I left him... that would disappear as soon as I crossed county lines, as soon as I entered bridal hell. My career had a definite impact on my life; so much that I wasn't even cognizant of who owned a blue dress, the interview with a woman named Monica, and a house colored white set in controversy. I was oblivious to high school antics that proved fatal in Columbine, Woodstock set ablaze, a little boy named Elian, a new movie about a witch in Maryland. The only thing that hit me was John John's death at sea. My career had an impact on my personal life. Go back to a time when you were a new mother. Your baby had colic. Or the first time she got an earache... the crying, screaming, whining all day, all night. Think ten-fold. Welcome to my world...

I was stressed from the Bridesmaids from Hell screaming in my face "We don't want to pay now, we want to leave a deposit." Stressed from the affluent Scarsdale-bred girls, bitching that the cost of alterations was higher than the dress. Stressed from the mother of the bride "You f' in s—t! My daughter is cryin. Who da hell told the mother-of-the-groom she could wear ivory. It's wrong." Frazzled from the "God-I-feel-sorry-for-her-fiancé" shrew insisting she was a size 24, insisting she hadn't gained any weight, cursing and shrieking at the top of her piercing voice. Drained by the pregnant brides, and there were soooo many, reiterating that "Mira, mira. We were going to get married anyway. It just happened." (Ever hear of condoms?) Stressed from the lawyer, Ms. Corporate America, who pulled a tantrum because her dress was cut a little too short. Don't worry, we'll get you another dress and do the alts for free. "Don't worry!!! It's my wedding!!" (boo hoo hoo) "How could you ruin my dress!!! I only want that one! You f'in morons. You stupid pieces of shit. I'm going to sue your ass." Frazzled by them whining... "I wanta newwww wun!!!" This was in-stock bridal- you tried it on, you bought it, you took it with you. And those brides, demanding a fitting room, even though they didn't have an appointment, even though there were 20 people in front of them. Weary and teary from the threats of the boyfriends: "Yous made her upset.Yous better watch your back, bitch." Stressed from the dyeable shoes that matched perfectly (under fluorescents) then magically turned another shade. Stressed from a ceiling that leaked, stressed from registers that went on the blink, STRESSED from bathrooms that overflowed, STRESSSSEDDD from a store that never functioned properly... Stressed. Stressed! STRESSED!

I was stressed, frazzled, drained, weary and teary... Those brides. They came in all shapes, all sizes, all ages, all colors, all backgrounds, all looks: Cinderella's hag sister, Orca, who would need two dresses to swathe her girth, the Bulimic (that would be a tough alteration!), the almost 30 year old "third time's a charm", the "I finally got him to agree after 10 years"... Those brides. How did they manage to get engaged? To find a man to love them? I wanted to tell their fiancées to RUNNNNN! Get out now before it's too late.

Those brides. They didn't want to hear it! Everything had to be perfect. They didn't want to hear it. And on top of their shrilly voices- the phones. They didn't stop ringing. Line after line was put on hold when the $99 sale hit. Help!! I was stressed from the poor planning on corporate's part. With sales increasing exponentially, the buyers forecast had landed short, a top vendor went bankrupt, and the company couldn't deliver its infamous "the three weeks or less" dresses. It had been a four-month wait in some cases and the wedding was in three days. Help! I didn't blame them for yelling, screaming, demanding, having temper tantrums; those horrific "terrible twos" spells (except these were adults). It was their wedding. The most important day of their life.

"I want to speak the manager," they said. "I want the manager," they demanded. "I want the MANAGER," they screamed. I looked too young to be in control. I wasn't married so I couldn't possibly understand how they felt, what they thought. "I want the manager!!!" Uhhh- that's me, with the serious faceless demeanor!! That's me. But I was only one person. I had my standards. I tried to please, in every way I could.

Stressed as I drove south on the Bronx River Parkway. God- always a bottleneck. Frazzled as I crossed the Triborough Bridge. Get out of the EZ PASS lane! Can't you read? Drained as I drove around for 40 minutes in his Astoria neighborhood looking for parking, crossing one block to the next, crossing avenues, finally squeezing into a corner spot. Would I get a ticket? It didn't matter. I was weary as I raced up to his third floor walk-up. I just wanted a hug. I just needed a hug. Just wanted him to throw his arms around me and hold me, kiss me on the cheek as he always did each and every time I arrived. The stress gone the moment I reached him; the former tense air I possessed, dissipated... Luke. He was there for me in the simplest form- hugs. A sentimental gesture on his part? So simple, yet they would pick me up, my spirits would be raised momentarily... It was about sex, he didn't like to kiss passionately; yet, he was compassionate.

It continued. It got worse. I had lost my moxy. I became dark, somber, and crippled as the weight of the world shrunk my five foot frame. I never smiled. I never laughed. My neck was always tense, my muscles tight. BOO! The tears were always behind my eyes. Boo! I couldn't take another 12-hour day. Boo! I couldn't take another 14-day workweek!

I lost my moxy as they screamed. Loudly. Blame it on those damn buyers. We could sell the product but we couldn't deliver it! The constant yelling in my face, daily, nightly, to me and only me. I was the only one to bear the brunt. I couldn't blame them. They couldn't walk down the aisle naked. Boo! The tears building. I lost my moxy. I wanted it back. Where was it? **Boo!!**

I also lost my best friend... We had a simple misunderstanding. She once asked me to be the godmother to her first born (since I was her maid-of-honor). She doesn't recall this conversation. As a result, I received an invitation. She invited me to her house but stated I didn't need to attend the Christening. I never showed up that day as she kept watching for me, waiting for me. I couldn't tell her how I felt. I just took the coward's way out and didn't go. I couldn't be the me that she expected, that she would have respected if I had told her off, spoke my mind. I couldn't be that me. I just didn't go. I neglected to call her. I just didn't go (because it hurt too much). The stress (from my job) took its toll. My brother's death had an impact on me. I lost something... Oh yeah- my moxy...

BOO! I was caught in a political twist between recruiter and District Manager. Boo! Two unfilled management positions I had earned. Boo!-when the Chief Financial Officer decided to spend the day. Boo!- as the investors paid a visit. My store, of all stores. It was a flagship, but still... I was only one person. The company was going through an IPO and I was the one they chose to lead it. (On this day, I soared. I knew my business. I wasn't intimidated by their horn rim glasses, Armani suits, Coach briefcases, the fact that my answers determined whether the company was taken seriously, got the money they needed to go public.) Why me? As if I needed this?

Boo! as the President and his mistress paid their weekly visits. I spoke to him. I opened up to him. He new he could get the scoop, the real scoop from me without rummaging through the amount of bullshit everyone fed him. Boo! As I was chosen as a test store for the couture line. A test? Why me??

My sales were exponentially above what had been planned. Why weren't they filling the positions? It had been months. Alone. This wasn't big business. It was retail!! A game of politics that they chose to play at the most ill-timed season. Give me anyone, someone just to help me a little, just until I find my moxy. What else could they heave upon my stooping, rounded shoulders??

And then... Luke wanted out- my only salvation. Six months. The marker. Six months. The deciding point. He broke up with me. Like a summer Gulfstream gale, this break up came with virtually little warning. I didn't have time to prepare myself for being alone, once again. Why hadn't I paid attention to my inner-alarm, that gut feeling you get but usually ignore? My inner-alarm hit piercing, shrilling, ear-splitting levels yet I didn't hear it. I should have broken up with him. I was too weak, too vulnerable, that certain frailty like a twig being snapped. With a little pressure, it was a forceful impact. Boo! I cried. Boo. I jumped. Boo!

The signs were staring me in the face; however since the countenance that dressed me was not my own, I could not have known (though I should have known). The signs were all there... grabbing my ass in public, and not knowing the color of my eyes. He didn't care. He obviously didn't want to gaze deep into my soul. I am positive that in the reflection of my eyes, he probably didn't like what he would see: himself! I was always at his house on a Thursday or Saturday night. What did he do the rest of the week? The signs were there... Stupid me! His roommate walking in... seeing Luke and some girl, an oversight or a commonality? Something he'd grown accustomed to? Luke- in coitus. The roommate said hello. Luke held a conversation with him. Luke didn't stop. He kept right on doing to me what he had been doing to me as he continued the conversation. I got pissed.

The jilted lover, cruelly jilted...

I should have broken up with him but the sex was good, great, exciting. Yet it was missing something... intimacy? We were two joined as one... but one in our thoughts of achieving personal satisfaction. I should have realized he didn't care. Luke had no respect for me even though he was nice to me. He wanted to see other people. We never talked about a commitment. I didn't think we had to. I didn't think his eyes would wander. I pleased him sexually. I lost some weight and looked good. I never thought he would leave me for another... I wasn't going to fight for him. If he wanted to start seeing other people, okay.

One month passed. He agreed to help me with my resume so I invited myself over. We started with the Grey Goose. He made dinner. We sat and talked. Resume?? What resume? His roommate got a call. Ten minutes later, he handed the phone to Luke. Something was happening but I was still without my moxy to realize what. Luke left the room. I should have ripped the phone out of his hands. I should have told her to fuck off. He's mine. I should have. I couldn't. I had lost my moxy. He said he wanted to leave- "Lets go play pool." I didn't ask questions. He just said she was some girl he was seeing and she was mad I was there. How did she know? "She heard you laugh." Huh? Since we got drunk at the pool hall, I spent the night. Luke put me to bed but left the room. When he came in hours later, he took off my shirt, held me naked but didn't go any further. He wanted me. He was torn. He could have had me. I was afraid to initiate. I couldn't fight for him. I lost my moxy!!

I went back two days later even though I wasn't allowed to come over. Luke's rules. I wanted the truth when I drove to his apartment on a spur-of-the-moment whim. I didn't call him. I wanted to know it all... I asked him when he became pussy whipped? I was shocked that he liked bitchy women, women that yelled and cackled, women that flat out demanded his undivided attention. He never seemed the type to be whipped. When had he become the pussy? The truth hurt but I needed to know... He lied to me. He hadn't gone fishing. He had been with her. The woman in the photo... And that's when he told me "I can't see you anymore. She won't allow it. I have to give her a chance, etc..." I lost my moxy. I hadn't found it yet. I could not fight for him. Triangles, damn triangles. He left me for another. I didn't want to fight. If he wanted me, he would come back to me...

Luke just wanted to be loved. He may have thought I was in love with him. His ego called for it, demanded it. He was lonely. No job. She promised to help him. She was a wealthy debutante, living in California. Did he go for the money? Did he go for the security? I couldn't give it to him. I lost my moxy and was just understanding the clues as to where it was!! I couldn't fight for him. Damn triangles.

And work. It kept getting more difficult... the 12 hour days... Like a tornado out of nowhere, I was spinning, spiraling, swirling, breaking apart... Where would I be when the storm subsided (if it subsided)? I had had enough and they knew it. I asked my boss for a transfer (to another store). I asked for a de-motion. I asked to be considered for the Queens store. It was close to home, a new store (one that was set up properly), a new environment, a chance for me to start fresh!!! A chance for me to find my moxy.

Corporate politics got in the way as my boss resigned. The new Regional Manager said I had to prove myself. ("*We'll get you support. We'll get you managers.*") "Fuck you, bitch" is what I wanted to say. Prove myself? I thought I was doing that, carrying it all alone. (Is that why my boss had resigned?) I wanted to pick up the phone and call the VP, call the head of HR. I couldn't. I lost my moxy. I was too weak, too intimidated, too not me. Prove myself? Bitch! (She wanted me up or out). My choice for assistant was turned down (She couldn't work Sundays.) That Regional Bitch. She told both Pat and myself that if we came up with an agreement (concerning the Sunday schedule), Pat would get the promotion she deserved. Agreement made, the Regional reneged her offer (couldn't make an exception to the rule). Bitch!! Six months alone, help!! Someone help me. I asked for help. I finally swallowed my pride, asked for help, but it never came... I wanted my moxy back. How was I ever going to find it?

BOO! I went to the Doctor. She could see the tears behind my eyes. She could see that my career was taking control of my life in a negative way. I was given the drugs to take the edge off. I felt a little better. BOO! I jumped... but only a little. One month later, I stopped popping those magical pills. When I realized the drug induced an altered state, I started to feel more anxious. I didn't want anything fucking with my brain! Boo...

I finally got a vacation. A trip to a spa in Ixtapan, Mexico should cure my ailments.... but it was too late. Five days of massages, five days of facials, five days of aromatherapy, mud baths, seaweed wraps... couldn't relax me, couldn't loosen up the tightness, couldn't release the tension... Five days of deep tissue massage could not break through the barrier that had crippled me. Boo...

And on top of this, the Pap smear came back abnormal. Nice office. They left one message (only one) that scared the hell out of me. When I called them back, the office didn't know who called me, what prescription? Who are you? Which doctor? My health was at stake! Assholes. The doctor never got back to me as I called the office four, five times, leaving messages with the service, leaving messages with the office, leaving a slew of telephone numbers so they could find me, even calling from California as I met the monkey on my back. Ten days later, someone finally returned my call. The mid-wife told me it was a minor bacterial infection. Mid-wife. I should have known better. (She was the one who told me I had a serious yeast infection while my legs were prone in the stirrups. I think not, considering I never had one before and had none of the symptoms.) "Fill the prescription. You'll be fine."

Why was this happening to me? It was too much. I couldn't fight the extenuating circumstances that I should have been able to control. I couldn't do it... I lost my moxy. BOO. I jumped but ... I still possessed a little piece of that type-A personality. I knew I had to make decisions and they had to be mine- no outside influences, no advice from those who cared... I had simply had enough. All the money wasn't worth relinquishing my health, my happiness. All the money in the world... See ya!! I finally asked for help and it wasn't coming. Like *The Perfect Storm*... George Clooney alone with his men to fight the elements... Me. Alone. I resigned. I gave the company two months to find someone. Blink! like genie popping out of nowhere, one <u>qualified</u> manager appeared. I kept forcing the issue of promoting my lead person. "NO!- We can't make an exception!"

Help me, someone help me, please... I wanted to scream. I was a strong woman. I could make sound decisions I kept telling myself, kept reminding myself... Boo! I lost it. Boo! I cried! Boo! I cringed. Boo! I couldn't do it! Boo! Help me, please! Help never came...

I quit. The best decision of my life- no regrets, no looking back. I decided to pursue my passions, develop the artistic right side of the brain I had let stagnate. I enrolled full-time in art school. I wanted to paint the world... to experience life in a colorful arena of lights, darks, tone on tone. After-all, I was a Renaissance woman... I needed my moxy back. Wanted it back. I would be able to find it. The blinders had been removed. Tunnel vision no more! I could think. I could create. I could be me. I was poor but money was irrelevant. My eyes started to show a slight glow, that brilliance that had been tarnished, now golden, warm, alive... I became happy.

I also became an introvert, the downward spiral of closing oneself off from your family, friends, the world... but finding peace with being alone. I converted... to my own spiritual guidelines, rules that I followed (and was allowed to break if I chose to). These parameters gave me a sense of identity again. Somewhat. I knew this wasn't me but it was the me that would make me whole again... one small step... a giant leap... My moxy... like the groundhog... would appear. Boo- I'm not afraid of my shadow! I would use this time to develop a portfolio for graduate school- a masters in advertising...

5.

I SPENT THE summer with my best friend: myself. I worked but the pressure was off. I had resigned. Closure on the bridal hell. The monkey was gone. Luke out of the picture or so I thought... In September, Luke agreed to meet me, a game (or two) of pool. He finally responded to an e-mail. He had ignored them for the last three months. He had ignored the lighthearted messages I left. He told me- "She was helping me find a job. I've known her for a long time. I wasn't allowed to talk to you anymore. I wasn't allowed to read, respond, send e-mails. I wasn't allowed. She wouldn't let me. You know- you're uninhibited when it comes to sex. She was jealous. Too jealous. It's over with her." I sent him an article from Cosmopolitan on "Biker Chick Girlfriends from Hell". He got a good kick out of it. We were friends again. He told me over and over again... "It's over with her." A few days later... her e-mail came.

6.

I DID NOT quite understand what I was reading that morning as I checked my e-mails and opened one from him. It was directed to Luke yet it enraptured the spirit of his many conquests through our own correspondence. I was not internet savvy so I could not comprehend that she had copied/ pasted all of his former girlfriend's notes to him so that it looked like we were all caught up in his cyber web being devoured simultaneously by his charms, the shit he had fed us for so long, the shit that became our sustenance...

"You say you love me but you seem to be saying the same to them," she cried, as if we would all join in as one womanly soul, heartfelt and crushed sisters, united in pain. She continued, slandering my name... "You fuck Rossana and you're probably still fucking her..." She slandered my name, a definite defamation of character sent to everyone in her address book, Luke's address book, and I don't know how many others... My name, slandered across the internet!!! Underneath her love letter, she had copied our recent e-mails to Luke.

I could not let this go. I retaliated by forwarding this e-mail to all my friends calling her the "psycho girlfriend from hell". My friends got a kick out of it- they were glad I had regained my sense of humor. I retaliated further by replying to all. I informed her that I could sue her based on an old blue law that protected the virtue and chastity of an individual (the one thing I retained from my college business law class). What would her boss think, her boss who ran one of the top accounting houses? For some reason, I believe she worked for Pete Marwick. And besides, she was using company property to slander a private citizen. A double indemnity. I wanted to get her scared. I wanted to get her fired... I wanted to get even!

Luke had yet to read the e-mail when I called him, laughing at first. The more I thought about that e-mail, the madder I got. How dare she slander my name! I called him back later demanding an apology, demanding some form of retribution. "Don't do anything," he said. "Too late," I replied.

I felt sorry for him. I felt sorry for her. Luke and I had been friends (a little bit more than that) so I offered him some womanly advice..."Luke- she seems to really love you. If you love her, maybe you need to give her another chance. Maybe she's just jealous and not thinking straight. If you really love her as she thinks..."

Luke got back with her. He didn't tell me. He ignored me from then on.

7.

JUST WHEN LUKE was done, the stress unbearable, I had finally thrown the monkey off my back, the Pap smear came back abnormal- the third time. (I sometimes think that the deterioration in my health was due to the fact that I internalized a lot.) Thank goodness I had changed doctors. The first group shouldn't be practicing. They told me I had a minor bacterial infection and prescribed a vaginal cream. Thank god for the internet. Too much information but within it, I discovered that abnormal pap smears are viral related and aren't treated with generalized creams. Idiots. They made me wait three months before another pap was taken. I was bleeding again. This time I knew I had to take my life into my own hands. My moxy was around. I found my common sense. I changed gynecologists immediately!

I had to tell Luke even though we had been careful just about every time. You never know. Luke wouldn't see me when I called him from the pay phone, the airplanes noisy above. I was at the Mobil station, next to La Guardia Airport, on the Grand Central Parkway, on the road that led to his neighborhood. I needed to talk to him. Luke's rules. I had to call first. He said I could not come over. He said he wasn't allowed to see me. He had gotten back with Psycho Chick. (My doing?) She wouldn't allow him to speak to me.(Ooh- this was going to be harder than I thought.) I proceeded to tell him. Of course, he didn't understand. Of course, he was pissed off. Of course, he blamed me. (He was the one sleeping with two women!) I told him to get checked out, to have his girlfriend checked out, and if he needed info to check the internet. It's his own fault he made it so impersonal.

I blame it on Thomas. I loved him. We never used protection. I was in love with him. It had to have been him. The thing that no one talks about, the one that leads to cervical cancer, the one that was caught in phase one and a simple freezing of my cells would take care of. I should have told Thomas. I loved him but I couldn't forgive him. I should have told him. Maybe that's why... just when I stepped forward, just when I felt grounded, two footed, just when I started being me again...

The Devil paid me a visit.

Chapter viii. Forced Entry

So many men that I gave myself to willingly and wholeheartedly. So many men. Fuck me- written across my forehead, chiseled in marble. I did not deserve the final outcome of these relationships... Relationships- I choose this word because there was a mutual respect and some sense of caring. In my eyes, they were relationships. I had reclaimed my virginity by this time (eight months). The main reason was that a certain abnormal pap smear led me to realize I wasn't invincible. Always careful but not invincible. I didn't want to sleep with just anyone. My libido, which had been on a sexual overdrive, was now on a long-term sabbatical. I was controlling my lust. Sex wasn't everything. I wanted to be a lady, to be treated as such, friends first, lovers eventually (or so I thought and wanted to believe).

I have "fuck me" written on my forehead- that and a million dollars will get you nowhere...

MY MOXY HAD slowly started to appear, slowly and carefully I could be myself. I could paint the world as I wanted. I was enrolled in art school full time, pursuing my passions, finally. I say "finally" because as a child I was gifted with an artistic talent but I didn't develop it. I did not conform. I didn't want to be like every one else and go to a local college. I rebelled. Eighteen years later I was finally pursuing my passions!! Cross that off my list. I would never have to ask... if only?[23]

Just when I started to feel better, I was dealt another blow. Knock out!! Two steps forward. Ten steps back. "Mother, may I?" If I had known he had an ulterior agenda, I would have said "no" to our date. It should have been a whirlwind romance, three months, the ring, you know... honeymoon baby... an easy relationship. An easy situation. Easy love. I was ready. I thought he was ready (to settle down). Instead...

He threw me down, pulled off my sweats, and entered me in one swift movement. It was a violation- not only of my body but also of our childhood, our friendship, our mutual friends. I had known him for 16 years. It wasn't right what he did...

We met for drinks after my painting class. He lived two blocks from the school. Just drinks. Two cosmos later, we were still talking. Four hours later, the conversation never faltered. We had grown up together. I knew his sister from high school. He was Stephen's childhood friend. We had so much in common: number three of six kids, both from Queens, both wanting to get married and live conventional lives like our siblings, both a lot of fun.

He was opening up to me and by doing so, I thought that meant he was viewing me in his future, wanting me in his

---

[23]As I painted the world brightly, my mother wanted to grasp (with good intentions) her daughter's (me) woes. She couldn't understand (why her daughter gave up her career) but wanted to share in my pain. I said nothing as I left for school each day, eager to create. She took a position with THE bridal company I had left even though I advised her not to. My advice went unheeded. Only then, could she be me. Only then, could she become me in the fullest extent of its meaning. Short lived. She had to drive to work each day knowing she'd return home in an emotional turmoil. She came home with that same look on her face, the reflection in her mirror not her own. She reiterated the same emotionally-battering tales. She resigned eight weeks later. I didn't need to say... "I told you so!"

future. (I guess I just thought too much.) The conversation was so relaxed even though the subject matter was intense. Relationships. Men don't talk about these in a free flowing form. I don't know. Maybe it was me. I never judged. I could hold a conversation with anyone, about anything. I listened carefully and interjected my thoughts. I challenged. I complimented. I agreed. I was funny, witty, wise. Dick was comfortable with me or so I thought.

By three am, we were splitting a burger. By four am, he changed. His behavior became (pause) weird, strange, just strange. Almost like a lion waiting patiently, seeking out his prey...

We opened up the couch in the living room. He would be sleeping in his bed, in the other room. We had planned it that way. We had discussed it, prior to this date, that I would sleep over. I thought I was safe... The next thing I knew, he was on top of me- a 6'4" 240lb. frame I could not fight off. It took me by surprise. There was nothing gentle about his movements. It took me by surprise- this date rate. This doesn't happen when you're both professionals in your 30's. It doesn't happen to ordinary people. We were living ordinary lives. It doesn't happen a second time, to people like me; except ... well, one kiss and I can get them going. I didn't kiss him this eve. I DID NOT kiss him this eve. It doesn't happen, it shouldn't happen, why is this happening to me???

I didn't scream. I didn't fight. I didn't kick him in the groin. I couldn't. He was a friend. I was too embarrassed. My moxy had run away. The energy to protest had left me, to protest his unwelcome probing maneuvers. Most importantly, it happened too quickly. Most of all, I was too afraid. I just lay still as he pummeled me hard- too hard to please, hard- it hurt inside deeply as his penis hit again and again my cervix. Ouch. It hurt. Ouch, I had just had cryo-surgery one month earlier. OUCH!! I was too dry. Ouch.

I just lay still as I stared at his hairy chest. I became a dead fish- no movement, no response, no life. Ouch! When was this going to end?? Ouch. He realized what he was doing and in a moment of tenderness, slowed down his thrusting, planted wet, sloppy kisses, tried to calm himself and focus on his erratic breath, uncontrollable breathing, trying to slow down so he wouldn't climax, trying to pretend to make love to me by gyrating his hips slowly, looking at me, kissing me, trying to get me to respond.

I continued to lay still- the dead fish and whispered in an affirmative, disgusted manner "STOP! (pause) Get off." I was not crying but my voiced cracked He listened even though I knew he was about to come- his body taught, his rhythm erratic...He pulled himself off of me... I turned away, tried to sleep, make myself pass out... Make myself forget.

It was a guilt stricken morning. I was the one who felt guilty as if I should have satiated him. Guilt.

Two weeks later I sent him a Christmas card and apologized to him. Guilt! I apologized to him. Guilt. One year later when I was asked by a friend "Why don't you go out with Dick? He's a great guy!" (Uhhh, maybe because your best friend raped me one night.) "Dick's not interested in dating me. Just sleeping with me," I said sarcastically, as the tone called for.

Guilt. Why couldn't I be emancipated from this guilt stricken event?

2.

AS MUCH AS I never wanted to see this man again or recall that night, I saw him eight months later at Stephen's birthday. Small circles. Stephen's birthday. What do you get a man who has everything and has "had" everyone? It was a milestone- #40. Stephen didn't want a big celebration (so unlike him since he was always at the center of attention) but his family insisted. I wrote this fable and read it (acted it out) during the speeches (more like a "roast"). I hoped that the brotherhood of bachelors (attending) realized that the moral of the story was an amusing parody of their own lives, not just Stephen's. This tale is essentially *The Bachelor's Credo*...

From The Sea Captain's Ledger
In Search of the Maidenhead

A LONG, LONG TIME AGO (not the Don McLean tune)...
in an age when fairy princesses were held captive by their
ruthless wards and the knight in shining armor was still in
diapers and waiting to grow up, when women were quiet and
demure, and men were brave, noble, compassionate... Oops-
wrong tale! (Knew it was too good to be true.) Men
compassionate?

This story begins or the EPIC commences- because it's been a
very long journey...
-In an era when technological advances were so numerous, the
ordinary citizen did not know whether reality was virtual or
existing...
-In a time when it no longer "snowed" in the summertime
-Bachelors were numerous as was the propriety of the day and
lived affluent lifestyles due to smart investments, fast cars, and
a little pill called Viagra.

The Sea Captain made what was to be his last voyage, to a port
of unknown origin, in quest of The Maidenhead. This quest
proved to be a difficult task considering, that, since he was a
boy, the virgin ratio had been at 99% but now fell somewhere
short on the bell curve, taking a nose dive like the current stock
market, lost, gone, the rewards never to be recaptured (partially
due to his own prowess).

The Sea Captain was in his prime- good looking, trim, and a fit
180lbs on a slender, yet muscular build. His manner of dress
had greatly improved since his hay day of Izod shirts and
designer (Sergio Valente) jeans. He was proud to be an
American; however, he now preferred to dress in Italy's
fashionable manner, with style and flare, ahead of the trends.
He even traded his "oh so fast" Camaro for a faster and
ostentatious convertible (Porsche). After all, he was allowed. He
had earned his right... a right of passage.

He took care of himself, especially after a reunion of the sort
where all present sported "Michelin Man" bellies more evident

than a woman in her third trimester. These friends of his youth proudly displayed their "Mr. Clean" heads. Their once thick locks were no longer a part of them and like the flocks in winter had decided to go south permanently. This realization that someday, he too, may succumb and look like them gave him more incentive to groom daily with Retina A, work-out with the fury of a body builder, and continue_____ like an 18 year old boy on the brink of manhood. This date with his destiny made him realize his mortality and inevitable fate. He decided, at this moment, on this day, he would remain forever 31.

The Sea Captain was in a time of his life when he could laugh at the misadventures, mistakes, and diabolical schemes of his early manhood. A time when he could view, like a scene from his favorite movie being replayed over and over again, his numerous conquests, literally and figuratively. He could recollect with lasting impression, the multitude of friends he had made for they were infinite... He was simply a friend to all and continued to be so. The challenges he now faced were small because the years had added a certain docile maturity to his youthful demeanor.

It was at this time that he decided to "search" once and for all, the last time. For he had everything, and in truth, had everyone he could ever want or need...

... The Sea Captain reached his destination and rang the bell, the captain's bell, once, a bell which harmonized the victorious toll of life's fulfillment, a man about to reach his goal. It sang of his approach for many miles. It told all of his intended landing... He slowly moored the boat to starboard, a vessel mirrored by the size of his ego. He expected to see only the shore before him- white, soft, pristine- always reminding him of the first woman he ever ____. Instead, it was a vision like a rainbow, an array of colors, arms waving, the sounds of a royal welcome! He no longer was "a legend in his own mind" (as many teased him)- but now "a legend"!

He pulled out the bifocals and surveyed, close-up, what may have been deceiving his Azure eyes. Before him they waited, anxious and somewhat perplexed like the moment before one's first kiss, a certain tension with a positive electric current. Some were happy and jubilant like the couple on the day of their firstborn. Some had tears slowly trickling down their cheeks, as if their fingers had just been pricked. Some were pensive- not really understanding the moment at hand.

It was their one last chance to capture his heart, a painstaking fight justified of its reward- HIM!!! They had known him. They knew him. They wanted to know him. This search (in quest of the maidenhead) was infamous- re-known for its purity in thought and reason, more talked about than that long ago slipper whose owner had accidentally slipped and run off.(But how did they know of it?)

And so- there they stood:
-the brown, doey-eyed one whose once innocent stare matched her now mischievous gaze;
-the succulent golden-haired beauty whose crowning glory once bright as a midsummer's night day was now mixed with autumn's subtler warm hues;
-the ravishing red-head who could never be inhibited for her thirst remained unquenchable- hot and fiery!
And a mix of fuschia-colored, nose-clipped, tattooed, silicon breasted beauties whose ages ran the gamut from the "naivete" to the learned "those who don't say"...

They were all there- his past, his present, and his future– all waiting and wanting... He wondered how they could have found him since this destination was un-chartered. He realized that his charm had surpassed a magnitude of proportions he thought he could never peak! What was he to do?

He thought carefully and seriously as the boat started to rise and fall, quickening like his heart which had started to beat wildly. Was he finally feeling what he so longed for? (Or was this a panic attack- uncontrollable?) He continued to view the scene, placing himself on the outside for once, strategizing what his next move would be. For once, he was thinking with his head (the one above his shoulder NOT his lower half). What was he to do?........

......For he whispered parting words and knew it would reach them since the gentle north wind had favored his voice and brought him to this place:

"You are all beautiful. You are all nice. You are all witty. You are all... the perfect woman."

And with that, he blew one last kiss, confident that the early morning mist would place it on each one's cheek... and motored quietly away in search not of "her", but of the many great adventures in lands which were still not tarnished by the fast and tumultuous world we lived... Alone- a man, his boat, (a photo of his late 1ˢᵗ mate) and the great sea which belonged to him and only him!

Stephen. A man whose ego was larger than life... Stephen's party. "His" friend's party. Our friend's party. I was hoping that some legal calamity (he is a lawyer) had taken that man (the Devil as I like to call him) out of New York and he would not be present. (I choose to keep him nameless because he is not worth personifying.) Wishful thinking... "He" arrived late. I ignored "him" throughout the eve. I acted as if he were a mere figment of my imagination. I looked through him when our eyes crossed paths. Even when he stood next to me near the crowded ice-block, vodka-shot games we were playing, I pretended the space was empty. When he casually brushed my back to get my attention, I ignored him; however, I was instantaneously thrown back to that one December night- goose bumps (of the bad kind) running through my body, evident in the heavy August air. I got the heebie jeebies. It was a buried event I was forced to recall...

My savior was the birthday boy's "Coastie" 29 year-old cousin. Sweet little Robert swept me off my feet and twirled me around the makeshift dance floor. I call him "sweet" because he was always the little boy who managed to hang around "us" teenagers. As we matured, he was still viewed at sweet cousin Robert. He was a 29 year old man now, blonde hair, blue eyes. He was a man (now), a very good looking, intelligent, mildly-mannered (had a bit of a wild streak) man. He became my savior and pulled me away from the bar just as "Dick" (alright-

I've given him a name) was about to engage me. Robert didn't know that this little innocent maneuver of his saved me. We danced for many songs...

At this party, I was, for some reason, the center of attention. "He" must have noticed. (I knew he kept looking at me.) I don't know why but I was the center of attention. Was it my fuchsia floral dress or the pashmina conservatively draped to hide my décolletage? Was it the cascading curls that partially hid my black-lined, sultry, smoldered amber eyes? Was it that the majority of women present wore shorts, t-shirts and sneakers since a party was no excuse for them to get dressed up... The compliments did not stop as one after another of the married boys exclaimed: "You look great." They were flirting with me and it was evident in the daggers their wives threw. The married men. It didn't make sense because my self-esteem was low. I had gained unsightly pounds, felt a little thick in the middle, and my hair was a boring darkened shade of brown (though the color in the box promised me light auburn). I was the femme fatale and I didn't want to be. You would have thought it was my party, my night. If you walked in and didn't know me, you would have thought I was playing the hostess, with the utmost in gracious airs.

I should have just accepted their compliments as what they were- real, some thoughtful exclamations. (I didn't know how to accept a compliment.) Anyway. I was confused. Why were all the men paying attention to me? I should have accepted their compliments instead my guard went up- thanx to that asshole looming nearby that made me feel guilty. When would I be emancipated from that event??? Did they all just want to sleep with me? Was "fuck me" showing through the veil of conservatism I chose to wear this eve???

Because of that incident in December, "Dick" is the main reason that I chose to take a back seat, to never make the first move on a man, to not sleep with anyone, to remain pious. (I took the back seat yet became the center of attention.) Guilt for blaming myself for what happened. My dark secret that fed its way to the surface of my closed heart. I was the lady in waiting- where was my knight in shining armor? Why was he always disguised? The evil warlock underneath his mask...

That December was the beginning of my rebirth as a virgin. I became a virgin once again. Yes- I reclaimed it again. Guilt was the extraneous factor! My commitment was to myself and no one else.(The August event that evolved later which forced me to recall only fortified my commitment to myself.) I didn't want to be hurt emotionally anymore. I didn't want to be hurt physically anymore. My guard went up. I didn't want to meet anyone. I didn't want to date. (I hated dates anyway.)

A man (any man that I deemed worthy, that is) would have to kiss me first because from me- a kiss was to be rightfully rewarded (even though I still needed the next man to take charge, to make the move, to seduce me but slowly). My guard went up. I had fuck me written on my forehead. I needed to be careful, very careful. No one would take me in and hurt me again.

No one...

TANGENT

We had such a nice evening. Playing games. We stayed up later than expected. We had so much fun.
Him. I guess she's got a new one. Playing games?? Really!!! at their age. Probably sex games.

She's a blast.
She?

She's so understanding.
She????

She's such a great person to be with.
SHE???

She's the person who makes me happy. And so young with so much energy.
When did she switch teams??

She's two. She's my goddaughter. Children are so sweet.
But you get to give them back. You're not around when they're crying, coughing, whining, calling your name every two minutes- "mommy", "MOMMY", "MOMMMMYYYY!!!!" They need you all the time.

But....
I don't get to wake up to "Mommy? Mommy?" in her cutest voice at 6am.
I don't get to wake up "I want shereal" when you ask her what she'll eat for breakfast.
I don't get to wake up to the giggles, smiling faces, hugs and kisses. I don't get to hear... "I love you."

I wake up alone.

Chapter ix.
Lost in Space

What was it about on-line dating? I was getting hurt and I never even met the guy. They were blowing me off- due to what? My verbal repartee?

1.

I WAS BEING hurt just as much as a real rejection. I was on an emotional roller-coaster, a never ending ride of gut wrenching twists and turns. I needed to stop being so sensitive. Stop asking myself- what am I doing wrong? Stop questioning- why doesn't he write me? (Call me?) I needed to take it all in with a grain of salt. I needed to remember I was just one person in a chasm, an abyss of endless potential mates. I needed to stop running home, turning on the computer, waiting to hear those three words... You've got mail! (It was three other words I really wanted to hear.) Cyber dating- it gave me endless opportunities. Then again. It gave them endless opportunities.

I was on the treadmill at the gym at the end of February. With the plastic surgery came a slight weight gain (you thought I would say loss), not too much but enough to make me miserable since my clothes were tight! I was tired of everyone preaching that I should go out on dates... I should meet a man... I should do this... I should do that... They didn't know about my December experience... I was on the treadmill reading Businessweek, and a tiny article caught my eye, an article on cyber-dating. How ironic was it that the largest population of single men lived in the same west coast town as my true love? The article postulated that California's Silicon Valley had the best ratio of men to women, intelligent men, men whose IQ's were as large as their deep pockets. This California town replaced Alaska as THE destination place to meet a man, catch a man, marry a man or at least date a man or two or three! As if I was going to jump off the treadmill and fly west! Not a bad idea, though, considering my true love had moved to a city in which I thought he was safe since there were few women. That's where she stole him from me even though she had her choice of men. I guess she knew she seduced the best.

What a coincidence that I called his best friend in Boston and in my friendliest "I should have chosen you" voice asked him to meet my sister and I for a drink. His tone, one of shock and disbelief, surprised me: "I am in San Francisco!!!" He was usually a sweetheart. How ironic is it that Thomas, my true love, was walking down the aisle when I called. Does anyone object to this marriage? Ring. Ring. I do! (me on the cell). How ironic. I knew he was getting married. I didn't know when. (How ironic that the FDA would approve VIAGRA just as he returned from his honeymoon.) I will always love him but I could never forgive him.

This is what brought me to cyber, cyber space. I was a new woman, a woman of the 21st century, pious and puritanical in mannerisms, triple x in thought. It took an operation and the fact that my true love got married that made me realize... realize what? My knowledge of the world and quest for love... No! It wasn't a quest; it was a quest to fall in love, "reached far beyond the confines of simply being the pediatrician's unmarried daughter". Was *Sex in The City* a story about me or was I leading my life around the plots in it? I was a single woman in her 30's and being reminded of this every day. I had been alone for the last four months. I hadn't had a "relationship" in over a year. I guess I was feeling lonely...

And so I began my foray into space... with a 30-day free trial. I could be anyone. Quite frankly, I chose to be me because "me" is quite interesting and my mother was whispering into my subconscious..."always tell the truth, no one will be believe you." I chose to be me with a byline that said: "witty, whimsical, friendly and happy with old-fashioned family values". If that didn't get their attention, then this would strike their fancy- a body type that read: "curves, all curves." I made sure that the "no one can break my spirit" was in BOLD print. And that I was attracted to a man who wanted to "encourage our spirits together!" Okay- so I accidentally slipped on the keypad and put in the wrong birth-date. Oops! Anyway, a gentleman should never ask a woman's age. As for the personal habits that really irritated me... foul language, foul body habits, and a man who'd prefer to watch football on a rainy day than make love.(Not for me so need not apply.)

I utilized cyber to keep me happy, to keep me busy (it was an excuse from remaining in Hotjobs! Or Monster! Searches), keep me... Well, let me venture into a love search universe. It was a time of 1sts: 1st blind date; 1st grown-up date; 1st lasting friendships with the opposite sex; 1st chemical de-action. It was a time of firsts...

I could do anything. I was a new woman with an attitude of "you can look but you can't touch!"[24] At least this was what I was telling myself. This was what I was psyching myself up to be. Those poor men. They were like that suffering child in the candy store who is told he can't get anything. My self-esteem was low so it became my experiment, like Pavlov's Dog- how often could I make them salivate. One kiss and I got them going. You can look but you can't touch...

Read. Write. Respond. A continual cycle. It was a vast universe of lonely hearted souls like myself. Everybody's looking (though no one's actually seeing), evident in the number of profiles. They would have good intentions, pure intentions. It was a reputable way to meet someone single, someone who cared, someone who wanted to get married, someone who wanted to be loved, and vice versa. My naïveté coming forth in thinking, believing, looking for the good. As I was a novice in this sport, I didn't know that people lied. I really thought cyber offered quick solution, a way to zig zag ahead of the curve, a way to get to know someone based on themselves not their looks (ok- so he's fat!). It reminded me of that lost art of the last century, the art of letter writing; whereby, "you wrote a letter the same way you would speak to a person". Except, you no longer had to wait for the Pony Express. The Stallion became a quick click of a Mouse. The Postmaster General had personified into an ISP.

I could be anyone but I chose to be me. Where were all my future husbands? You've got mail! Not! They hadn't found me, like a needle in a haystack, soaring through open space of inherently appealing women. They hadn't found me in cyberspace, the boundaries limitless, heights infinitesimal, a world yet to be conquered. Cyberspace... they hadn't found me. I guess I would have to initiate... off to the races. I was a filly waiting to take home the Triple Crown. But, don't tell my

---

[24] The new enhancements turned me into a prude. I was afraid to touch myself. The thought of anyone else squeezing, sculpting, molding, playing was enough to give me an anxiety attack!

parents. They wouldn't understand. They couldn't understand. They had been married for 40 years. They fought on a tour bus through Europe. My Mother- the Italian tour guide. My Dad- the obnoxious gum chewing, feet-on-seat, American medical student. Fate crossed their paths two years later when they met again, fell in love, and within three months, they were married in a civil ceremony. Three months after that she was walking down a church aisle getting married before God. I tease her that she couldn't wait to loose her "vestal virgin" appeal. After-all, the bride wore white! Anyway- my parents wouldn't understand. Cyber dating was as indecent as running a personal ad... "Ro- why are you laughing?" I covered the monitor from their gazing, eavesdropping eyes. "Ro-why are you laughing?" Nothing. This was just one of the covert maneuvers I had to keep and camouflage when conventional terms dictated my family's Christian doctrine. It's what I needed to do without raising suspicion. Don't tell my Mom and Dad!

I looked for a common interest, a key word that made me write, write and write. "Hello... I always like to begin with a simple salutation," I mailed. I picked one commonality and continued to play whether it was a favorite movie, a favorite activity, or most importantly a stress on family, family values. And the questions that were always asked first and foremost by those that met less than their expectation: Do you have a photo? How old are you? (I guess a gentleman you are not!). I didn't want to be a stereotype but I was- the biological clock (which I didn't believe in) was ticking. I wanted a whirlwind romance and I thought cyber would speed things up a bit. And from what one of my male friends told me ... a women will say one thing and a man will interpret it another way:

She: I'm going through physical therapy.
Interpretation: She's gained some weight.
Hey wait- I was going through physical therapy. (That pervert of a therapist who took liberties with my body. I mean a massage is a massage except when it gets personal, and he's heaving, sweating, foaming at the mouth... I stopped therapy soon after. I kid you not!)

She: The photo is from two years ago.
Interpretation: She's gained some weight.
Wait- that's a great photo of me even though it's from two years ago. The Ladies in Red photo.

She: I'm looking for friendship.
Interpretation: She wants to get married.
I wanted to be friends first and yes... I am looking to get married.

She: I'm curves, all curves, just curves.
He:(intrigued) "Uhmn... This could be good!"

I was different (or at least wanted to believe some were like me). I didn't lie. Why did people feel that they had to embellish? Tell the truth... no one will believe you... I met them all in cyber. The was the hermaphrodite. She was a woman who posed as a man. Was she writing a thesis on dating habits or was she really a he/she? Ohhh- that scared me. Next came the PhD. with his Oedipus complex. He blew me off on our first intended date. I walked up and down Moran's, amidst the crowd of well dressed, fast talking, debonair (so they think!) men. Moran's. Up and down Thank goodness it was a quiet day. I finally called him from a pay phone- "I'm in Long Island," he said annoyed. Huhhh? Idiot. I was too good for him.

Anyway- it started to rain. All at once, I had dates (a lot). On one such weekend, I had three. I hated putting myself on parade. I hated being a searcher. I hated dates but I was forcing myself to go out, to meet someone, to go forward with my life. My true love was married (my true love who I will always love but never forgive). My sister, Angela, kept asking where I was meeting these men. Ahhh- lets see I work for French Design Company. He's French. He's one of the buyers. Uhmm- he's a friend of Margherite's. Let me think... I went to high school with his cousin and bumped into them at the gym. Yeah- that's it...

I was going to a Mardi Gras Happy Hour sponsored by The Children's Aid Society. It may have been a fundraiser but it still was a pick- up, singles scene. Who's kidding whom? The shy, demure me was coming out. I hated bars, meeting people in bars, being picked up; nevertheless, I e-mailed this poem to one of my potentials:

<u>If you decide to go Friday</u>...
In a room full of women
who look the same
with shoulder length hair, maybe longer
neatly coifed manes
The air fragrant, attitude high
who'd take the chance to faithfully malign
each other with a few dirty looks
the warnings not mistook
Will I be
petite and FUNky dressed
though I'll be sporting the smile
wearing the CROSS on my neck, twice blessed!

...He saw me as I turned to my left, laughing, head thrown back. It was a casual moment. I caught his eye in this darkened room of "hoping to hook up" men and women, the same men and women who went to fundraisers as a civic duty because they hated singles bars (right!). I noticed the two because of their opposing mannerisms: one- confidant, the other- anxious. One urging the other to move forward, pushing him forward. I guess I wasn't appealing to him because he hesitated a little too long. Or the red Baccarat Marybeth cross on my neck wasn't a big enough clue? I said cross... I never said what type of cross!

One down... 100 more to go. An infinite number to go...

I met them all but only when I knew I needed to, when they initiated "the date". Ahhh- a few men with balls! I didn't want to. The shy, demure me still present. I was so insecure. My personality could come out in an e-mail but the me, when it came to men, meeting men for the first time, was so insecure. I didn't have enough self-confidence to realize that maybe they liked me. It was that "I have fuck me written on my forehead" stigmata. It was that "temporary adornment" cycle that I wanted to break (but didn't know how). But I psyched myself up. Self-confidence is a sexy attribute. I kept hearing that, kept reminding myself to possess it...

"Peppy le Pew, Adieu, one. two". The Frenchmen – Pierre. I showed up at the café in the Village. I looked sexy/conservative in my cashmere sweater and black stretch jeans. He decided within one minute he didn't like me. Based on- looks? We had coffee but when the subject changed and he said, "You should try Matchmaker.com.", I knew he wasn't interested. Snob! Cultured bastard! Artistic ass! My feelings were hurt. What was it about me that he didn't like? I was too embarrassed to go home. Like a little girl, my feelings were hurt because my date had ended in less than 20 minutes. What would my Dad think when I went home, early? I couldn't go home just yet. Too many questions would be asked. I would have to face the dreaded parent tribunals of my youth, questions that were asked because they were curious but would make me feel like it was my fault. I didn't want to face my parents so I drove around the neighborhoods I used to hang out as a teenager: Flushing, Bayside, Bowne Park, The Triangle, all of those places where we snuck beers and acted like big shots. A trip through my youth would take my mind off of him not liking me. Who did he think he was? Eurotrash!! That High and Mighty fixated on address', a "Manhattan Elitist" who thinks THE CITY is comprised of only one borough. Queens? Where's that? I guess I wasn't interesting enough. (Though he did make me realize I should take more advantage of what THE CITY, all five boroughs had to offer...)

2.

PALMER... MY FIRST grown-up date. He wined me and dined me. I should expect nothing less. This is the standard I should go by, always (but I didn't). We had been conversing on line for two months and continued our facetious banter. I can't remember what caught my eye about his by-line. He seemed to have a lot of energy. He said he would make reservations for dinner. I got lost driving around Nyack but finally arrived one hr late, found the coffee shop but didn't see a man with his description. He was 42? He was wearing a brown jacket?

There was only one man sitting alone among the crowd but he looked old, weathered, with a stressed appeal, and he had on a blue shirt. I ran out to find a pay phone. How was I going to call him since I didn't have the $4.00 in change? (His cell was a New Jersey number.) Think! He probably thought I stood him up. I turned around to go back and he was standing there, behind me with a big smile. The "old man". On closer inspection, he was quite handsome, a Mel Gibson twin, gray hair (a full head), blue, blue eyes, a big smile, a nice body, tall. He was just missing the Aussie accent, although he spoke with an Atlanta twang. He was divorced and bitter because he said he wanted children and his wife had some gynecological problem. My first grown-up date. And he was divorced. (Don't all divorced men want to get married again? I wouldn't have to worry about commitment phobia, I thought.) He kissed me hello. We took a walk around the town. He wanted to get to know me first and ease the tension. (Probably wanted to see if I was worth the dinner expense. See how insecure I am?? Confidence- it's a turn on. Confidence- it's sexy. Remember that. Remember that. Remember that...) I was nervous. He could be an axe murderer luring me into a dark alley (and the alleys were dark!). The little girl was coming out. Nervous Nelly. The stupid, giggly child. He held my arm as we walked as if we had been a couple for many years. (Think mature! Think grown-up.) I was a great conversationalist when the little girl didn't come out. (I'm not schizophrenic!) We stopped on a dock overlooking the Hudson. It was a beautiful May evening and the lights from the Tappan Zee Bridge glowed sensually on the calm water. After some casual conversation, we finally went to dinner. He ordered. My first grown-up date. I looked the part- with the Ann Taylor white silk duster, a vintage pin on the collar, side-zip brocade pants. High heels, of course. I took off the jacket and knew he was staring at my body- the black t shirt clung to my breasts. (Too bad he didn't know he was only allowed to look and would never get to touch!) My first grown-up date.

When the check came, he kept looking at it. I just sat, politely. I didn't offer even as he kept staring at it. My first grown-up date. He made reservations. He asked me out. I just sat- it was beginning to get awkward. I hated dates for this reason. Who was going to pay? The etiquette. If someone asks you out, they should pay. If you ask someone out, you should offer to pay. If he's a gentleman, he'll pay. In a man's eyes, a lady should always at least offer. Too bad on this one. He asked me. He was a grown-up. He was a Regional manager for an internet company. He made money. I was the lady and acting the part. He should pay. I just sat there. He paid. I said thank you. We walked through the town and ended up in a bar, listening to a blues singer, drinking Cognacs. I love the blues, so erotic, such a turn-on for me. My first grown-up date. He kissed me. I drove him to his car. He wanted to go out the next day. Fast! (They always wanted to get to know me fast and then ... see ya!) I had a Communion party... I only know that one kiss and I could get them going. I got him going as he left. He just sighed and looked at me with those baby's blues- sparkling. He would have to wait.

He called the next day. I was surprised. He wanted to come to the party. As usual, I dressed well. I wanted to continue being a grown-up, a sexy grown-up. I wore a paisley deep pink and orange knee length skirt, pink wrap top, white sandals with little flowers on the straps, and of course the pale pink Pashmina shawl. Pink is not my color but I still looked nice. Everything matched.

Big mistake! My friends with all their kids. My family with their kids. Kids. Kids- everywhere you looked! Big mistake. He seemed out of place, even though he came from a big family. I was out of place considering everyone was married with children- two or three children. But I had known this group my whole life. They could have been a little nicer to him instead of their usual cliquey selves. The clique! I should have known better. We should have left sooner but we stayed until the cake.

We went to Coco's in Huntington for a drink, outside, on the water. A little bit better, just me and him. I bought the drinks but I made him go up to the bar. Grown-up date. I wanted him to continue being the gentlemen, even though I asked him to kiss me. I made him kiss me: "Kiss me, you fool," I said with devilish smile in the parking lot of 7-11. As we drove on the

Long Island Expressway, he serenaded me. He started with Broadway's tunes and drifted into an operetta. He had a wonderful tenor voice. It was his passion and if he could change places at this time, he would be singing at The Met. As we drove, he continued to sing throughout the hour long journey. I asked him to sing *Bocelli's "Ti Parturo"* and he did. I explained to him its importance to my family- my sister's wedding song, which became my brother's funeral song. He sang it with strength and sweetness.

There was one thing that bothered me, really bothered me. He kept rubbing my shoulder, moving his hand underneath my shirt, moving his hand to the side of my breast. I kept moving it back to a safer place. He kept sneaking it back there, caressing me, rubbing my thigh. The caressing was nice but this was a grown-up date. He would have to wait! And he was driving. He asked me to go to dinner but somehow we never went. As I gave him a tour of my parents garden, as we sat and talked on the upper patio, as we began to kiss, my mother stuck her head out the window from two floors above: "Rossana? Is that you?" Grown-up date. More like high school.

...More like high school is how I was acting but Palmer proved to be a grumpy old man, that scowl faced schoolmaster. Mel Gibson had disappeared. Someone else had replaced him. My two friends, Kim (34) and Marybeth (30) had been recently diagnosed with enlarged hearts, hearts pumping at 20% capacity. Two sisters (each with two young girls): the same disease, separate stages. The doctors believe they were missing a gene that shrunk their hearts back after their pregnancies. The doctors were unsure of the diagnosis because they had never experienced such in women so young. Marybeth had just turned 30, her face ashen, she had just had a de-fibulator put in, had just been given the a-o-k to begin life again. Kim was in better shape, the decimation on a smaller scale since she had bore her second daughter one year after her sister...

My two college friends as different from that school as myself. I first noticed the two because they looked so much alike and stood out or should I say above the rest of the crowd. Their hair, which you might expect to be golden (like most southern blondes), was dark as midnight. Quite frankly, their hair was Farah Fawcett fluffy: a little too much care, a little too much effort, a little too much Aquanet. It was the 80's. They were from Richmond, Virginia- five years behind the trends as my 1st and only butched haircut depicted. What really set them apart was their fur-jackets, probably the local hares that their Daddy hunted and scalped in their own backyard. Even though they were statuesque, of model proportions, and beautiful, I could hold my own since I was smart. We became friends as unlikely as this should have been. I guess the commonality was that we didn't care! We knew we were different from the Buffy's and Becky's that had dominated our college campus.

15 years later we were still friends with that same "who cares" attitude. They had not changed one bit. Still gracing 6 feet, slender bodies, thick midnight hair. The only noticeable difference was that Marybeth's slightly auburn tinted hair covered her many grays. Too young to look old, heart failure had set them back and slowed them down but you could not tell even though their smiling, giggling, farting appearance was a façade, hiding the effort it took to breathe!

Girls night out on a July night in Downtown Richmond, Va. Girls night out to celebrate life because we weren't sure how long their lives would be (and my own "growth" that was being watched carefully). Girls night out, just like in college (except one sister didn't drink) as we danced with the little frat boys, laughed, did *the Bus Stop, the Hustle,* and got wild to the sound of *Saturday Night Fever* with the lighted dance floor. It was 80's night in this downtown club. Marybeth, as usual, kept pulling me into her breast. Marybeth- what a nut. Rosy O'Donnell except at 5'11", lean and curvy she looked like a super-model. Her sister, at 5'10, had been your typical Hawaiian Tropic Bikini model. My two beauty queen friends. The little boys couldn't believe that most of this outlandish group was married, happily married.

On the drive home, we were giddy, we were high, we were thankful to have experienced this carefree, entertaining evening. As we passed Monument Avenue, someone started to tell the story about the controversy surrounding putting Arthur Ashe's statue amidst the Confederate Generals. Wait! I told them about this man I dated, my first grown-up date, his Great Grandfather had been one of those Generals- a hero of the old south. His Great Grandfather was well known. OH-NO!! Like in *OHHHH, NOOOO, MR BILLLLL!!*: His Great Grandfather's head had been sliced off and replaced with Arthur Ashe. Oh, No!! We couldn't stop laughing at the absurdity of this but in the south (deep south by my NY standards), white was white and black was black. No diversity. No in between. Controversy. Arthur Ashe was a hero to the blacks: for defying conventional standards, defying prejudice, building his own tennis stadium when he was shunned from the "whites only" country club, for teaching the children of Richmond that pride prevails, for being sensitive to the needs of his race...

We were laughing, crying, the tears streaming. It had been a long six months, six indecisive months, a long time since my two friends had laughed and let loose. We were celebrating life and the simplest things seemed funny, innocuous things, hysterical, and this story, hilarious. Thrown back in time to college, nothing could stop us, no one could stop us from our pranks and practical jokes. Amidst the Taco Bell food-fest being devoured at 2 am, I called Palmer. Laughing. Choking. "Palmer- (choke) I'm in Richmond." (hee-hee ha-ha)... "Your Great Grandfather's head was chopped (gasp) off and replaced with Arthur Ashe." (hee hee ha-ha...) "I can't deal!". Click! Ouch!- that bruised my ego. (If I had only read *"The Sweet Potato Queens Rule Book"*, I would have known better. It clearly stated that these late night calls can only be made if you are engaged to the fellow.) He said he had a sense of humor. He seemed to have a sense of humor. Who put the stick up his tight ass? Maybe no one likes to be awakened at this hour, but he didn't have children to worry about, a nagging wife to console. He lived alone (or maybe he wasn't alone that eve?). I sent him an e-mail explaining. He never responded. Insensitive! He could learn a thing or two from Arthur... Arthur Ashe, who stands proud amidst the white Confederate Generals... The good 'ole south!!

3.

I COULD BE myself, words and phrases revealing my outgoing, shoot from the hip, bubbly demeanor. I could be myself and write witty retorts, whimsical replies to their questions... Gavin. He appreciated me for my sarcasm. He appreciated my humor. He had a similar personality. Our families were the most important things in our lives. Gavin... *"whose hair is dark as a moonless night, the sunshine's warmth reveals the chestnut mane of a thoroughbred, racing through the wind, fearless, blight... Eyes crystal clear like the Mediterranean on a calm and quiet eve, effervescent, looking glass, piercing deeply into my soul... Two pillars of strength, steel, a body of exuberating force and power on which it was built- lean mass. Voice, deep and resonating, pitch high and low..."* He had a certain homeboy allure with his long hair and dare-devilish attitude. Gavin, the musician, who wanted a girl just like him. He didn't drink. He didn't smoke. (He did toke.) His personality reminded me of my stoner friends- too laid back, too complacent, to set in his hazed-out ways. Okay- I'm looking for a reason we didn't mix, like vinegar and oil. However, shake us up with a few added indulgences and you've got a spicy dressing.

Gavin. He wouldn't return my phones calls to be interviewed for this book. Gavin whose current girlfriend prevented him from being my friend. Gavin. I wrote that poem on tax day, our first date. I had yet to actually meet him. He e-mailed me a picture. I wrote the poem as I drove the fifty miles to his house. The words just popped into my head. This was my "poetic period" anyway. Every man reminded me of something poetic.

Our first date was suppose to be a picnic, a casual lunch with a casual motorcycle ride. I chose carefully from the Italian deli: eggplant, boccancini, cold cuts, cheeses, salad with homemade vinaigrette, tira misu. I also brought with me a bottle of Brunello di Montalcino (1996) that I purchased on my recent trip to Italy. I planned the lunch very carefully and very tactfully, spending well above what an afternoon excursion should cost. Gavin liked my artistic flair. But he could have been a serial killer... luring me into his soundproof recording studio. I was scared. He voiced my fears. We laughed. We were at his parents' house in Westchester. My only disappointment was that he didn't drink; thus, the wine remained unopened. (I relinquished it to his parents' private collection of other fine vintages.) In addition, he ate healthy- too healthy. I believe the plain iceberg lettuce was his favorite part of the meal. (This should be to my advantage since I wouldn't be able to poison him with my cooking.)

Gavin. He is a nice guy- one of the few that really exist. i.e. he thinks with his head not his dick. I mean that. He satisfies his sexual urges by taking industrious bicycle rides through the mountains, jet skiing 'till endless hours, snow-mobiling on trails that don't exist (rather than picking up strange women, getting laid, having sex with a friend). He is truly a moral, kind being. Why can't all men be like him? For once, a man who leads with his heart. He never leads a woman on.

When I met him, I initiated it because he was "an enigma". His byline said: "lying, cheating, no good scoundrel that's lazy, fat, and ugly!" Just kidding. It said: "honest, active, passionate, happy and at peace, looking for the same." He didn't write anything else about himself. Gavin, into spirituality and family. The musician. Talents that he kept hidden. Only once, did I intrude on his privacy. It was the first time I heard him sing. I forced the issue by popping his *single "Keep Writing Me"* into the tape deck... Gavin's fantasy about his online woman, his mystical princess, his very young (twenty-one) princess.

Gavin and I are still friends. We will always be friends even though some woman always gets between us. Triangles. I never want to be a part of but I always am. We never consummated "us" though there was an apparent chemistry. I asked him once what he would do if I kissed him. He replied he didn't know. I told him once I didn't think I was thin enough, healthy enough, athletic enough, or young enough to be his girl. God- why was I so insecure? (What happened to my "You, over here. Now!" attitude?) I was definitely intelligent enough!! I never made a move, the fear of being rejected was too great! (Hello, moxy? Where are you?!) He never made a move. He liked us as friends, movie friends. (I got tired of going to the movies with him, usually seeing something stupid, far from a cultural classic.) Friends... But... I still dream of our date, a date that got ruined by the rain... Our date...that should have been...

... An autumn ride into Bear Mountain, me holding him tightly as I sat on the back of his motor cross bike, an autumn ride off the beaten path, the dirt trails resplendent with a tree curtain, the sun peaking through as if afraid to light up the hilly terrain, the wind beginning to blow....A sudden downpour. Two upturned picnic tables, there tabletops meeting, one on top of the other, became our makeshift cabin. We would wait out the storm not realizing that ...The heat of his kiss would force the shivering cold away from our bodies, the mud becoming our fashion statement, as we turned and rolled on a bed of twigs and fallen leaves. Crunch! Snap! Sigh! Aahhh! We never realized the squall had passed, the sun shining on a panorama of red, yellow, orange and green, a blue clouded sky above, the valley before us...one majestic view for our eyes only, a perfect finale to our coupling....

Gavin never judged. He didn't seem to care that I was in a transient state. He didn't seem to mind that I hadn't quite found my moxy and that my career was on hold while I experimented in different fields. I was working in the New York Design Center because I needed the money; however, it was a transient state because I wasn't fully utilizing my potential. I knew I could run that showroom with my eyes closed but I wasn't quite ready. I kept quiet, observing every mistake they made. Those asses- they had the potential to make a lot of money (lots, if I was in charge). I was working for a French design company. I realized that I loved interior design and wanted to be a decorator; however, I didn't have the blue-blood elitist attitude of the trade, nor was I a gay male! Remember, I didn't quite have my moxy or the attitude that I could combat anything. I was still looking for a new career, wanting to get into PR or marketing as I waited for my grad school results... Until, that one day in June. I chose to be happy. It all happened at once. One day in June, a day that changed my life and made me who I am today. I found my moxy once and for all!!! One day in June...

4.

ONE DAY IN June, Murphy's Law had changed my life: what could possibly go wrong, did go wrong, all at once. It changed the way I thought, the way I acted, the way I was. One day in June...

1.   I called the recruiter. I was waiting on a high paying position with the Louis Vuitton Group. I had gotten great feedback from him saying the French were very impressed with me, I had interviewed well, made a positive impact, thus far, with someone as tough, snobby, and resilient as Jean-Marie, the French District Manager. My moxy had been showing a strong presence; however, victory was short-lived. I didn't get the job. It seems the Regional manager, a New Yorker born and bred, didn't like me.

2.   That day continued with a disheartening call in to Gavin: "I got back with Maria"(for the third time since I knew him). I wanted to ask...and what about us? I couldn't. I wanted to ask him what we had been cultivating? I couldn't. I guess I was just his "movie date". "She's jealous of you. She surprised me and came up this weekend." Gavin- couldn't even be my friend because of Maria, *"Maria, I just met a girl named Maria"* (*West Side Story*) In my view, their relationship was more like the song from *The Sound of Music*: *"how do you solve a problem like Maria, how do you just make it go away..."*

3.   I got home and opened the letter. "We were impressed with your application. We found it enjoying; however, your portfolio wasn't strong enough..." I didn't get into the grad school.[25] What was I going to do in September?

---

[25] I received a second rejection letter two weeks later. No kidding. It seems the school decided they wanted to take a personal interest in my humiliation. The Dean wrote a letter. Bad enough once but a second slap in the face. Ouch! Luckily, I had a tough hide!

4.   I received a call from my gynecologist: "The MRI validated that you have a tumor..." I didn't know there was an empty cavity behind my fat ass. One lonely tumor... and it was growing!

I could become a manic depressive, cry, transcend my happy little life into a negative spiral or ... This was a hard one... or laugh since "I didn't even have my health!". I chose to be happy. From this day forward I would always be happy. I DIDN'T EVEN HAVE MY HEALTH! It was a lot to handle. One day in June. I found my moxy, once and for all!!

5.

JUNE GOT BRIGHTER and hotter. It seemed that I finally was going to get a new full-time career, in the same field I wanted to leave behind me, but more upscale, on Madison Avenue. June... the summer's onset. June...no-one could break my spirit because my moxy was here. On one day, of all days, in this volatile city, someone decided to jump in front of the tracks. Only in New York. Only on a day when I needed for things to run smoothly, the subway stopped in the tunnel, somewhere between Queens Plaza and Long Island City. The Fire Department turned off the electricity, which in turn caused the air conditioning to be shut down. Only in New York, is the morning's rush hour demeanor more concerned with their own sweating selves than the poor soul who decided to take his life. Only in New York. On this early morning, the humidity soared as we were stuck in a cattle car with no ventilation, stifling, heavy, shoulders to shoulders, faces to breastbones, heads to armpits. I was lucky enough to have absconded a seat since my departure commenced at the first stop.

On this day, of all days, I had switched bags, and I needed my inhaler, which never really had much of a purpose other than taking up space. I rarely used it. I always had it except this day. I couldn't breathe, scared of passing out, scared of joining the lost soul who had caused this mess. On this day, I had an interview and I was stuck. I couldn't breathe and so I began to count backwards, slowly, breathe slowly, close my eyes, relax, count, breath deeply. Ten minutes. Twenty minutes, thirty minutes. Stuck in a hot, closed subway car. Forty-five minutes. Someone, open the windows, please! Keep counting. "Think calm," I told myself as I wheezed, as I sweated, as I swooned. Finally... air back on. I would not become a calamity. Finally, moving again.

I arrived late, harried, flushed, a mess. I made a joke of it as I explained my appearance to Elena, the Director of Stores for Nickermil. What else could I say to defend my unappealing self? Despite my grand entrance, the interview went well, conversational, free flowing, relaxed, no trick questions, no hidden meanings.

I followed up with Michelle, the recruiter for one of the top firms, with offices in Chicago, NY, LA, Atlanta: "She loved you"...as the praise continued... "however, she went with another candidate." Disappointed but at least I had made a positive impact. Or so I thought. I called back a day later, as the company was hiring for an Assistant position in Manhasset. I liked and believed in the Director's ability. I liked this company. I liked their product line. I wanted to work for them and would humble myself into any position. I called Michelle back. I got Fran: "Listen, Rossana.... They liked you but she said you have a mustache! (Her tone was condescending and nasty). She liked your skills but she said your hair was dirty even though you dressed well and spoke well but... you're simply not polished. Image is important and they hire for image...May I offer some advice, maybe you need to get bleaching done"

"STOP RIGHT THERE!!! I GOT to know right now..."

I was floored, taken aback. Her assistant had just given positive feedback a day earlier. The truth hurt. The truth was unfair. The truth was unprofessional. What truth? This was the most bogus job denial I had ever gotten. Lawsuit? Anyone know a good Jewish lawyer? This screamed discrimination!! A company that hired for image not skills. Plain and simple-discrimination... but it would be difficult to prove. Anyone know a good lawyer?

See ya! Your loss. Another door slammed in my face... another opportunity somewhere... *"some-where o-ver the rain-bow"*. I am a dreamer but I knew that the horizon looked blossoming... After all, I had my moxy back!

6.

I CONTINUED TO interview. I need to find something before my September deadline as I had already given notice to the design firm. Public relations or marketing. I would make my goal. Yes!! Opportunities fell into my lap. I chose wisely (hindsite is 20/20) I reached my goal... working in a corporate, Monday – Friday 9-5pm position, managing a toy account for a marketing company. (The office atmosphere replicated a *Babes in Toyland* paradise. The childhood energy canvassed every wall, the laughter echoed through each temporary structure.) I could also continue taking design classes down the block at the Fashion Institute of Technology. Finally, one goal in my favor... And, it started to rain again that fall...

INSERT

...And I wondered why you stopped calling me. I am your friend. I spent a lonely summer, alone, in Long Beach, sometimes sharing the day with my 1 year old god daughter. How sweet. How innocent. How much fun as she ran around naked. I am your friend. I kept asking you to join me. Oh! You're in a blue mood- your fiance is a confirmed alcoholic and doesn't want your help. You want to stay sad. Okay. It's your prerogative to remain in a dreadful mood... but I'm your friend. Now I get it. I'm happy. I choose to be happy... and the last thing you want is me, all smiles in your face. That one day in June... changed my life forever... I choose to be happy.

Most of us can't understand- in fact we rather surround ourselves with those feeling the way we do- miserable! Happy person is that pain-in-the-ass always smiling, always laughing, always carefree. She doesn't understand (or so you think) your harrowing lifestyle:

- the painter who arrived just as you were leaving to take the kids to school
- the phone ringing non-stop just as you put your daughter down for a nap and you need this hour alone, to yourself,
- the hot water tank exploding the day after you installed a new carpet

or best:
- at the school fundraiser, you (PTA Mom of the Year) find out your four year-old is the kissing bandit, chasing all the boys, making them cry, and the leader of her "girls rock rule" club.

...It's always something! If you're not screaming at your children to pick up their toys or yelling at your husband to put the kids to bed (not play with them, and wind them up)... It's always something... Happy person! Smiling person! You think she's judging you so you'd rather not have her around... Well, your loss. I choose to be happy.

Chapter
X.
Let's Just Call Him
Fast and Furious

Cyber cooled off, no longer a novelty. Too many men, endless opportunities, and most were asses. So...

I CALL HIM "fast and furious man" because I wasn't putting out (poor time management on my part because "being good" was getting me nowhere) and he was all over me on our first date. When he called, I thought he was someone else- the someone else described as successful, well-established, good looking, a great guy- Constance's nephew.[26] She told my Mom she wanted to set up her adorable nephew with a nice girl- I being labeled "nice" at this time. (What was I doing at this time?) My Mom, a newly ordained "yenta", gave out my number willingly and blessedly, without hesitation, not caring whether I would comply (knowing I would comply with her gentle urging)...

Instead- he called. He was Constance's friend. He asked her if she knew any nice girls (any new single women) since everyone he knew, everyone and anyone, he had already dated, dated by conventional standards- *achew!!!slept with!!!*... Even the chat rooms had run out of new options for him. Chat rooms- I should have said no to our date...

He called me that first week, every day, every hour. He made me laugh during crucial e-mail freezes and computer crashes. He continued to make me laugh as I became stressed and more stressed fitting in a full work day, night classes, then back to work for conference calls... I listened, carefully.

I was intimidated by his age. I knew that I needed to look hip, sexy, with an attitude of "I can have anyone" for this date. I wore a blue matt -satin stretch (a few extra pounds) suit with a floral blouse opened just so (ok- it wouldn't close) to reveal the black tank underneath. A full face of makeup and hair blown out to a perfectly coifed look (me? coifed?)! I may have looked good but boy was I scared ringing his doorbell! Ding dong. The seconds deciding my future... husband??

He was cute- handsome really, blue eyes, medium height, expansive chest set over a flat muscular stomach- no gut!, looking good for 47. As for his shoes- move over John Travolta cause the Saturday night fever was just about to sizzle! Capezios (in disguise as loafers). I wasn't crazy about the

---

[26] Constance is my mom's client.

mustache- I kept imagining how it would chafe my thighs and rub the makeup off my face. Ok- I was horny but get your mind out of the gutter! I said i-m-a-g-i-n-e.

Lets see, small talk (nervous), small talk (still nervous), drive through Gold Coast neighborhood (nervous but impressed), walk on beach one minute (oh-oh- awkward very nervous moment- whew! escaped that one without a kiss),dinner (glass of wine confidence builder), back to his place (nervous? who me? I was feeling no pain at this time)... *He kissed me and I took control (no pain, no gain) knowing that one deep thrust, a small suckling on the upper and then lower lip, a quick peck on the cheek, a peer into his eyes would get him going...a pause, soon becoming a grinding of bodies and contortion of limbs...He kept wanting me to move upstairs- me keeping a "safe" perch on his Living room couch.* Second base was a far as I let him go-I was caught up in a moment where nothing mattered. (Slut! Tramp! Come on- remember being caught up on the moment when nothing matters?) Second base was as far as I would let him go though I was taken away, especially when he kissed my belly, his hands finding their way south, cupping my ass, massaging my thighs...

I wondered if I could feel again- it had been so long (over one year) and the last time had ended up with a "supposed" friend taking advantage of me in the kind of situation no women should be in. Would my body know how to react? respond? Ahhhh. One kiss of his lips on my right breast sent me swirling. It was only when he exclaimed out loud between suckles "God I love your breasts. Are they real or are they fake?" -the bubble had burst! A moment of rude awakening. I was brought back down to earth in a second! Pig! I thought. One thing is to whisper dirty little thoughts –it's another to add injury to insult. "If you have to ask, then they are what they are," I replied as I gasped, one final breath, pulling away. Two points for me. He didn't know. He couldn't tell.

I know what blue balls feel like. Not exactly, since the female anatomy does not testosterone make. It was "the let down"- the point of no return, inhibitions running wild, and boom its over and I felt empty not sated. I stopped him, yet I wanted to have him, needed to have him, wanted to feel like a woman again. Constance had warned him not to sleep with me on the first date as his usual norm, 'cause I was a nice girl. I wanted to though I had not intended to. He didn't have to seduce me- it had been too long. I guess maybe my body language stated black and white "I'm easy. Take me. I'm yours." My mind said no. My body said yes. Yes! YES! Fast and furious would have to wait. I was not so easily had. My body. My choice. My decision.

I listened carefully... He mentioned that what he always wanted, wished for, longed for on his birthday was a homemade chocolate cake with chocolate frosting- BING!- file that away under "best recipes to win him over". Months later, after dinner, I presented it to him- Duncan Hines chocolate pudding at its best. He accepted it politely and left. Too overwhelming?? My simple gesture was an affectionate act of kindness, of friendship. Oh well- they say that a way to a man's heart is through his stomach- I guess I can't even win one over this way. At least I can bake. Come to think of it, I can cook also- rare for a woman to do today yet alone admit to. Blame it on Mom- teaching her girls to cook so that they could marry well (three out of four isn't bad). Nice- too nice-that's me. We are still friends. The platter which held the cake reminds him of the sweet girl much too young for his "oh too aged" virile self.[27] 47- acts like he's 60!

---

[27] It was he who took me 90 miles each week to find my house on the Northfork, negotiate a final price, inspect, compare. It was he who took me recently to test drive my Miata- a car I dreamed about for 10 years, wanted for 10 years, had to have now as a measure of my self-worth. He pointed out in an authoritative, fatherly way the pros and cons of driving a stick in NYC with its pot holes, traffic, and other obstacles. I decided not to buy it. My choice. My decision. His good advice. However, it proved to be a "bait and switch" maneuver on his part for he was selling his Mom's 560sl Mercedes convertible- "special price for you". Once I was behind the wheel, I knew I had to set my sights higher- I was Mercedes woman. I am a Mercedes woman. "Yes, I am woman!" I didn't buy the car. He's still holding it for me. It was to him that I made a booty call, bearing bakery-bought chocolate mousse cake. Needless to say, I chickened out- It was with him when I realized I can't even make a booty call anymore! Ahhh-virtue.

DEPARTURE

As I recollect, there has been too many men. It serves me right that I keep getting hurt, keep giving 110%, loving unconditionally. My record wasn't always so "nice". Look what I did:

Daryl Dog "dawg". I hurt him, so dearly. The 6'4" string bean with his Van Halen choker, Van Halen shirts, Van Halen memorabilia in every corner of his room, and his Van Halen look... Oh, those romantic walks on the beach when I stood perched on top of a boardwalk wall so I could see him eye to eye, kiss him lips to lips. He was too quiet and I recall trying to instigate a fight just to get a reaction out of his stoned demeanor. He smoked too much pot. We lived together in Pacific Beach, Ca. and had a wonderful time exploring each other when we could. My first lover, as an adult. He worked as a sous chef nights at the Catamaran Hotel. I worked mornings as a waitress. We had the two-hour overlap of shifts- I made sure I was consumed with work in the kitchen. My puppy dog who, once I left and moved back east, vowed never to cut his hair... One day, when I returned two years later- he proudly displayed his hippy locks that grazed his ass. Who says romance is dead? He vowed never to cut his hair until I returned.

There was Robbie. (I was his high school sweetheart.) I first saw at a St. Francis Prep HS football game. He was so cute with his blonde, blonde hair (and a virgin when I met him). My first high school crush (*and they call it puppy love...*). He was in my friend Maddie's core (homeroom). I was only 14. We met again later when I invited him to a party. My parents were in Italy. (Never leave your 15 and 16 year-olds home alone!!) My brother and I were up to no good, having fun as teenagers do when they possess their first bout of independence... and we were lucky that the house didn't get torn up, demolished, destroyed... Robbie asked me out again a few months after I ended our two year relationship. He loved me his friends said. I kicked him to the curb... I had found another...

I would leave Steve (my high school sweetheart) to go away to college, 365miles south. My independent being felt that a girl should NOT stay home because of her boyfriend. All the Queens girls attended St. John's so they could be with their sweethearts. (Most of them got married soon thereafter). Not me! He was attending Fordham. I could have easily attended any school within 100 miles radius of him. Away I went and away he played, sleeping with all my friends including three of my best friends. "You cheated on me first," he said." "Yes, but I only kissed him. You slept with all of them." "You cheated on me first," he continued, psychoanalyzing his actions. Not his fault. In his mind, he was the victim. I'm the one who lost three best friends... In fact, this is when my insecurity complex first surfaced. I don't like triangles- someone is always going after what is mine. Ok- "if it's yours it will come back to you, if it doesn't, it never was." Yeah, yeah. I've heard that before. He never came back to me.

And who could forget Andreas, from Cyprus- dark hair, brooding eyes, and mysterious grin. I met him on a school trip to Greece. We kissed, necking as 17 year-olds do, for many hours in the lobby (and terrace) of the Pantheon Hotel. This time, the Pantheon illuminated the smog-filled air in an iridescent afterglow. We wrote to each other quite often over two years until he said he was moving to NY or DC for school. I freaked. I had a boyfriend (Steve). I never wrote back. I disappeared into the rolling Virginia hills.

"Rosebud", so nicknamed because he brought me a rose. My friends made fun of his gesture. I liked roses at this time, had never had them given to me. I didn't want to date him! I didn't give him the time of day because he wasn't my type. Did I even have a type?

Vinnie... such a nice Italian guy. I blew it. Dating him and "Mr. Body Beautiful", simultaneously. Mr. Beautiful looked like John-John, 6'2", curly hair, and a body that you'd die for... God, he was hot!!! A senior in college. I felt so grown up strutting around with him on a nightly basis at Gantries Pub. The crowd at this local bar all wanted to know who he was.

The girls had lust in their eyes (and daggers behind their backs). Vinnie really liked me, had a genuinely nice quality about him. I was such an idiot! I guess I wasn't ready for another relationship, another boyfriend after Steve. My heart was with Steve, trying to get him jealous, as I sowed my oats. Didn't work, obviously.

I hurt them. I hurt them a little. I hurt them a lot. Now it's poetic justice, that turn of events, that I am hurt again and again and again. But you see... I'm not a bitch. I'm too nice.

Chapter xi.
"Catch My Lucky Charms, They're Magically Delicious"

It was the night before Christmas and all through the house...
He was thinking and contemplating, he sure was a louse...

THE NIGHT BEFORE Christmas Eve, that is! He canceled plans with his friends, telling me he didn't want to go because it was a night out with all the kids. He didn't want to deal. Instead, we went to the movies. He picked it. "Ms. Congeniality", a light hearted and funny flick with comic overtones throughout. He didn't want to hold my hand in the theatre. Strange. The seats were comfortable. Why was he sitting away from me? He usually received my affection well. I just wanted to hold hands. ..."Let's go get a drink where we first met," he said as we turned south on Bell Blvd. "What? Taking me out in public. Are you breaking up with me?" I teased. I was in the holiday spirit. He was quiet. "Hey, Scrooge..." I was laughing. Did I just put my foot in my mouth? He remained quiet. "WHAT?!!" I said in an astonished tone. "You've got to be kidding. It's Christmas." He started to speak. I didn't want to hear it. "Take me home." He pulled over once because he wanted to talk about it. Talk? I was bursting with venom like a snake about to strike. I knew that words spoken would not be nice. I chose to be silent though my eyes were filled with raw emotion. I maintained a silence so deep- lost in my own world, lost in a pea soup fog. I don't even remember opening the door, entering my home, and crawling into bed still clothed. You jerk! It's Christmas!

It finally hit me. I couldn't sleep. How dare he break up with me? Jerk! I was only kidding. What in God's name made me kid around like that? I know I'm a witch but foretelling the inevitable? What made me say that? I couldn't sleep, tossing, turning, my mind burning. I drove back to his house in Bayside. Jerk! He was still awake: "I'm going through something. I always go through something during the holidays. I need you to call me." "Call me," he said three times. "You need to call me." Jerk! How dare HE break up with me? "I have your gift," he said. "I don't want it," I replied. "I have your gift. It's even wrapped. It's right here," he said, as if the breakup was not planned, his last minute escape. "I don't want it." How dare he break up with me. This was a man I wasn't interested in. A man I ignored all summer long. This was man I blew off more than once; always coming up with excuses to not meet him: "I'm getting my hair done." "I'm babysitting." "I'm this..." "Sorry, I'm doing that." This was the man I finally went out with and said to me, yes, he actually said these words and I quote: "Lets get this relationship going. Three months is too long to wait." Jerk! How dare he.

"You're a great girl." STOP!! I didn't want to hear it. "You're a great girl," he continued. "STOP! I don't want to hear it. I know what I am." I said. "I can't give you what you want," he said. He didn't know what I wanted. We never talked about it. About our future. About us. Everything's copasetic. No pressure. Just two adults enjoying each other's company. (Or so I thought.) He didn't know what I wanted. He didn't have a clue. It had been taken from me so long ago. Jerk!

This was a man I met in cyber-space because we both loved our favorite childhood movie "March of the Wooden Soldiers". *Dun duh duhh, dunna duh duh dunnah.* (AGHHH- besides, the movie had more "wood" than our sex life!) Like me, this was a man dedicated to his family. This was a man who grew up in the next neighborhood, a man in which we had mutual childhood friends. I was a high school friend of his cousin's. Jerk! This was man that taught we how to roller blade down by the Throgs Neck Bridge. Jerk! This was a man that took me to dinners with <u>his</u> friends in trendy (passé) places and then a walk through the Village for espresso and tira misu. A night out on Bleeker street for some live music. With HIS friends. This was the man that I planned to spend New Year's at his place in Mt. Snow, Vermont. We had plans. Everything was copasetic. Everything was fine. No tension. No controversy. None of those point-counterpoint battles of wit that begin to snowball. Everything was copasetic. I should have stuck to my motto... never go out with a man who only has brothers. They just don't understand the needs of a woman. Jerk! How dare he break up with me. Me. I'm smart, very intelligent. I was probably the sexiest person he ever went out with (probably the most excitement he had sexually!). I was probably the best-dressed woman he ever went out with. I was probably the happiest and funniest woman he went out with. I was always smiling. At least when I finally felt he cared. At least when I finally felt secure. At least when he finally made me feel comfortable. How dare he! With his looks. And he sucked in bed! How dare he break up with me. My self-esteem just took a nosedive.

Did I invade his space? I only asked him to pick me up at the airport on both Sundays. I knew I should have made other plans but after working in Minneapolis and New Orleans, I wanted to see him. It had been two harrowing business trips. Did I invade his space? I called him from the car because I went last minute Christmas shopping at Bay Terrace and wanted him to join me. I was only down the road. Wait- he invited me over for dinner ...didn't ask me stay but he did kiss me, longingly, out of nowhere, passionately. (I only wondered what brought that on.) It ended as soon as I became aroused. Was this a test for what he was feeling? Should have been feeling? The kiss made my knees weak. It's about time he kissed me! Did I invade his space? He lived alone and was use to it. The few times I was allowed to sleep over, during our morning coffee, I'd spontaneously get up, jump into his lap, throw my arms around his neck, and kiss him. I love to kiss. A small peck on the cheek. A soft kiss on the lips. Or maybe a deep one. I was just being affectionate. Did I invade his space? He wanted me to redo his home- a task that eventually had us redecorating every room in the house. I wanted his home to look more masculine instead of being a reflection of his dead mother, a cross over every doorway. He had great antiques and wonderful knick-knacks that thanks to my decorating savvy you could now appreciate. UHHH. That ugly wall unit. Gotta go and it did!! Wait- the couch is on the wrong side of the room. And those chairs! Lazyboys. Gross. Downstairs to the basement. What a great marble sideboard! Perfect for a bar. Waterford. Gorham. Such beautiful crystal. OOH- check out that DECO bed. Upstairs into his bedroom.

His bedroom. His bed... we made love eventually. I don't recall how or when but I knew him for five months by this time. I was in my catholic school-girl mode, along with the white panties... not really wanting to be with anyone, not wanting anyone, just anyone, to touch me. (This was my time of "You can look. You can't touch." thanks to my new boobs.) I wanted it to be right. I wanted someone to make love to me. It had been ten months since that bad episode, eighteen months since someone, anyone had been intimate, really intimate. He seemed to care. He didn't push, sexually. He liked me. I thought he cared. Ouch!! Those damn fingernails. He was always slicing me. I'm sure my vagina looked like I had run through a thorn bush or cactus meadow, naked! Ouch! Those damn fingernails. And what was up with him not being able to do it from behind? He kept his balls locked between his thighs. UHMM? Well in time- we would have to get used to each other. We would have to learn how to please each other. That's what he said. That's what he made me believe.

Chemistry? (Not!) I was confused. Chemistry. I never knew what people meant when they said "there was no chemistry." Until now! I guess I didn't feel any with him. There was something about him. He wasn't good looking but he grew on you, my leprechaun... but he didn't have a pot of gold at the end of the rainbow. He didn't have a pot to pee in as they say. And he needed to get those teeth fixed. He had no prominent incisors, no center, the top blended as one continual line, kind of askew. And the cigars- you know how they make the teeth green. He had a pear-shaped body, no muscle tone whatsoever in his chest, with a large ass. He didn't dress well. The khakis were way too short and the creases didn't fall correctly. And the stripes. Horizontal! Add some weight where it wasn't needed. His habits were enough to turn any woman away. Recycling the dental floss. I thought he was kidding- just teasing me- but there it was, hanging over the towel rack. Gross. Ok- I would be a little more compassionate. He said he didn't always have money. Ok- he had been poor. I guess he was just being economical. Still... gross.

He was a geek, a professor who taught a Policy class at City College. Intelligent. I always did like a man for being smart. And he did ski. One eve, he played his guitar, played it to me, played it for me. I guess it was the little things that I read too much into. A blatant act would have meant nothing. These subtle, little things meant the world to me as if I was special. And he was nice to me.

Something, though. I couldn't quite figure it out. He didn't like me spending the night. I kind of had to ask, insist, state "I'm

sleeping over." He didn't like to open up to me about certain
things. He didn't drink. Alcoholic? Dope head? For some
reason, I never really asked him. He had that way of closing
himself off that wasn't worth prying into. Anyway, I wanted to
keep everything copasetic. I didn't want him to think I was
nosy. (He felt we would learn what pleased each other in time.
I felt I would get to know him in time. When he was ready.) He
only said he had a lot of former vices. A few things he revealed
but never in detail. I know his business went bankrupt in
Silicon Valley. There was some animosity with his cousin who
wouldn't bail him out when she possessed every means to.
That's all he said about his former life in California. Anyway, I
discovered the papers, and of course read them, when we were
moving things around. I just found them. I didn't ask him
about them. I couldn't pry. The moment never seemed
appropriate. (In time, though.)

I FINALLY understood what people meant when they said they
don't feel chemistry for someone. I always have chemistry with
every man. My periodic table is usually a vast array of
elements, their physical and chemical properties endless... but
there was something about him. Something. As if he was
playing a part because society dictated he should, though he
didn't want to, he didn't like to. Something. Maybe? Yes! the
moment of reckoning... what he said to me makes sense:
"There's probably a reason I'm not married at 39." Yes, there
is. You are gay, a closet homosexual.[28] After all, I have
chemistry with every man.

This was the man that I felt comfortable enough to reveal my
secret, a secret I had been harboring for six and a half
months- "I have a tumor. One. Behind my uterus."[29] I was
scared and I felt comfortable enough telling him as I lay in his

---

[28] Let's just say... I hit the nail on the head. Recently, I saw two men roller-blading by
me as I sat by the water's edge in Bayside. They were holding hands. One turned back
and smiled at me. It was not until he skated away that I noticed that fat round ass.
[29] My gynecologist found the tumor (a cantaloupe-size fibroid) on my follow-up visit
many months earlier. He wanted to leave it alone. "What are you waiting for?" the
Doctor asked. My biological clock (which I didn't believe in) was ticking. "What are you
waiting for," the second opinion questioned me in reference to starting a family. "...a
boyfriend, a husband, a house, a baby...in that order. Would you like to harvest my
eggs?" I answered. After all, I felt I had at least another 10 years of child bearing.
NOT! -according to the statistics.

arms. "You'll have to get a hysterectomy! My cousin did." he said. Jerk! So insensitive.

Maybe that was it. Was he scared we would have no future? Was that it? End it now before it gets too deep. What did I do wrong? Everythng's copasetic... Jerk! And I gave myself to him. I chose to give myself to him. I hadn't slept with a man in, gosh it was so long... since the incident. And that doesn't count. I hadn't given myself willingly to a man since ... Luke, my rebound. I chose to give myself to him, this leprechaun. Damn it! I should have remained the coquette, keeping up my good girl image, relying on "You can look but you can't touch!" Still, I gave myself to him, that night under the bridge, with a full moon cascading on the water, in the car, as the windows fogged up, no one around. We started out "necking" and I just let go. I was tired of being such a good girl. What good is it being a good girl? I didn't want to hold back anymore...

the shadow of a bridge
traversing two separate worlds
it was me, it was him
in a dark desolate corner
where others chose to perch nearby
on this cool winter's night
our room, four corners of steel
passion arose
"throwing caution to the wind".

He had been a gentleman, taking his time, cautious how he handled me. He never moved his hands to where they shouldn't be as we kissed. He massaged my sternum once. It was very relaxing. Yet still, I kept pulling back, holding back. I didn't want to be the tease. I gave myself to him because he wanted to "get this relationship going". And then HE stopped me. I chose to give myself to him, like a virgin sacrifice, and HE stopped me. Ok. He had a point. He wanted it to be safe. We continued... later... back at his house but the moment was lost, lost in the wind... I thought he cared. Jerk!

I wouldn't cry for him. He wasn't worth it. (I cried a little.) That night into the next morn. I just didn't understand why this was happening to me again. Why? Why couldn't someone just love me? I was good to them. I was nice, too nice. Everything's copacetic. I never fought with him. I never brought the volume up. I gave 110% when he made me feel secure. I spent Christmas Eve alone. I had to drive my parents to my brother's house in Manhasset, 20 minutes away because my Dad had just had hip surgery. My mother was asked to get out of the car. "Get out of the car! I want to speak to Rossana-ALONE!!!" he yelled as a husband of 40 years has his right. "Don't do anything stupid. Merry Christmas." He read my mind. He must have known I was hurting. I was planning something. I was tired of being hurt. I was tired of being taken advantage of. I felt morally degraded as if this affair had dishonored me, once and for all. I didn't want anymore short stories, minute interludes. I just wanted... *"If your heart is not on my side..."* That song by Belly King suddenly popped into my head, a song that would remain there, the thought making its way to the surface of my conscious being each time my gut told me otherwise...

My Dad is a smart man... because of his words, I wouldn't do anything stupid. I couldn't do anything stupid. Instead, I made a strong Cape Cod (Grey Goose vodka (Luke!) & cranberry), pulled down the two paintings I had created eight and a half years earlier in simple colors, simple form and put my energy into finishing them as a gift to my niece.

I took the negative, the dark cloud of despair, the depression that was brewing and put it into creating a masterpiece, a pencil and watercolor painting of Barishnikov in a warm, colorful embrace with his lover, a cascade of intertwining hues and images. The more I blended, the more I added depth and highlights, transparent and translucent tones, layering color upon color, I felt better. My broken... No! he's-not-worth-it, I reminded myself... My tainted heart began to heal. I realized that my love was very strong, a bond no one could ever break. My love was indestructible...

...my love for the children, my nieces and nephews. I created a masterpiece. I felt much better. One thing I can thank him for... I began my house hunt. I wasn't going to wait for any man. I could take care of myself. Buy my own house. House hunting. My energies went into settling my future. Alone.

I returned one of his gifts to Tiffany's, a sterling-silver cardholder. A gift with the name of his new company engraved on it- Wild Ir'land.

Wild Ir'land. Kiss my "you can bounce a quarter off of" ass!

PDQ

I KNOW YOU may not like me. You're probably trying to figure out who the hell I am. I guess I'm still trying to figure that out. I know I'm not a heartless whore because I felt something for each of them. I really liked them and looked for the good in all of them. OPPOSITE? A heartfelt whore. Maybe. In the absence of any real love, I became a "virtual prisoner of my own imagination, a slave to my own desires." But the desires spanned between a desire to be a good girl and the desire to be wild. Maybe it was congenital- a sickness that tormented me and drove me to become a woman of ill repute. Maybe I should just accept the balance of opposites that comprise me.

I never thought of myself as a slut. I did not jump into bed with them. I never even had a one-night stand. From a conversation I had with my girlfriend, everyone has had one, one night of just sex, new sex, sex with someone you've just met. Not me. But the boys, the men... they led me, made me believe that they cared, that they wanted to make love to me. I only kissed them. One kiss that made them come back for more.

But I was also the shy girl, a part of me that no one believes. I was outgoing; except, when it came to men... I became a little girl, stupid and silly. I knew I appealed to them but I was still insecure... there had been so many times of being the ugly, short one in a crowd of tall, thin beauties. I was only a girl intimidated by your natural beauty, your all-American looks. The girl that was boxed out in conversation because he was only interested in getting to know you. I was only the girl that looked better dressed up because I couldn't carry your look of jeans, t-shirt, no make-up.

I had so many periods, dry spells, by choice. Periods where my single friends coaxed me to go out but I said no because I was getting to know someone, the someone being me. I didn't want to be hurt anymore. There had been too many men. I wanted to just be loved. And it's not a false modesty. I had this good girl inside of me- the Christian morals that had indoctrinated my youth. But what good is it being a good girl?

I know you're probably even trying to figure out your own life. Are you content being the "good mother"? Are you content being Soccer Mom? Minivan Mom? Just Mom?

Are we all just a product of our generation? That generation that Madison Avenue overlooked, forgot about, or didn't think we were significant contributors to be titled, marketed, labeled. A generation that's unique? or unimportant? A generation that didn't understand our roles. Born between 1960-1971 give or take a few years. Who am I? Who are you?

Post cold war- too post! Our parents were getting married, moving to suburbia, having children (us).

The Hippie generation. In the age of love and peace, we were babies, toddlers, and pre- pubescent. We were still innocent in this era of fornication and drugs.

In the age of Women's Lib, once again we missed the movement. When it resurfaced, ERA could not get passed. You know equal pay, equal rights. I was in high school. Where were you? I know I wanted to have it all, be it all, wife, homemaker, career woman. I dreamed of this.

There were the Baby-Boomers, the Yuppies, the Buppies. Some of you may have hit the tail end. Most of us were struggling or starting a career and we didn't have enough disposable income to get labeled. We were not important enough.

By the time Generation X was labeled, we were too old. Generation Y? We were very much out of the loop.

Who am I? Who are you? We were a generation that played with GI Joes, hoola hoops, Tonka trucks made of real steel, Mrs. Beasley dolls, and don't forget Chrissie whose hair miraculously grew (when you yanked it out of her head!). We wore catholic school plaid and dresses with smocking. Little boys pranced around in shorts and knee socks. We watched the first landing on the moon, the second, the third in a home with one television set, maybe two. Street games consisted of running bases, ring-a-levio, manhunt through open backyards. We could wait for our school bus alone at age seven. We could walk to school with our friends at age ten.

We grew up when disco was born. We should recall the Disco Sucks/Sex, Drugs, and Rock and Roll counter-clash. We may even have become a part of it, traipsing to kiddy discos 'til 10pm or wearing our "Who" t-shirts proudly.

But how come we never got labeled? Who am I? Who are you?

We went to four-year colleges to get a BA/BS. We may have even gone on to get an MBA/MS (not a MRS. Degree). We lived in an age where we had to get a job, no choice but to get a job, so we started careers (at lower pay). We got married; we kept the career going, we had children. We finally settled in the role as mother, homemaker, and wife. And some of us became very successful in our career, made sacrifices, but now have the money to create the balance with nannies and maids (but it's not enough). Some of us are still struggling but don't have to work, have the beautiful home, the healthy kids (but its not enough). Some of us are working, raising the kids (because the husband doesn't help, doesn't share in the kids.) And some of us had no choice but to keep working, waiting for the prince (still waiting) to take us away from that boring career. Yes. Some of us are still single.

The blankety blank generation. The PDQ generation: pretty damn quick.

Don't you realize that you are the mirror image of your mothers; however; you are NOT a little more wiser NOR a little more adventurous, NOT a little more feminine in a masculine role nor a little more parental BUT...a little less patient, a little more I wish for it, I can have it, I WANT IT NOW!

You never have enough time. You are always on the run.

- The pest man that you left in your house (whose probably stealing your Christmas gifts) since you invited him in (to check for spiders between the floorboards) because you had to run out to pick up your daughter from cheerleading.
- The construction crew you couldn't leave alone. You had to supervise every, last detail instead of just leaving them to be the professionals that you hired. Blame it on them (not yourself), you were late dropping your children at swimming.
- Oh yeah. There's your next door neighbor who left your seven year-old child alone with her two year-old because she had to drop her oldest off at soccer. Luckily, you were looking out the window when she backed out of her driveway. You watched the children from the hole in the fence so no harm would come to their nimble limbs. Now you can't even trust your neighbor because she's also always on the go. Too much for her to put <u>all</u> the kids in the car.
- You can't finish a conversation because your six-year-old must have your undivided attention RIGHT NOW!!!!
- Let me see, oops, I'm sorry I interrupted you scolding your eight-year-old because she's not doing her homework. Could be she's just helping her sibling go potty?

Here. There. Where? Now. Then. Before? Always on the go. Super Mom. Pop-up mom. Pop-up mom?

Pop-up and your cookies-n-cream mom. Next moment, pop-up and you're PTA mom or the Pop-up carpool mom or the Pop-up professional mom. Pop-up and you can be "Party mom" drinking non-stop shooters. As a result, pop-up and you're dancing-on-a-bar mom! Next day, pop-up and you're church mom (with halo and all). The pop-up maid. The pop-up homemaker! The pop-up wife! The pop-up lover! Pop up and you're...

Pop-up mom. Who are you? I couldn't possibly understand your life, relate to your life. Not me. I'm single. You still live your life through me, your single life. Well, I am sick and tired of hearing you complaining. You have a husband that loves you (in his own way), you have healthy kids, you have a house (maybe its not as big as you'd like). You have a career- its called motherhood. You have a career- its called wife. You have a career- this is your career.

I guess I'm getting to my point... I am single. I have loved. I have been in love but I'm still single. I don't want to hear from you again "Oh- you just don't understand". Yes- I do.

I face different obstacles, different challenges.

Chapter
xii.
Let's Just Call Him John
Unrequited...

1.
Dearest John

ONCE AGAIN I was in a triangle and this time he wasn't even my lover. I wasn't even in the "irresistible grip of physical love" yet it was an infatuation that did not ask questions nor expect answers because it caught up with me so unexpectedly. The "Dear John" e-mail was a surprise- it came after my coquettish invite for him to escort me (opportune word) to a wedding. I was just trying to bridge the gap that had widened even though I continued to visit DC, continued to ask him to be adventurous (with me), continued to be his friend (and wanting to be his confidante). I patiently (like getting involved in tasks, laborious tasks baby-sitting my two year-old niece) waited one week to send the e-mail when I didn't hear from him, when he hadn't called me back...

——-Original Message——-
From: Rossana@aol.com [mailto:Rossana@aol.com]
Sent: Sunday, November 04, 2001 10:08 AM
To: jck@.mil
Subject: waiting with baited breath

John-
now that I got your attention- did you delete my voicemail?? I would appreciate an answer re: nov 17- my friend. ok- you think of it as a weekend when it's really only 12 hrs of your time I need.
Ciao, Rossana

In a message dated 11/5/01 8:39:40 AM Eastern Standard Time,
jck@.mil writes:
Let's talk tonight.

Unlike him, since he always responded quickly, instantaneously to me. I knew I could count on an e-mail (or two or three) from him. I knew that I would always hear "you've got mail" and his envelope would be postmarked daily. He finally called me but only after I sent him that e-mail, only after I had persisted in getting him to respond. So unlike him. His conversation started off strange- something about long term relationships and how they don't work (What long distance relationship? What relationship? He couldn't have known that my frequent trips south were for our benefit. He couldn't have known that my intention to move to DC was for our benefit. He couldn't have known 'cause we never discussed it, never discussed "us").

He went into some diatribe about how two people are never on the same wavelength about how they feel for each other at the same time. His words, he had "subconscious quilt". What the hell is subconscious guilt? I should have asked him at the time but was afraid of what he'd say. Anyway, his girlfriend went home to Turkey for an indefinite period of time. I only wondered if she had gotten booted out of the country after that day the world watched. I should add that he upgraded her from "the woman I date in DC" to "girlfriend" ("You know Rossana, when you keep dating someone they become your girlfriend."). Duhhh. Sorry. I didn't know you had started sleeping with her. Anyway, she wasn't around and wouldn't be. John and I were friends. We had always been just friends so I didn't understand why he had guilt about meeting my family. I only suggested he stay in my sister's guest house, a small studio on her historic estate. I wanted him to meet her husband anyway since he had agreed to design the architectural plans for John's school, a school that John professed to build in Africa (and needed a lot of help). I just wanted to help him with his humanitarian efforts. John, formerly of the Peace Corps. John, who didn't judge people by the color of their skin, race, religion but by their actions. John, with his instilled Christian values. John, whom I revered.

I was the only one of my friends who still lived with their parents and I didn't want him to feel awkward. I was lucky to have a family I could rely on. I was lucky to have been fortunate to return to the home I grew up in, a large tudor house with a gazebo and fountain set amidst the landscaped gardens that beautified the blue stone patios. I was fortunate that this house had always been a home, open to all, and had welcomed me once again. Months earlier (nine to be exact), I had lost my job for the second time (from the same company) on the day that I was finalizing the contract on my house, check in hand for 20% down, sign on the dotted line! That's how I ended up in Africa meeting him. I decided that since I couldn't buy my house, I would build houses for the poor. I took the negative energy that was surfacing and put it into something positive.

Back to that wedding. The event was in NY. I offered to fly him up. Airfares were extremely low since no one wanted to fly the deathly skies. I viewed it as an opportunity cost, the same as the dinner he bought me the week before, a dinner I didn't want him to pay for (though financially I needed him to pay for). This wasn't a date. We had been friends, only friends who met for dinner occasionally. "You have never asked me to dinner; therefore, I don't want you to pay." I made it clear I had wanted more but didn't expect it since he never took the initiative. His male ego intervened.

I just wanted an escort. A date. I wanted him... to simply go with me. To see the feminine me. To see both the serene and sassy me. I cleaned up well, and besides, he had only known me in construction gear, sloppy baggy clothes with a dust covered face. Anyway, it was my chance to see where we were going, "IF" we were going anywhere. The significance that it was a wedding was irrelevant though weddings do have a certain way of setting the mood since they are usually fun, emotional, romantic. I was very upset (not teary upset for he's not worth crying over), red-faced upset, when he indirectly said no (for the second time) to coming to NY. What was it with his aversion to NYC? Me?

He was definitely confused. Aren't they always confused? Do men ever grow up? When we spoke about the wedding details, I had just gotten back from being out with a friend. He kept asking me "who's the friend?" I answered "a friend.[30]" "A

---

[30] A "friend" was actually my friend Michelle but I never told him that.

boyfriend?" the jealous note apparent in the inflection in his tone. I know I didn't imagine this or wish it to be. He seemed "concerned" that I was out with a man. The green-eyed monster had just bit him in the ass! Jealous fool. I sent him an e-mail as a follow up to our conversation. Subconscious guilt? Huhh???

Subj: AN AFTERTHOUGHT
Date: 11/8/01 6:57:10 PM Eastern Standard Time
From: Rossana@aol.com
To: jck@.mil
You know-I chose my words very carefully on that vm-escort and friend don't imply date and lover so guilty subconscious need not apply. You should have called me last week- there was no reason to deliberate.

This is why I said I need a man with gulones. If you're jealous- do something about it!!!! Unfortunately, he did something that really threw me for a loop... Dear John – that's how he should have started the e-mail. Dear John. It was ironic that he possessed the same name as this euphemism. Dear John. I always felt sorry for those men who fought in the wars to defend our great country and then received their Dear John letter from their cheating, fooling around, infidelity-breathing wives. Dear John, out of the blue. So unexpected. So unlike him. Dear John...

In a message dated 11/9/01 5:40:55 PM Eastern Standard Time,
jck@.mil writes:

Rossana:
I thought you said that after you yell at someone, it is done with and it is over and it is forgotten. Are you still yelling at me? Rossana, there are a lot of people who call me and I do not get back to right away. I am sorry I did not call back right away. That is all I can say. I know you did not say date or lover, but the reality is that even when we talk on the phone, your eight year-old niece asks if I am your boyfriend. The

reality is that going to a wedding may not be a date, but it is close. Don't say that you do that often with Stephen. It is a different situation with you and Stephen that has much history. Rossana, I think the world of you. You are as bright, pretty, creative and you have a one of a kind personality that I enjoy. But I do not think we are right for each other romantically. I told you that it is very hard to have two people right for each other at the same time and that is how I feel. Although you are saying down below that it would not have been a date, is that completely true? Do you want to date? I definitely have gotten the impression that you would be interested in that with me from some of the time we have spent together. And believe me, I have often considered asking you out. But I do not think we are right for each other and would prefer to remain friends. And don't you dare be mad at me for speaking frankly here since you just told me the other night that is the only kind of communication you prefer.
OK, you can start yelling at me again now.

Dear John... so unexpected. Throw an egg in my face! Yank the rug from under me. Giant step .50 steps backward. Who was he kidding? Did he really think I believed his bullshit? I heard it in his voice, the jealous tone...

Subj: dear john-
Date: 11/9/01 9:53:47 PM Eastern Standard Time
From: Rossana@aol.com
To: jck@.mil

John: I am not yelling. You needed to call me back "soon" because it was a wedding and on an army base and the names needed to be called in-ok.I think your ego has gotten bigger than your britches and I say this with the utmost respect. I can only say that you confused me much a few months back with things you said (like flying back from some forgotten city to meet me initially) and e-mails you wrote (about questioning being intoxicated by me or alcohol).

I do have to tell you that I ended our dance in that that club in DC because I felt very comfortable in your arms, too comfortable. I believe the chemistry was mutual;–

nevertheless, since you never made a move (and I refuse to make moves on a man) nor did you initiate a night out- I kept it as friends-more than anything I have tried to be your friend.

I don't want to be the assertive one and I am finding that this is expected from most men. I don't need to be told about me-the good or the bad cause I know who I am. As for my eight year old niece, she says that to all the men I talk to as she only wishes the best for me. I guess that no matter how I tried to be your friend you may have perceived it otherwise- I would have asked you to that wedding in person however I chickened out ...and I do have to say one more thing- you insulted me by calling me too intense. I am not the social butterfly nor the affluent debutante- I have to remind myself every day to be happy (especially since I didn't get what I rightfully deserved a few months back) and if being with friends consistently is what I need right now and being "intense as you say it", then so what? I have many different facets (like the shy and demure me) which I tend to hide these days.
Anyway- a good friend said to me once "its only money" and if I want to fly my friend up for a wedding, so what? If the roles were reversed it would be acceptable.
ciao
-Rossana

Tit for tat. As I said, we were like two adolescents who didn't know how to express our feelings for each other when we were together. We used e-mail as our means of communication, as our means to disguise our feelings. In hindsight, I realized that the written word could be much greatly misunderstood. Nevertheless, he answered in his six-year-old crybaby voice: "If you think I'm too big for my britches, you're wrong. I am always getting shut down by women... Can't we just put this behind us and stay friends?"

Oh, I was seething! Foaming-at-the-mouth-mad! I wanted to face him, tell him all the things I believe he felt. It was about time that I take the initiative. Face to face. I'd be right about "us" or make the biggest fool of myself. I never wanted him to be an "if only". I demanded he meet me in DC when I returned from Mexico.[31] We never met because he didn't call to confirm (I kept staring at my cell phone wishing it to ring.) and I wasn't about to call him (though I wanted to). We never met. Of course, being me, I couldn't let this go. I needed to do something. I wrote him a letter, the handwritten kind. I wrote him everything I would have said face to face. I called him on his bluff. I wrote him, from the heart but never mailed it. For once I listened to my friend Michelle's advice: do nothing. DO nothing. DO NOTHING!!! When you are a woman of action, this proves difficult.

What would he have done if he had gotten the letter? Would he finally admit to his feelings? Would he come to NYC and declare his intentions? love? Ok- that's pushing it. I'm always the dreamer, hoping, wishing, wanting only a happy ending. Most probably, he'd run into the arms of another (since this was always happening to me.) Why me? Damn triangles. John. Jack. Jack- ASS. Not making his move! Jack-ASS, my unrequited (What does that mean anyway?)

Do nothing. It was killing me. Month one. Month two. The season was supposed to be jovial... I couldn't be jovial as I waited and hoped, despair the temporary winning contender. Somehow, I pulled myself out of the despondent mood with sheer will-power... Do nothing! Do nothing! It worked. He sent me a very intimate Christmas card. The end of it said "if you received this card then someone special is thinking about you!" DO nothing! He sent me another e-mail when I didn't respond: "You're being very quiet these days, Rossana."

Do nothing. It works; however, it brought me back to a place I didn't want to be, which was saying goodnight, every night "I love you JCK" as if my guardian angels would carry these words to him, plant them deeply into his subconscious. Maybe they did... subconscious guilt?? You don't say...

---

[31] I had an interview set up for a position in Georgetown, a position (in retail) I really didn't want but needed to get.

2.

"Sunshine On My Shoulders... Makes Me Happy"

IT BEGAN SO innocently. I had decided to go to Africa to build houses for the poor since I couldn't buy my house. Can't buy one, build one. I got fired because the VP didn't like the District Manager candidates I had recommended. Second time, in a matter of two months, from the same company. (The first time happened as one of those "We've closed the NY office. You no longer have a job." kind of mornings. Three days later, they hired me back) I got fired, unexpectedly simply because they didn't like the people I wanted. Hell- the candidates got screened in Dallas by the VP's own people. Scapegoat, they needed one, to buy some time on the account, to fulfill their obligations to their clients. Assholes. Scapegoat- me! And only one week earlier I had gotten my review- excellent in every category. My boss loved me. He liked me for the decisions I made, the clear communication I had with him, the relationships that I had built with our clients. He didn't stand up for me, support me like he should have. Maybe because the President of the company, sitting in as judge and juror, was his father. Jon- couldn't stand up to Daddy, could you? Wimp. Where were all the strong men? Me: guilty before proven innocent. I thought we lived in a democracy? They tried me in absentia. No reason. I got fired. Five cautious steps forward, ten giant steps back. Mother, may I? Ouch- that hurt. No house. No job. No man. Uhmm... sound familiar? Once again, I would transform the worst situation into a brilliant opportunity. Remember... no one could break my spirit, still going strong... like the Ever-ready Bunny.

It began so innocently. I was going to Africa to build houses. Why not volunteer? My ulterior motive: meet a man. It was just my fortune... no men on this trip. I actually thought about canceling and going to Fiji instead but after speaking to John... he had that type of personality that you knew you could trust. He seemed to have the same facetious temperament as myself. I spent an hour and a half on the phone with him during our initial conversation. He was good about e-mailing. Our flirtation began so innocently...

—-OriginalMessage——-
From:Rossana@aol.com
Sent: Tuesday, April 17, 2001 3:31 PM
To:jck@.mil
Subject: Re: Misc.

John- or should we call you ali baba, sultan of
the harem about to embark...

Rossana

ps how are the donuts??

Rossana,
please invite guys on this trip so I can talk football and say
politically incorrect things, etc.
Donuts are almost always good (no matter what the Admiral
says)....John

John,
I am sure you can find some women to talk
football with though I'm not one of them and
I wont pretend to know something just to be
with the boys (its the men Id rather talk
to...There are definitely other things you can
have a conversation about, especially with
10 caddy women. You better be ready for
those hormonal ups and downs.... My men
friends are all pre-occuppied and don't want
to join in on the fun....
Rossana

Rossana 4/17/01,
...I am sure you will like the other women on this trip. I will
keep searching for men to join up so we can have some
balance here. That does not mean women are imbalanced. I
am guaranteeing I will get in trouble on this trip, between my
inherent wisecrackerness and the PC environment we now live
in. I've got to get another couple of guys on this trip and
hopefully they will be like Archie Bunker so that the heat will
be off me! Talk to you soon. John

John- always crossing his t's and dotting his i's so as not to insult the female gender. The flirtation continued, as John sent reminders regarding our upcoming trip...

From: Rossana@aol.com

Sent: Sunday, May 06, 2001 2:09 PM

To: jck@.mil

Subject: Re: FW: Whoops

Dear Dad:

Yes- I took my pills as planned so there will be no more accidents and

dismemberments.... regards, Rossana

From: John

Sent: Sunday, May06, 2001 3:09 PM

To: Rossana220@aol.com

Subject: RE: FW: Whoops

Get used to this constant pestering young lady! And work on that attitude. Whoops, never mind, you are from New York.

——-Original Message——-

From: Rossana@aol.com

Sent: Sunday, May 06, 2001 3:47 PM

To: jck@.mil

Subject: Re: FW: Whoops

Yo- whatsupppp! What attitude? It's just a little bit of whit and whimsy...hey- if you'd didn't follow up, I'm sure there would be a lot of things forgotten. See ya friday, Rossana

---

——-Original Message——-

From: jck

Sent: Sunday, May 06, 2001 4:10 PM

To: Rossana@aol.com

Subject: RE: FW: Whoops

Was the dismemberment comment wit or whimsy? Just wonderin...

:)-John

I had yet to actually meet the man... I just "knew" when I finally did. I just knew when I finally saw him. I still believe we were meant to be. I knew when I saw him, in the African desert heat, pushing that heavy wheelbarrow, bearing the cinder block load that ... I loved him. Too strong a word. Too strong a feeling. Thumpety, thump, thump. My heart was beating, beating strongly. Thumpety, thump, thump! Once a hopeless, always a hopeless romantic. I still see him in that light... his broad shoulders struggling with the weight, the tie-dyed Dead-head shirt glistening with sweat, the worn out jeans showing off his muscular jogger's legs, his hat surreptitiously covering his oh-so-bald head, his slight sun-kissed Scottish skin turning pink. I just looked at him and knew! Thumpety, thump, thump. Thumpety, thump, thump!

We were in Africa. He was our group leader on a Habitat for Humanity mission. I was one of eleven women, eleven independent, strong willed, able-bodied women. Eleven unemployed (mostly voluntarily) women, single women, women much like myself. I hated women (well, they hated me). I much preferred to be in the company of men. This trip was going to be a trial. This trip was going to be good for me, cleanse my soul (as if it hadn't already had a good enema!).

The ladies used me as their scapegoat (at this point in time I was a pro at being the goat!), hiding behind the fact that they were either involved with another, or just recently graduated from jail bait status (much too young), or just too... well, she was an octogenarian (though the term "age is a state of mind" proved worthy as she entertained other ideas, when she purposely left her black bra in John's sleeping bag). They used me and embarrassed me so much I couldn't speak to John. It served me right. I was just having a good time, busting his chops from the onset. "John, are you straight?", I asked him as his jaw hit the table at the first group meal. I just happened to shout it at a moment when everyone chose to be quiet, the lull in a conversation going four strong.

It served me right that they got on my case about him. On the fifth day of the trip, the fifth day of relationship discussions, the fifth day of discussing the differences between men and women..."John, tell us about your girlfriend" as I shone a flashlight on his face after the tribunal dinner. John was sitting alone at the head ...the rest of us in a semi- circle around him, the light piercing into his nervous eyes as the jury of his peers listened attentively to his response. It was at this same dinner that someone asked him if he liked witty women or nice women. Poor guy. Nice was not what the majority wanted to hear since this group comprised mostly of witty women. He could never win with us; however, since he always spoke in PC tones, he remarked: "You are all witty. You are all nice. You are all beautiful. You are all the perfect woman!" (John made this line infamous.) Thumpety, thump thump...

I stayed away one day from the site, feigning illness. John came by to visit- making sure I was okay. Nothing special. He did this with all the ladies, his role as the team leader. My eyes lit up when I heard that early dewy morning knock on the door, heard his pacifying voice. He-man, come to the rescue with a cup of steaming coffee to welcome in the day and a grapefruit. As we sat on the terrace, viewing the sunrise over the valley below us, I told him how I felt. I confided in him that this group of ten strong had intimidated me. I didn't feel comfortable around him; hence my ability to be elsewhere when the team split into groups, my ability to not be in HIS group. This group put me on the spot when it came to John. John didn't notice, hadn't noticed... Duhh. John- chose to have a deaf ear? John? John? Hello, Mc Fly?[32] Where were you when all the ribbing, kidding, and jokes were loudly whispered about you (and me)? You and me.

He was surprised that I, of all people, was intimidated. After-all, I was just being my usual facetious self. This trip was a retreat for me. I could be me. I could be free. I didn't have to think about all the negative things that had just disrupted my goals, my plan for my life. The group thought I was "intense" yet I felt they were ganging up against me, especially in reference to a rendezvous with John. I told him how I felt as his cheeks flushed the color of a beet. You know me by now to understand that I always speak my mind. He remained red and I didn't have to feel insecure anymore. The schoolgirl crush suspended for the time being. Anyway, we became friends.

It was Africa, a land where we mingled and trespassed with the animals in their natural habitat. Africa, where the daily trek through the backyards and grass alleyways of the wards had us sidestepping the donkey's doo, returning stares to the bewildered cows, and running absentmindedly through the flocks of the chickens milling about. Africa...

Our adventure continued from Botswana to Victoria Falls, that mystical, wondrous, unbelievable marvel of the world. The roar of the Falls first heard before being seen...powerful! breathtaking! As I first walked along the perimeter of this great natural phenomenon, I saw before me a vision of twelve separate rainbows- hues brilliant- each representing one of us, each a little bit different; each personality- its own shape, own form, own beauty. The prism of light reflecting different points, a spectrum of unmeasured velocity. The depth of color intensified by the individuality of thoughts, reminding me of each person on this trip:

---

[32] From Back to the Future.

- Red- passionate like Kit's anticipated reunion with her former lover or June's desire to keep all things living-breathing;
- Orange-electric as my own personality striving to maintain its positive current; the combination of two HOT colors-an energetic force in Maria's dancing;
- Yellow-happy as Karina's disposition; Sunny as the glow on Beverly's cheeks, the light in her eyes.
- Green-wholesome as Julie's Midwestern charm,
- Verdant like Elena's down to earth demeanor.
- Blue-freedom representative of Michelle's approach to being equal like the men; Laura's cool/calm manner until the punch-line delivered.
- Violet- where passionate and calm meet as in Nancy: with age comes wisdom.
- Indigo- dark and mysterious: well none of us fall into this category...

The rainbow: its magnitude as determined as John's quest to keep us all peaceful and content. Its shape similar yet not - each arc determining the height, direction it (we) intended to take. For some, the beginning- somewhere in the depths of the schism, untouchable, unreachable, immeasurable, The end- somewhere yet undetermined, reaching upward, endlessly into the sky, a continuous line. For others, its start/end evident in its simplified form, its perfect half circle, its contentment to just be.

Victoria Falls is THE most romantic place in the whole wide world, so beautiful with its endless rainbows, rainbows that went into the chasms of the earth, then escalated into heaven's hands. Rainbows... John should have been ecstatic to be there with eleven women. I would have liked to have been in heaven, with him, if he wasn't still acting like the group leader. He couldn't relinquish his role. The ladies wouldn't let him relinquish this role. He didn't have to be in it anymore. He could have been one man in a group of eleven women. The odds (or Gods) were in his favor. Instead, he still chose to wear his "Habitat" cloak, the cloak of the good Christian. Instead, John, still the leader, the fearless leader encouraged the pensive few, in this placid void..."See what you eleven have forced me to do... J-U-M-p-p-p-p-p!!!!" as he bungied from the highest point over the Zimbawe river...

Bing for my BANG! and vice versa. I needed for him to take the lead. We were going head to head in a battle of wits. I wanted to run wild and free, like a filly on an open field... and have him catch me, throw a lasso around my neck, rope me in carefully, delicately, deliberately. I bucked and whinnied and threw him into the air with my facetious banter. Ever determined, he came back for more. Calmly, slowly, he'd tame my feral ways. I wanted that. I hoped for that. I needed that. I needed a strong man. I was a strong woman but I could not break free from the bonds that imprisoned me.

He flirted with me constantly. During the builds, during the game drives, during the bungi jump. I would casually gaze across the savana and out of the corner of my eye catch him looking, a stupid grin forming as if he knew I knew he was watching. I flirted back somewhat, returning his smile but I also observed very carefully. There was always one woman at his side, everywhere. The same woman. Do you think I didn't notice? I had been trained in attention to detail, a close observation of events, things, people. One woman, always at his side... I wouldn't interfere. If she is what he wanted... then so be it. No wonder he kept the Habitat disguise on. One man. Eleven single women. I told you they hid behind the fact that they had boyfriends. She hid behind the fact she had a boyfriend, yet she was always at his side, sharing a shovel, mixing mortar, building a wall...always sitting next to him, on the sandpit at lunch, at the table during dinner, always sharing, always discussing, always captivating his time and attention, always his Siamese twin, joined together by some nether region. I paid attention. I didn't interfere. If she is what he wanted... oh well.

Africa ended... an experience that's surreal. But after Africa... back to planet Earth. Back to New York but my mind was in DC. My heart was in DC. I wanted my body to be there also. I was always interested in him. He was a nice guy. He had a strong, personable attitude. Hell- he survived eleven women,

24/7, directing us on a construction site (with no motorized tools, even in the 21st century), camping in the bush (myself, the city girl- never camped before!! Hello- panic attack.), bungi jumping in Victoria Falls. SURVIVOR– Africa was as easy as jumping rope compared to what John had to succumb to. He survived us. I dare any man (or woman) to take the challenge. Immunity? He carried that idol consistently.

He was untouchable in Africa, always the leader, always keeping us safe, never compromising his position, yet still flirting. When we returned to the States, our flirtatious dance continued. Who knows who else had signed his dance card?

... He sent me an e-mail thanking me for the team journal entries.[33]

I replied.

———-Original Message———-
From: Rossana@aol.com
Sent: Wednesday, June 06, 2001 11:14 AM
To: jck@.mil
Subject: Re: FW: Two journal entries

John-
huhm- Does that mean you are indebted to me??? I may call in the marker when I need to get out of NY. - Rossana

In a message dated 6/6/01 11:55:33 AM Eastern Daylight Time, jck@.mil writes:

You should assume you are always indebted to me. That is the safest approach.
Thanks! -John

---

[33] We had been each assigned two days by John, aka "Fearless", to write about our experiences, to be culminated into a team journal. I volunteered to type them up.

It continued. Back and forth. Back and forth as if the two us (and only us?) were engaged in fast moving conversation, a conversation about anything, a conversation about nothing with substance, everything with substance, a conversation regarding our trip and the journal we were writing ...

John-

I beg to differ... Ouch! Now you have me begging. What have I become???

...Have a great day at work.

-Rossana

In a message dated 6/6/01 4:01:10 PM Eastern Daylight Time,

jck@.mil writes:

...Maybe I will write something up about the day that was not covered. That is a scary thought isn't it.

Evening...

From: Rossana@aol.com

Sent: Wednesday, June 06, 2001 6:18 PM

To: jck@.mil

Subject: Re: 4 more

John-

I agree- its interesting to see opposing views/similar views on a single event. Scary? I don't know about that since no one has read anything from you. All kidding aside- I know that id be interested in reading your perspective on the trip, an event, the women. I've designated you for May 11/12th- a. ny airport b. jo'berg airport- the deadline is this weekend so throttle forward! The other date is May 28th. In your case- I'd say write from a testosterone point of view. Have the other tenacious ten been in touch?

-Rosana

Rossana:
Of the other Tenacious Ten, only Kit, Michelle, Julie so far... I will not be done this weekend... Sorry about that. But I will start thinking about it... So you want me to write about 2 airports? Can I please have a blander topic.
-John

John and I had open communication yet we were like two children, afraid to show, say, feel the tormented emotions cultivating out of what I wanted first- friendship. After-all, he was dating someone, "the woman I date in DC" as he referred to her. I refused to be in the middle. I guess I was in the middle, but not in a sexual way. He was a man though I kept thinking of him in a priestly way: calm demeanor, even toned manner of speech, pleasantness of just being, a purity of soul, of body ... or so I thought. He kept reminding me over and over again that he wasn't- priestly that is. I just wanted to revere him because he kept telling me, on several occasions how different he was than his male gender: "I am too nice", he said. Too nice. He was always the one being dumped and shit upon by women. Too nice. He was always showing he cared. Too nice. Sounds like someone I know. Was he my mirrored reflection?

John never pushed things...and maybe this challenge was one of the reasons I wanted him more. I had a hidden agenda when I sent the next e-mail. I'm sort of asking him out, making that first move (subtly?). I invited our other friends, other single women so the evening could proceed without any formalities, the evening would not be perceived as a first date...I had a plan of action but it would be enacted at my pace, a comfortable pace because he was dating someone, "that woman I date in DC" as he referred to her (constantly). I didn't want him to think I was blatantly attracted to him.

——Original Message——-

From: Rossana@aol.com

Sent: Monday, June 04, 2001 11:08 AM

To: jck@.mil

Subject: Re: to broads abroad and fearless...

You're welcome. I truly hope you write that article - an interesting perspective from an all male viewpoint- though some of your women-libber team members might have your head on a platter (me excluded)!

-Rossana

Ps. I'll be in DC from June 14-24th so expect a call from me- those bitchy women await your gentlemanly charms...

He replied with something to the extent that he "always enjoys regaling with bitchy women" and he was "expecting my call." At this point in time, I started to feel confident that he wanted to see me, even if it was innocuous, a simple meeting of friends.

From: Rossana@aol.com

Sent: Monday, June 11, 2001 7:54 PM

To: jck@.mil

Subject: I realize something...

I don't have your phone number- would you
mind?? I'll be floating between DC and Richmond
starting Thursday- hope we can meet up (though
regaling with bitchy women may not be on the
agenda).

Ciao, -Rossana

He replied that I should call soon. Call soon (he meant like
right now). I lost out. I thought I was being coy, not calling
right away. He had another woman lined up for a date
(probably the woman he dated in DC, the woman he hadn't
seen in over two months). Call soon. I waited two days. I didn't
want him to think I was interested in him. I lost out. I played
by "the rule book" and lost out. However, John still wanted to
meet me after his date. In the meantime, I made other plans.
Stephen and I went out with a group of his friends, about
sixteen of us. I wore a cute black Gap mini-dress with white
polka dots, a strand of pearls, low black open-toed sandals.
My hair was twisted back into a tight chignon. As a tribute to
the conservative appeal this town demanded, I dressed in a
somewhat understated (for me), preppy mode; nevertheless (as
I've said), men find me sexy no-matter what. I spent the night
looking over my shoulder, checking my cell phone, instead of
just enjoying the company I was with, those few that wanted
my undivided attention, those few who may have really cared
had I shown them interest. John left me a voicemail at
1:30am...that his date had attacked him and he got detained.
At 2am, in his next voicemail, he asked me out to Sunday
brunch. Couldn't do it 'cause I had no choice but to help
Stephen with an important errand. Anyway, John and I agreed
to meet for drinks, Thursday, after he returned to DC. I had to
wait patiently and it was worth it...

A big bear hug hello, his arms around me, a warm inviting
kiss on the cheek. G-ahhh-d, it felt nice. He felt nice. He
looked gleeful, relaxed, happy to see me outside of the realm of
a third world poverty stricken universe. He told me that he
came back to DC for me, that his boss had wanted him to

remain in Chicago. I gave him one of those could-you-come-up-with-a-better-line looks. "No really, Rossana. I flew back to see you. She wanted me to stay." Too bad the bar closed early. I can kick myself for not inviting him back to Stephen's for drinks? Stephen was away. Alone at last- I could kick myself in the ass for listening to Stephen not to bring anyone back to his house. This night could have been our night, John and myself, alone. I could have used Stephen's array of wines to get John drunk, to take advantage of his priestly ways, to tease him. I listened to Stephen, kissed John on the cheek, and ran away. I didn't want to be second fiddle anyway. John was seeing someone (the woman always at his side?), even though he had flown back to meet me.

6/22/01 7:17 Pm

Rossana,

... It was good to see and talk with you last night and I hope to see you in July. Keep me posted on your schedule

-SOS

I kept wondering if this meant he was truly interested and couldn't wait for me to return. I kept wishing, wanting, pining....

——-Original Message——-

From: Rossana@aol.com

Sent: Friday, June 22, 2001 9:05 PM

To: jck@.mil

Subject: Re: journal

John-

Thank you.

...When will I get your first three journal entries?

-Rossana

Ps I don't live by a schedule but I'll keep you posted if you promise to behave. When are you coming to the city with the attitude???

6/23/02 1:24 Pm

Rossana,

You will not get my first three until I publish the whole thing. That is the way it is. Get used to it. (I'm practicing a New York attitude. Pretty good huh?). I will never promise to behave.

-John

Oooh! You know how much I love a strong, controlling man!! (Keep practicing...but I want to keep thinking of you as priestly- uhmn- does this mean you left me and met her (your usual motive of operandi)?- Call soon – means call now or I maybe I'll have a another shot at what's-her-name.-Rossana

Ok. I admit- this is just a little bit obnoxious but he originally intended (that first night) to leave her and meet me. He double booked himself, but I was still second fiddle and didn't like it... The e-mails continued. Back and Forth. Back and Forth. He told me to be daring. I had chickened out that one night, that first night, the night I should have invited him back "to view my etchings". Moxy! Hello moxy! Where are you??? I needed my moxy to transform me into the vixen once again. And since my moxy chose to disappear, dissipate when I needed it most, I guess I just needed for him to make the move, to show me he cared. I didn't want to be hurt anymore. The fear of rejection, his rejection was far greater a fear than never knowing. I didn't want to be hurt anymore since I was always setting myself up.

John ended "us" six months later (that magic number) with my reply to his "Dear John" e-mail. John...our ephemeral existence, a short-lived and fleeting courtship. I should have just put the wall up. I should have become an impenetrable fortress...maybe then it wouldn't matter. John. six months. He set the time limit. Not me. It ended by him becoming the person he never was, by him becoming someone who doesn't care, who takes advantage and then just leaves...but it began with my voice-mail. I made the move, my moxy suddenly taking the front row, an orchestra seat befit for a queen. My moxy, right beside me cause it had been too many months and I knew I needed to be daring. I was being daring. John kept telling me to "be daring, take a chance!" These words became imbedded in my mind and soon my actions followed. I left him a voicemail and followed up with...

John:
am being daring....
Return my call.
-Rossana

Rossana:
I have not checked messages at work or home for at least 3 days.
-John

I e-mailed him with one of my usual whimsical replies: "return my call period"- a simple statement that meant he would be lucky, a simple statement whose tone meant he would be lucky (followed by a soft sigh, the contentment whistling through). I explained that my statement was not:
a. return MY call- the tone which meant that I possessed one raised eyebrow, the slight inflection in voice; the slight demanding manner
b. RETURN MY CALL-mannerisms evident with my hand gestures flailing; my raised eyebrows daring him to;
c. RETURN MY CALLLLL!!!- at this point his best bet is to run, change his number and hide out with friends cause my face is red, I'm carrying a weapon, and I'm ready to beat him up and use PMS as my defense.
d. return (pause) my (pause) call (long pause)- in a soft spoken voice, the trying-to-make-him-feel-guilty voice; usually followed by a "Thanks a lot!!! I'm not talking to you." That implication of "if I continue to speak I may cry or say

something I regret so now I'll just give you the silent treatment" which will drive you crazy...

He understood my humor. He laughed at my playfulness. I think he understood I just wanted him to call me back, nothing more.

Rossana:
I guess I better check my messages...
-John

John:
Yes- check your messages but I only asked you to call me- no jokes left, no comments made, nothing said to make you laugh-didn't leave any details
-Rossana

He called. John replied YES! instantaneously when I asked him to a party that summer, that July, when we finally spoke. That is why I called him, why I left him that voicemail, why I needed him to return my call. He wanted me to be daring. I was. I asked him to an event. He said yes. I would not have to be alone, to go alone, to face the relatives and friends once again, alone, single. He said yes (I never told him that it meant more than he could ever imagine since this event fell on a date, July 21, that...) He said yes! I didn't even have to go into details. He didn't ask. He just said YES! as if he wanted to go with me, just be with me. For once, a simple closed-ended question, a simple closed-ended response. My heartbeat raced...however, my blood sugars would soon dip dangerously low. Joy short lived. He would change his mind. He would change his mind because he said he thought the event was in DC, something about his commitment to work. At least I didn't have to tell him it was my sister's party. I knew that would be a quick NO! The way I looked at it, if he survived eleven women in the wild of Africa, he could easily experience eleven family members in the wild of New York. The guests invited were his age anyway. Alas, he said yes and then changed his mind. Ahhh, my disappointing, usual norm.

I guess he felt bad, but not enough to come to the party, not bad enough that he could surprise me. As an afterthought he wrote to me and asked a million questions about the event, specific questions, questions I should have ignored. I answered as if it didn't matter he couldn't come, as if my invitation was a mere afterthought. I should have let him know how my heart ached, how I was disappointed, how my happy persona had become sad. I should have ignored him once and for all. I couldn't. I wanted him in my life. "No problem" is what I conveyed. "Shit!" is how I felt. I am too nice. Everything is copasetic...

Rossana:
Good to know this is not a situation
-John

He always rationalized the situation at hand so that he would come out looking like the good guy. If he had only made a move when he felt something, when he thought he cared about me. If he had only kissed me that night we went to dinner, that night of the slow dance, "When A Man Loves A Woman" was playing... that night in the Club (Polyesters) whose inhabitants encompassed one-quarter of our income level, one-third of our IQ, and one-half of our age. That slow dance as he held me in his arms, as I cradled my head in his shoulder, as I looked up at him, into his eyes... and then I turned quickly, so quickly you would have blinked and missed my escape... I casually sauntered away, ran away!) still holding his hand, hoping he would pull me back into the embrace, our embrace. I ended it because I was comfortable, too comfortable in his arms, the chemistry apparent. It was... *a moment suspended in time, the pinnacle of contentedness, like a movie scene where the two are about to kiss, THEN that knock on the door!, a sudden crash to the floor!!, a shallow scream!!!. Anything to interrupt, to disperse "the moment".* We were two people... on separate paths about to converge... a sudden detour... not meant to be. I ended it because I was too comfortable in this room of loud 20-something music, this room full of gyrating bodies, a room filled with smoke and blinding lights that didn't matter. It was me. It was him... not meant to be.

He confused me so and he continued to confuse me as he portrayed mixed signals, wrote mixed messages. He confused me so. Back and forth. Back and forth as we continued to e-mail, continued to flirt, continued to... I sent him one e-mail that he shouldn't drive while intoxicated. I was concerned one night that he drank too much and that his road trip home would end as a calamity. He responded: "intoxicated by which drug: alcohol? or Rossana?" I intoxicated him. What was I to think? I made him drunk from my playful seduction? I wasn't trying to seduce him. I did not aim to titillate. I just wanted him to lead. I had signed his dance card but he needed to inform me when it would be my turn. I needed him to lead, as men should. Un' uomo senza spina dorsale. Back and forth we played.

A few months later... What was up with his comment to me to check out his socks, his "lucky" Irish socks, as he pulled up his khaki's. "Can you find the four leaf clover, Rossana?" And stupid me, bent over, tipped the barstool precariously, and looked carefully, adoringly, at his ugly green and white clovered feet. (The former me would have grabbed his foot, stripped off his sock, and sucked on his toes as he sat with a look of disbelief. Where was that me?)

His four leafed clovered socks... Did he wear them because he wanted to get lucky, with me? Did he wish for me? Did he desire me? We were just having a drink. Now you know why I wanted to call him on his bluff!

He confused me so. His actions confused me. I dreamed. I pined. I wanted. I imagined. I imagined how it would be, could be...

His electric kiss that pulsated through me, that kiss that would raise the follicles on my arms running down through my legs...those goosebumps chilling me... and as he continued, the slow warmth, the glow spreading like a wildfire as my knees buckled, the mischievous glint sparkling in my eyes, my dimples evident as my smile radiated...one kiss from him that would get me going. I would kiss him back with equal passion...

I knew we were meant to be... One kiss that I imagined as so... His kiss... I AM hopeless. I still believe we are meant to be.

I set myself up for failure. I never made a physical move on him. Maybe this was the one time I needed to take charge? Where was that moxy when I most needed it? I set myself up for the letdown... yet I kept coming back ... determined not to be the loser in a cutthroat game of catch, tag, and release...

determined to keep playing, to win the game I was finally learning how to manipulate... MANHUNT! that game we played as children through open back yards, across the neighbors lawns, running down safe, empty streets... Manhunt! Track me down and make me your prisoner, save me, release me from my torment of being a "slave to my own desires", a desire to be loved...

~The End~

Book First

Whore by default

~ Frankie ~

<u>Book First</u>
<u>Whore by default</u>
Frankie

It's been ten years since someone, anyone, told me that they loved me... that's why I'm a whore, by default. Without love, there is only s-e-x.

So many men. So many little boys. I've kissed and gotten hard, instantaneously, kissed and they wanted more, of my body not my heart. I've kissed and they've fainted. I've kissed. I've fucked. I've lusted for. There has only been one, truthfully, who I've kissed and who kissed me back. Only one, who captured my heart, locked it away in a magnitude of proportions that could not be emulated. Only one I loved, was in love with, I was true to. There was only one who reciprocated. Only one who loved me, told me he was in love with me- the type of love that you've heard about, read about, wished for- so innocent, so just, so pure. It was ours and no human being could take that away from us, no triangles, no human obstacles...

I am a whore, by default.

I remember clearly that day that my life changed so quickly, my life turned, the moment that had decided my fate. My sister, Chiara (Kiki), came running up the stairs to the first floor landing, shouting between floors: "You'll never know who I met at the gym?" "Who?" I yelled down from my bedroom. I was tired after a long day at work, a long commute from New Jersey, a long ride on three trains, two buses. "Frank," she said. "Don't worry. He gave me his phone number and said he wouldn't call you, out of respect- you should call him," she teased. "Frank?" I yelled in a perplexed tone. "Frank who? I don't know any Frank's." I thought. "Frank. He said he knew you from the Beach Club. He came up to me at the gym and asked me if I knew you."

Frank? My brain racked. Who the hell is Frank? Then it dawned on me- the moment of recognition, the lightbulb being turned on, the moment that turns from acknowledgment to rage. I was appalled! Frank? Frankie? Oh my GOD!!! Could it be that Frankie? The Frankie that used to chase me around the Beach Club and ask me out, year after year. The Frankie, who on one sunny day I saw coming toward me as I suntanned with my friend, Joanne, as we baked our baby oil and iodine slicked skin. I closed my eyes and pretended to sleep. I was wearing a red floral bikini- my first two-piece and adventures into being a woman. The small pouch protruding from my fourteen-year-old nubile body embarrassed me. What would he think about my birthmark that ran southeast across my torso? It wasn't even that- I didn't want to talk to him. "Hi- are yous sleeping. Wake up! I saw yous from across the way." He was always pestering me.

Could it be that same Frankie that I saw one day as I body surfed in the ocean? He was on the shoreline, waving his arms, seeking me out. I quickly swam far away, beyond the breaking of the waves. We always did that- far, far out until the lifeguards blew their whistles. This was pre-Jaws days- the ocean was our playground, a water-park of adventure that rose and fell like its crests and waves. He couldn't possibly find me way out there with all the other adolescents. My only escape route: keep swimming, stay close to my friends, keep my head above water only when necessary to breathe! If I see him coming, swim FAST AND CATCH THE NEXT WAVE IN. Next thing I knew, he was right beside me. "Hi- it's me, Frankie. I saw yous swimming and I wanted to join yous." The vast ocean could not protect me from his boyish persistence, as annoying as a horsefly buzzing about!

Was this THE Frankie who stopped me, trapped me, on my way to my boyfriend Jason's cabana? On this mid-summer afternoon, I walked pass Frankie's cabana, F28, to get to Jason's cabana, F10.[1] The distance short- the journey terrifying. As I passed Frankie, trying to ignore him, trying to get pass unscathed, trying to casually saunter by him, he put his feet up. He had his brother do the same from behind. I was stuck in the middle of these two punks. Like the game of London Bridge; they took the key and locked me up. I could not escape. I was nervous and scared but didn't know how to be mean, to get angry with them. After all, the adults sat casually nearby. I couldn't make a scene. If my mother was called to the office one more time, I'd never be allowed to spend my summer at the Beach Club. Besides, this was "the" Frankie. The one who always got into fights, who was banned from coming to the dances and events, had been suspended from coming to the Club on numerous occasions. This was "that" Anthony, his brother, who wore a leather jacket, motor cycle boots and a drop earring in the heat of summer. (Anthony who once sent his seven-year-old sister running after me as I walked down the boardwalk to the ocean. Anthony called out from behind: "Rosanna. Ro-san-na!!! Come back here!!!" I turned around. "Who me?" I asked. "No, my little sister, Rosanna" as he pointed to the cute, skinny, little girl beside me. "Oh? My name is Rossana too." "My name is Anthony." I found out later he had watched me from afar, watched me as I strolled pass him numerous times, watched

---

[1] The Jason whose mom used to exclaim in front of me repeatedly: "Isn't Mary pretty with her golden hair?" Why his mom didn't like me wasn't obvious to my immature 15 year old mind. Could it have been the hickies I left on her son's neck? Talk about demoralizing. I felt so blasé because I wasn't a golden haired beauty. Insecure. Maybe it's her fault I started lightening my black Italian hair with Sun-In. To gain her respect, golden haired beauty I'd be; in actuality- bright, orange-tinted clown I became!

me, watched me like his brother. He wanted to meet me but he wasn't as bold as Frankie.)

"Don't ya want to tawk to us?" Frankie asked in that way that meant he wasn't going to take no for an answer. Somehow, I managed to gently push myself through this obstacle and quickly walk (run!) to Jason's. I could see they still were watching me. They made it obvious and they catcalled and whistled across the way, laughing, hysterical as if I was some pawn in their game and had won the point but not the match.

"Don't ya want to go out with me?" Frankie pleaded through the summers of my teenage years. "I come from a good family. My family lives in Jamaica not far from you. They're in sanitation." Jamaica? I thought. How could a nice white family live in that neighborhood, a neighborhood that my dad grew up in but over the years had gentrified into a negative spiral, the crack epidemic strong, and the shootings happened often, a neighborhood that white people didn't venture into (or so my naïve self thought)? After all, I lived in Jamaica Estates, my Dad was a Doctor. Sanitation? Did this mean he was a garbage man? I frowned. No way, Jose. "No. I'm sorry. I can't go out with you," I stated over and over again, as my body matured and my mind remained sheltered. "I have a serious boyfriend." "Break up with him," he demanded repeatedly. "I'll treat you like a queen." Yeah, queen of the garbage ghetto, my somewhat stuck-up self thought.

Oh my God! Could it be that same Frankie? THAT FRANKIE! I SCREAMED as I ran downstairs, half undressed. "Don't worry. I gave him your number but he said he wouldn't call you, out of respect. You should call him," my sister cowered at the bottom of the stairs, the anger apparent in my red-faced scowl. "I CANT BELIEVE YOU GAVE OUT MY PHONE NUMBER! MOM!! Chiara gave out my number to a boy I used to avoid like the plague and run away from at the beach!" "He said he wouldn't call you, out of respect," she yelled back, running up the staircase to her room, slamming the door behind her, fearful of me. Ahhhh! My past come back to haunt me. It was 1991. The year of the Persian Gulf War. The #1 hit that year would be Brian Adams' *(Everything I Do) I Do it for You.*

~2~

Frankie did call. He left two, three messages on my answering machine. "Hey Boobie, What's Up?" Boobie? Oh my goodness, I thought. He is such the quido. Boobie? Boobie?? Boobie-what the hell does that mean? (As he explained later, Boobie was a term of affection they used around the garage.) He said he was very happy that he ran into my sister, ecstatic that I lived in Queens and was still single. How did he know I lived in Queens? still single? I was going to kill my big-mouthed sister who had to tell everyone the story of our lives. Wasn't anything sacred? "He asked me if you had a boyfriend," she said later as I questioned her further, a Gestapo interrogation, about what was said at the gym.

I was curious, especially after the fifth message so I called him back. "I'm so happy you called, Boobie!" he said, a little too enthusiastically. "Don't call me that!" I demanded. I'd put him quickly in his place. "But Rosanna's my sister's name. I can't call you that. I'll think of you the way I think of her and that's just not right. There's always been a special place in my heart for you!" What a sap, I thought. "I'm so happy your sister gave me your number..." Why, I wondered? I did my best ten years earlier to snub him and he <u>still</u> liked me. I ran away from him. He kept pursuing me.

The truth of the matter was, I hadn't been dating anyone. I had no desire to go out, to socialize, to bar hop. I had no desire to date anyone. Steve (#3) had shot my self–esteem down two weeks earlier. My friends and I spent president's weekend in Vermont celebrating my birthday. Steve and I sort of dated, on and off the last year, in a chaste manner. We only kissed. I met him my sophomore year while attending one and only one semester at St. John's. He was like a priest. (He is now a priest which explains for his behavior.) There were ten of us in Vermont. Steve spent a lot of time downstairs in the bathroom, always washing his hands, never partaking in any of the games we played, the easy conversation, the closeness of friends. On the long drive back, he made a comment that took away my self-confidence and my whole persona: "You know Rossana," he said in his strongest Queens accent,

"You're a great girl and you'd be a great girlfriend but you're a little much. If you were a guy, your behavior, attitude, sarcastic comments, joke cracking would be great. However, you're a girl and it's not okay. You have too much energy, you're too obnoxious." These comments coming from a man who was just revealed his obsessive/compulsive behavior during what was a fun, drunken weekend. I kept quiet, very quiet. I kept thinking- what? My girlfriend Laura snapped: "What the hell did you just say? Are you kidding!? Say you're kidding or say you're sorry!" I remained quiet for the next two hours. This idiot, who had serious psychological problems, just took away a personality that I had always had, a personality that everyone loved, a personality that made everyone laugh. I was a cross between Mae "is that a rocket in your pocket or are you happy to see me?" West and Bette Midler. So what if I was a little loud? a little obnoxious? I was fun!!! Only a little bit assertive (and aggressive). It was a lot to absorb, an overwhelming amount to digest. No wonder I had no desire to go out with anyone.

But... could I turn down a date with someone who was thankful he'd met me again and repeatedly said so? Could I turn down a date with someone who left three messages a day telling me to be careful, stay out of trouble, be good? I was curious. He was definitely the stereotype, the way he spoke, his abuse of the English language, the run on verbs and sentences, the profanities that he kept trying to curtail but kept slipping out, profanities that made up most of his speech. He reminded of a gangster straight out of Al Capone's Chicago.

My first impression of him was one I can't forget. It's because I had yet to meet him and he already seemed to care about me. I remember I was sick, probably a cold that I usually got with the onset of my period. I told Frankie that I wasn't feeling well, a man whom I had spoken to only a few times but had left 20-30 messages on my machine. He sent me my first dozen long stem roses. Red roses. It had been over six years since he last saw me. He didn't know if I was fat, thin, a blonde, a brunette or what! Red roses... because I wasn't feeling well. I called to thank him. He just said: "There's always been a special place in my heart for you!" He was no longer the sap in my eyes. He asked me if I would go out to dinner with him when he got back from Florida. I said yes. I was curious. (Weeks later, Frankie would tease, "Did you thank her yet?" -a constant reminder that my sister gave him my number.)

I knew he'd be the epitome of a Brooklyn boy, a real "paisan", because of his voice and manner of speech, his use of complex word combinations and continuous syllables. He fit the stereotype to a "t". I wondered if he drove a Trans Am, Camaro, or Riviera with a statue of the Virgin Mary (the only Virgin left in Brooklyn?) on the dashboard. Instead, he picked me up in an old Buick Le Sabre, light blue with navy velour interior, spoke rims. "A good American car!" he exclaimed. Hanging from the mirror was one of those scented things that I hated, that made me sneeze, not a green Christmas tree as expected in a car as such, but a bent over woman that said "hauling ass". I should have run away then.

My expectations of his dress code were not high as I guessed, knew, expected him to show up in the typical "guido look": tight jeans, a shirt open just so, a gold chain or two. I was impressed! He wore a suit, a gray polyester suit (a statement of 1972 though in fact it was 1991): tight tab-front pants that were too short, a jacket that he couldn't close (due to his rounded belly), sleeves that rode up (his bulging bi-ceps evident), an ugly knit shirt (navy), and a striped tie (the type of tie you see on politicians, less the expense).

He said in describing himself: "Yeah, my hair is shaved at the side, short on top." Okay, I thought, he never left the 80's with his zipper head, the hair that's blown and sprayed backward (aka: John Travolta in Saturday Night Fever). Well, at least he wasn't sporting a mullet head! My perception was skewed once again as a bald man showed up on my doorstep. He had less hair than my Dad. There is no other way to describe him- he had a cue ball head!

He told my Mother that he would have me home early because he had sisters and not to worry. My mother replied: "My daughter has lived away in California and comes home whenever she wants!"

"But I have R-E-S-P-E-C-T," he said (the boyfriend in Betsy's Wedding).

I remember trying to find the perfect outfit for our date. I didn't like him but I wanted to look good. He had last seen me as a teenager and now he would meet me as a woman! I chose a black mini-dress, the orange and maroon Dior blazer with antique buttons, and my Mom's black pumps with the gold appliqué. I looked sexy (showing off my muscular legs) and classy (the blazer covering me up just so). He noticed. "You look be—e-youu-tifull and sooo-ohh sexy," he said with a lascivious look.

We went to dinner, driving to a section of Brooklyn that didn't look friendly, with it's broken streets, dilapidated auto's, crumbling sidewalks, and dark facades of the buildings mirroring the people milling about. Bamontes. That's the name of the restaurant. Something happened- a long wait or no parking, and so we drove across the Williamsburg Bridge, south to Little Italy. Angela's. We were given a beautiful table next to a garden. A romantic table for two. It was a nice dinner. I was inquisitive and didn't mind prying when he ordered seltzer, no ice. "I'm an addict," he said. (An alcoholic, I thought). His favorite meal (which he would order every time we went to dinner): shrimp cocktail, tomatoes and mozzarella, and gnocchi. He unbuttoned his pants at the table, the top button only. "I want to get comfortable so I can eat dessert." You should have seen my face!

Afterwards, I wanted to go to a bar. I wanted to party even though he didn't drink. I'm either the shallowest person you know or just naïve. I didn't care. Here he is, an alcoholic (I'm thinking) and I'm taking him to a bar, a local bar on Bell Boulevard in Bayside, one of the hot destination night spots in Queens, a Greenwich Village clone with bars, cars, restaurants, cafes, women, men, teenagers, all ages, all income levels. It had been written up as "a place that people flocked to from Brooklyn, from Long Island from all over". It had the energy and excitement that the downtown NYC scene is known for. I wanted to go there, be a part of it. We went. He informed me in his most courteous manner that he wasn't comfortable in bars, never went into them but for me "he'd do anything." We left after one drink. I could tell by his antsy manner that he really wasn't comfortable.

On the way home, he took my hand and held it. It seemed so juvenile, like a teenager on his first date. Then he kissed the inside of my palm saying he was so happy I went out him. He proceeded to suck on my fingers. He was a bad boy. I knew it. This was turning me on, especially since it was a forbidden taboo. I didn't want him to stop, the good girl was giving in as he sucked gently, more forcefully, rolling his tongue around and around each finger as if he was consuming me whole, like the food we had just eaten, the last great meal... and he was driving. It's no wonder we didn't end up in an accident as he kept looking at me, as he teased me, as he nibbled on my hands. When he pulled up to my house and kissed me for the first time, a kiss he had been waiting for... for the last 12 years, well... hot! sweet! fiery! gentle! All wrapped into a universal moment. The fireworks had started. The show had begun. Our breathing became erratic, we pulled apart. "Thank you," he said. Thank you, I wondered? "Goodnight," I said as he walked me to the door and I kissed him on the cheek.

The flowers arrived the next morning, early. Red Roses. Long stem. *"You're a Doll."* he had scribbled on the card.

Red Roses. Long Stem.

~3~

I went out with him a week later. I couldn't help myself, he
kept calling me. He was pursuing me. On this second date,
Frankie took me to eat at his Grandma's. I also met his
Mother. I knew that this was an "old Italian tradition", to meet
the family. Frankie wanted them to like me. I had this gut
feeling that Frankie was trying really hard to keep me around.
He had waited twelve years for me to pay attention to him.

His Grandma barely spoke English but I conversed with her in
what little Italian I spoke. It was a little embarrassing but I
wasn't worried. I was probably the first woman he brought
home (Although, I've been told that he attempted to bring a
very young, the-16-will-get-you-20 "lady" home. His mom put
a stop to that.) I was educated (a college-education went along
way in this family). I dressed well, conservative for me (a peach
suede micro mini, brocade blazer emblazoned in deep greens,
sandy neutrals, vibrant corals, green and gold flats). I smiled. I
was friendly. Everyone liked me. (I had that certain
charismatic attitude that Steve had failed to notice.)

After lunch, we went shopping to begin his transformation.
After-all, behind every well-dressed man is a better dressed
woman. It was funny how things evolved. I told him how much
I didn't like his suit on our first date, it was out-dated, and
that I'd teach him how to dress. My first goal was to attack his
closet and that wardrobe- a highly combustible array of earth-
tones (not one neutral, not one fashionable item). Help! He
was stuck in a time warp (1972)... *"It's just a jump to the left,
and a step to the r-i-ghttt...put your hands on your hips..."(The
Time Warp from the Rocky Picture Horror Show)* However, he'd
do anything for me; even throw out two-thirds of this calamity,
a polyester paradise. Anyway, he lived in sweats, sweats, and
more tight fitting sweats (you know, Sergio Tacchini), adorned
with his Ked basketball high tops. He was such the stereotype.
"Out! out! out!" I said as only a girlfriend would. "What! These
is good clothes," he said in reaction to me grabbing handfuls,
stuffing them, throwing them into a garbage bag. Even at this
early stage, he'd do anything for me though he suggested we

bring the three garbage bags of clothes to the poor. I only wondered who in their right mind would dare venture forth in these hideous things. Even a poor man wants to be proud. These clothes screamed burn me! He didn't fight me, or argue with me and was receptive to my actions. We settled on throwing out only one bag. After-all, even at this stage, I could do no wrong in his eyes.

First stop: Filene's- my mother's favorite shopping mecca. For a bargain, I could transform him into a dapper young man (or at least someone I would want to be seen with). As usual, the ladies dressing room had a huge line. Frankie kept coming out of his room, to get the approval of the ladies waiting: "So, look atallthese b-u-ti-ful ladies. Do ya think this looks good?" as he spun around. Moments later: "So is this o-k? What do you think of the color? Do my eyes stand out?" as he fluttered his eyelashes in a flirtatious manner. I had pulled various silk and linen shirts in shades of soft purples ("I don't want ta look like a fuckin' faggot- oops 'scuse me!" he stated emphatically.), green ("...to enhance your eyes," I said.), beige (a good basic). On his next catwalk, he blatantly stripped, took off his shirt as if he belonged on the cover of GC, flexed his muscles, showed off the tattoos. "Ladies, what do yous think of this?" as he proudly displayed the Matisse on his back shoulder. The line of well dressed women laughed. I was... I don't know how I felt. Embarrassed? He had entertained everyone the entire twenty minutes they were waiting. He was a goof ball and I knew I would have to get use to it.

Next stop: Macy's. I was working for them in corporate so we had the advantage of my employee discount. "I want the shirts with the man and pony on them," he said. Great. A classic Polo, a relaxed look for our casual afternoon. You can't wrong with that (or so I thought). At the Ralph Lauren counter, I handed him a medium but he put on a small. "Wrong size," I said. "I like them to fit this way. I ain't no preppy fuckin' faggot. Oops. Sorry." "Wrong size!" as I handed him the medium. "So what do you think?" as he turned to the country club couple standing beside him. "Don't this look oh-k? Don't I look good?" as he ran his hands up and down across his pectorals. The couple just smiled. "I think I look good," he remarked as he flexed. "I'll have two smalls, pretty lady," he said to the salesgirl. Ohhh- I couldn't believe this guy liked his polo's fitted, skin tight, stretching the fabric to its limits. I could get him into the classic line but I couldn't convince him to wear it the way it was intended. My preppy gangster.

For dinner, we went to a Portuguese restaurant in Jamaica, his local hang out. I ate and experienced (what I think is called) bouillabaisse, a large pot filled with shellfish: shrimp, clams, lobster, muscles. Delicious!... Later that eve, about 10:30 pm, as my sister and I drove into Manhattan for a night on the town, I didn't feel right. I felt queasy; my head hurt, my stomach was in knots. I asked her to get off the next exit, Queens Boulevard and take me home. "You'll be okay," she said as she continued driving west on the Long Island Expressway, pass the exit, not wanting to ruin her intended night. "No! Turn around. I'm sick!" I yelled at her, the way sisters usually do... I ended up with food poisoning in the worst way. I couldn't stop throwing up. I crawled downstairs in the middle of the night, into my parents' bedroom, to my Daddy: "Help me. I'm dying. I can't stop throwing up." "There is nothing I can do. Just keep drinking water and let it pass through your system." My Mommy helped me back into my bed; put a towel near me, a bucket on the floor, and a pitcher of water nearby. It was horrible night. I kept throwing up into a bucket. I couldn't make it to the toilet. I popped all the blood vessels in my eyes. It looked like someone had ripped my eyeballs out. Those red, blood-filled eyes. The hemorrhaging was not a pretty sight. The whites of my eyes were crimson. I was a mess!!! Frankie said he was sorry. "I eat there all the time. The food is good." The roses arrived that afternoon.

Red Roses. Long stem.

~4~

Red Roses. Long Stem. By Easter, Frankie had sent me my fourth dozen. I was being wined and dined and courted. Every day, that's EVERY DAY, there were messages, at least five, left on my machine. I woke up to them. I arrived home to them. As our relationship flourished, he'd call me at 6:30 am to wake me up for work with "Why aren't you ready for work yet? Aren't ya afraid you'll get fired?" He'd leave a message in the afternoon telling me "I miss ya. You're so sweet." I was amazed that this man thought so highly of me. Why me? What did I do to deserve these terms of his affection? He was too good to be true and too much. He got mad at me because I told him to stop being so good to me. I wasn't used to it. What would I do when he left me? He'd say, again and again, "I'm not going anywhere. Not unless you want me to!"

Seven months earlier, I had grown up, my first step into adulthood, my first step into being an independent woman, my first step into moving up the career ladder. I was planning to move into Manhattan with my friend, Jonathan. After stomping through the East Side high rises, storming up the West Side walk-ups, I decided I didn't want to rent. I would buy an apartment in the city and I would buy it smart. I investigated the market. I went to the auction and bought a foreclosure. It was a one bedroom, upper West Side apartment, one-half block from Central Park for $40,000. (Imagine what its worth in today's escalated market?) I didn't need a man to take care of me. I didn't want a man to take care of me. I was an independent woman. I'd show everyone!

I was at a point in time in my life when I felt I could do anything. I did not understand politics as they applied in the work force nor did I relate to life's little nuances. I was 26, at the onset of my career and taking on the challenges as they arose. I was in my prime, waiting for Mr. Right to find me as I bought my first new car, incorporated designer names into my wardrobe and now planned on buying my first home. I could do anything and be anyone. But then... BOOM! Frankie comes into my life and doesn't understand why I question his good deeds and affection. He upset my plans. It was city living that I wanted- the asphalt jungle would become my playground, an amusement park of concrete, steel, dirt, grime, innate nastiness and noise. 24 hours of non-stop action. He changed the course that I had chosen to take. He kept trying to figure out where he fit into my "Manhattan class structure", the caste system I chose to embrace. My equilibrium just went out the window as he continued to pull me toward him, bring me into his world, make me take that direction.

I told him once that he could "have my body and maybe a piece of my mind, but that he would never have my heart". I was a brain and not a body. I didn't want to be someone's piece of ass. I would never be a piece of ass. I just didn't have that physique. I wasn't sexy although I dressed well. I was more classic. I was smart but I was afraid of getting hurt. Frankie made me fall in love with him. He told me once I was his. All of his. He was right. I had given myself, all of me, body, mind, heart, soul to him. I also knew that he had given himself to me. After all, "he'd do anything for me!" He possessed me (and I possessed him). But where would Manhattan and all it had to offer me fit into our life?

As the affair blossomed into a meaningful relationship, the romance continued to flourish... One night, as we were watching a movie at his house. Frankie lay quietly, contemplating. This was so unlike him, he was always on the move, always restless, always rocking, always caressing me. He just lay there, very still, with me in front of him. "What's the matter with you?" I asked in my usual, tired-from-commuting tone. "I feel weak," he said quietly. He continued: "I have never felt this way before. It's a nice feelin', a new feelin'. Rossana. You make me feel weak. These feelings are overwhelming." The funny thing was I felt the same. I wanted to tell him (but didn't know how) that *I only knew that... "My knees tremble when I'm around you, not withholding their stance, You light a fire, long forgotten the dance... I melt when you kiss me, like an icicle on a warm winter's day... Two lovers to be? Will we teach and learn to play each others bodies like a concerto in progress, slowly, slowly, slowly, heightened, quickly, no less... the desire (or is it love?) burning, you've awakened it so... Could ours be true? I undoubtedly know."* But I would not tell him. I was scared. I was afraid about how much attention he paid me. I wasn't use to it. "I'm not going anywhere. Not unless you want me to."

I almost lost him once. It was my own doing. My own insecurity. I kept putting that guard up. I didn't know how to accept his love, to accept his generosity, to accept the fact that I was in love with him. I felt it deep inside, those butterflies, knowing (it's really true), you just know, that he was the one for me and I wanted to marry him. I know he felt the same way but I still was so insecure in thinking that someone would come between us. It always happened to me- my friends (my best friends), someone always stole my love, someone always took away from me what was mine or should have been.[2] I didn't want anyone to come between us.

We had a fight, one of those stupid, innocuous fights, the type that you don't know how it begins or why you're pissed off. We had a fight over who said "I love you" first. Frankie did. I didn't respond. I kept watching the movie. Later, I told him I loved him but he didn't say anything. I got mad at him, my voice raising an octave. We started fighting. It was so stupid. We are cuddling on the basement couch, his sisters mingling near us, wanting to participate in this event, being the usual sisterly pain-in-the-asses (to Frankie), trying to get back at him for always bothering them. It was the one time they shouldn't have been around... Our first fight and it would have been our last. Our first fight and it was over something beautiful. I got up to leave. I had enough. He followed me. The twins remained, looking baffled.

I remember clearly that look on his face, a look of remorse, as if he had lost someone that he loved. He was so cold and flat. No emotion. His green eyes, a dark empty void. I was about to leave and walk out the door. Frankie gave me a kiss and a hug without any emotion, without any feelings. A simple pat on the back. He was so cold. He treated me as if I were no more than a mere stranger, his adversary. The screen door was open, my

---

[2] My High School Sweetheart was named Steve(#1). My best friends, more than one, slept with him. He had betrayed my trust. They had betrayed my friendship. No wonder I was insecure?

arm holding the latch. I was stepping through it, my back to him. I knew that if I walked out, if I left, he would never call again. I would be out of his life forever.

Something made me stay. Some influential force made me turn around and walk toward him, into his arms, wrapping myself into him, giving him a deep passionate kiss, a kiss that he returned with equal fortitude. As Frankie would say later, he was trying so hard to get me to like him and I was so cold. I guess I was a heartless bitch. He said he didn't know what else he could do for me or to me to make me return his love. Little did he know, I already loved him. I was insecure, insecure enough to think that he was the one who wasn't returning the feelings or being honest. Thank goodness, something or someone made me stay. Frankie made me fall in love with him. My sweet Frankie. "I'm not going anywhere, not unless you want me to."

I was in love with him at this time. Though it had only been a few months, he was with me daily in my thoughts, desires, wants, needs... from the time he called at sunrise, until he picked me up on Midland Parkway, the last stop on the subway. (For once, I was happy to be living in Queens.) And everyday, he thought of me. It became obvious to us and all around us that we were in love... From the movie "Ghost", we started to say the expression "ditto" as a substitution for "I love you". Frankie hated it when I said "ditto" because he liked to say those three words because they came so easily now. I, on the other hand, wasn't about to say "I love you" when the room was full of people. I would reply "ditto" every time he said "I love you". I love you. Three words so simple to say.

I really put my foot in my mouth saying that I would never be a "Queen's housewife." I abhorred Italian New Yorkers, especially those that depicted the stereotype. Maybe my attitude developed while attending that Southern Baptist College in Richmond, Va. I had been typecast during my three and one-half years in Virginia. I didn't want to conform. I wanted to upgrade. For Frankie, I would have lived anywhere, even an apartment in Queens. Forget Manhattan. I would have lived with his Mother when we got married. He didn't need to persuade me. "I'll build an apartment in the basement. This way we can have some privacy but save some money." Save some money until Frankie could buy me our house, the stately colonial on the corner of my parent's block. The house I loved as a child and always wanted. He would have found a way to buy it for me. Somehow make the tenants sell to him. That's what he told me. "A girl needs to live near her parents, especially when the children come." How's that for love: giving up everything you set out to do for someone. I would do anything for him and vice/versa.

~5~

Oh no! Just as we pulled up, they were coming out the front door, my mother and a man wearing a dark shirt, white collar. Frankie wasn't wearing a shirt. I would definitely hear it. My mother had this rule that no one was allowed in her house without a shirt, a "proper shirt." My elder sister dated a guy who always wore white undershirts, short sleeve or worse, Fruit of the Loom tank tops. Frankie didn't like this rule. He once exclaimed to his mom: "Her mother. She's a nice lady, but who does she think she is? She makes me wear collared shirts every time I go over. What?!! Are we at a country club??" (giggle, giggle, hee, hee, hee) "F-R-A-N-K!!!!" his mom screamed back.

My mother- the utmost in propriety. In addition, this was her potential client, a very influential man that she was trying to impress. And he was a priest. HE was the MONSIGNOR! Timing. As we got out of the car, Frankie grabbed his shirt. Too late. He couldn't hide the four, five, wait, six! tattoos evident all over his body, his arm, his back, his shoulder. You name it- he had them everywhere and they were big and colorful (and it wasn't even trendy):

- His right bicep: a soaring, colorful Eagle, his freedom.
- His right forearm: a religious theme, The Cross: "In memory of Pop"- his eternal love and respect for his Grandfather (the only person Frankie ever cried outwardly when he died).
- His left bicep: a red rose superimposed over a cross "love you Mom and Dad", his wish for a complete family unit, his wish that only his father could have made come true.
- His left outside forearm: a big, bold symbol of who he was: "FCC" (though the last 'C' he wanted to delete).
- His back right shoulder: This one well... it was a long haired maiden, with one breast exposed (a copy of a photo he saw in Playboy). This one, by far, the biggest, spanning four inches across and eight inches down, a very vivid, triple-x rendition.

And last...
- His back left shoulder: those luscious lips, the lips that in themselves are a story.

"Hello Mrs. T," he said as he went up to my mom putting on his tank, the naked lady exposed. (Why couldn't he have done that in the car?) "I'm sorry about not being dressed. We came from the beach and it was hot..." (He always drove bareback.) He kept talking. I was definitely uncomfortable. "Monsignor. This is my daughter. And this is Frankie," my mother said giving me that don't-embarrass-me look. "Hi! I'm Frankie, Father. No disrespect. I was too hot in da car, no air conditioning. We was just coming from da beach. No disrespect." As usual, he was going into some diatribe about being hot, what a beautiful day it was, etc, etc... He didn't shut up! Usually making jokes, at least this time he had enough couth not to wisecrack the priest. I can only imagine what the priest was thinking, what he thought about Mrs. T's educated daughter and her lovely derelict (looking) boyfriend?

Later that eve...
"Frank. You have lipstick on your shoulder. Did Rossana kiss you?" my Dad said as we stood in the kitchen. My mother was making dinner: pasta (no wonder I had carb thighs!) and her infamous Bolognese sauce sautéing for the tenth hour. "No-it's my new tattoo. Isn't it great?" he said with a smile, like a new proud papa. He was so proud of these two perfect lips displayed on his left trapezius, two lips in a bright pink shade. What was I going to do with him? The simplest things gave him pleasure. I wasn't simple but I was his ultimate pleasure. "No more tattoos," I said later!

As our relationship grew... this man didn't mind (at least he didn't show it to me) waking up at five am and taking me home because my Mom had stated I wasn't allowed to spend the night. "What will his mother think? You're a good girl. You come from a good family. You need to be home before six, otherwise, it's like you're spending the night out." Okay, Mom. Great rationalization. Home before dawn. Home before the sun rose and the city woke up, his mother woke up (as if she didn't know who spent the night). I was 26. I had lived alone for three and one-half years in Virginia, two years in San Diego and I was now listening to my mother! "Wake up Frankie. You have to take me home. FRANKIE!!!" as he laughed and pretended to snore.

My funny, little Frankie. He cared for me and thought nothing of advertising it. He was so proud of me, his college-educated girlfriend (and liked to show me off)... Everywhere we went in the local vicinity, as if all of Queens was his own backyard, we would bump into one cousin or another- Big Frank, Little Frank, the Tony's, the Angelo's... Endless family invitations. Someone was either getting married, graduating, having a baby, or passing away- every festival commemorated with immense proportions. And there I would be. On Frankie's arm. At each event. The series of events seemed ten-fold; but, were in reality, a direct proportion to the size of his family, his Italian, catholic family. La famiglia.

On one occasion, we walked into his house only to be confronted by his mom's card group, a group of pleasant, mostly single, middle-aged Italian women. "Frankie, I didn't recognize you. You're hair is so short!" one woman exclaimed. "He's got such a good head of hair. I don't understand why he keeps it so short!" his mother retorted. I rubbed his bald head and exclaimed "Too short! He's going to grow it for me." "Let's not tawk about hair!" he sarcastically replied, glaring at my "you look like a nigger" (no disrespect) cornrows and satin bow, a result from my Bahamian vacation.[3] Laughter from the group... as our facetious banter continued. "Frankie, you're standing in front of me." I said, annoyed. "Sorry!" he said as he quickly stepped aside, lowering his head, so I could address the group without being blocked out! "See," his aunt Veronica nudged her friend, "he really likes her!"... His

---

[3] I kept the cornrows in for six weeks, pulling them back into a professional ponytail, adorned with a satin bow to match whatever color my suit was, as a fashion statement I am. I kept them in to bug him and to show him that it was I that dictated fashion doctrine-not he. A price to pay for beauty... headaches, spilt hairs running from roots to ends... five inches chopped! To shoulder length! I now looked like everyone else. Lesson told: Being a wiseass to a wiseass does not a winner make.

chivalrous mannerisms apparent to all. Always the gentleman to me being his lady. My knight in shining armor; however, with his sisters, his family, his friends... the court jester!

~6~

Frankie, whose every waking moment consisted of bugging his sisters constantly, always embarrassing them in front of their 15 year-old friends, "get-a-life-Heather" and "Coleslaw" (his own made up nicknames), tormenting Rosanna, whose favorite pose at this time was prone in her waterbed with a phone glued to her ear. Frankie would casually saunter by her door, stop, peer in, never crossing the line that separated the hallway (the free zone) from her space. He would just stand there. He'd grab her door and pretend it was a woman, holding it, caressing it, kissing it, talking to it as if it were alive. He'd act as if it had huge breasts and grab them and fondle them, laughing in his mischievous tone. Only he could mak ethsi inanimate object appear alive. "Gross!" said Rosanna who had had enough and slam the door in his face. However, Frankie, ever the more troublemaker, would lean in as the door was closing, the door bouncing off his forehead, the force never making an indentation into his thick skull! "Frankie!!" she would scream, slamming the door again with determining force. Like a statue, he wouldn't move. As she continued to chat in her girlish manner, she could hear him breathing, sighing, still caressing the door. Of course, she would have to investigate. "Frankie!!" she'd shriek as she opened the door. "What? I'm on the line- the Mason-Dixon line!" he grin and laugh.

You could never win because no matter how much he instigated, how much he teased, tormented, joked, embarrassed, you always ended up laughing. Even with parental authority: Frankie! was kicked out of the dinner table for being a wise-ass, time and time again. His mom, ever reactive to his antics: "Take your plate and get the f out of here!" Moments later, the telephone would ring, just as dinner with her girls had regained some sense of control. "Hi Mom. Can someone bring me salt?" Frankie would call from the upstairs line, in his sweetest, politest, let's-not-make-Mommy-mad voice. He'd push you to the limits and get away with it. "FRANK!!!" she'd screech, trying to control her hysterics, laughing.

Pain-in-the-ass Frankie who you couldn't help but love. Pain-in-the-ass Frankie who would take a can of Mountain Dew out of the fridge, pour it in a glass and go up to his sisters as they were entertaining and in the most mentally disturbed voice, the most mentally disturbed look, turn his head sideways, roll his eyes, and declare: "Pee-pee makes me strong! Hee hee hee!"... a story that had been told to Frankie by his cousin, Andrew. A story that had shaken up Andrew, the incident very disturbing. A story that Frankie never forgot, made fun of, and continued to use in his "bag of tricks". A story that begins with a trip to visit a sick friend in a mental hospital. One patient, a young man in his 20's, was drinking something. Andrew thought he smelled the "piss" but didn't think anything of it. This was a mental ward after all. He didn't think anything of it until the patient turned to him and said, "Pee Pee makes me strong" and drank his own urine. Yuck! Gross! The visual imagery is one you'd like to forget; however, thanks to good little Frankie, you were jabbed with it daily! He could take the most serious, disturbing issues and turn them into something comical. And you would laugh!!! Even if you were the most conservative, straight and narrow, educated individual... you would laugh! He was that funny.

Frankie... once handed his 12 year-old cousin a bill, an itemized statement from a garage on all auto repairs: "This just came in the mail for you. Uncle Frank (they were all named Frank) says you can work with me on Saturdays at the garage or after school until the debt is done. Until you pay off the damages to the car." She just stood there, mortified, the look never leaving her once innocent face. "Would you like me to call Uncle Frank and see if he'll let you answer the phones instead? Don't worry. I'll be there with you." She had crashed a tractor into her Father's partner's brand-new Mercedes. Worse, she was embarrassed at the thought that Frank, Jr., her first love, her crush for the last five years, would find out. She would become the laughing stock of the family (and the brunt of joke after joke for years to come). She started to cry. What was she going to do? She became hysterical, being the over-sensitive, naïve, pubescent child that she was. She couldn't stop the tears, not so much for the thought of

working, but the fact that Frank, Jr. would find out...
"Angelina, I was only kidding," Frankie would later say (hee-
hee, ha-ha), as he continued to laugh and snicker at what he
had gotten away with. The practical joker that he was...

...always up to some little stint. On his daily route while
hanging off the back of the garbage truck, he has to watch,
observe, tease, torment, keeping himself amused by always
playing games. "Garbage is beautiful!" his motto. After-all,
work could be fun, especially if you paid attention to your
surroundings, not just the debris you collected. On one such
day, some almost teens, at the age when saving face is
everything, at the age when hormones have just started to
kick in but the child still lives strong, an age when flirtation
takes on a literal meaning... Frankie was caught up in a game
he was not invited to play: As he threw the can over his
shoulder, Frankie noticed a devilish group sun-tanning
themselves around a pool. One little girl, whose budding
breasts peaked through her conservative one piece, began
carefully walking around the perimeter, delicately, balanced
not to fall in. Lo and behold, a smirk thirteen year-old skinny
boy, whose muscles barely stood out by themselves,
unexpectedly, snuck up behind and pushed her in. He
couldn't stop laughing as he hopped and skipped his victory
dance around and round. She started crying...

In a moment's notice, the little dancing misfit is being thrown
in the pool in his clothes. As fast as it takes to turn around,
Frankie was poolside. Superman to the rescue. The next thing
you hear is..."Oh- shit. The garbage man just threw me in the
pool." Frankie could be heard laughing and giggling as only he
could. The knight in shining armor coming to the damsel in
distress' rescue to save her honor... It was only later than
Frankie wondered if the boy could swim.

No matter what time of day or what vampire hour the clocked
chimed... this man could make you laugh. At 1:30 am, on a
freezing winter night, he knocked on his best friend's bedroom
window, as if the Con Ed man needed, at this very moment, to
enter and read the meter. (He was living in New York at this
time.) The front door was opened by a weary-eyed matron.

"Hel-loooo, Mrs. Santangelo. I'm sorry to wake yous. Does Johnny have a pair of dress shoes I kin barrow?" She got him the shoes, a little annoyed, but she would do anything for this man, her son's childhood friend. "Good-bye," Frankie said as if the disruption in sleep was to be overlooked, that his visit was no more than an ordinary social call. A few nights later, at a very odd hour, this time 2:30 am... she heard the same knock, on the same bedroom window. The front door was opened, once again, without hesitation. "Hel-lohhh, Mrs. Santangelo," Frankie said in his best afternoon, ball-park voice. "I'm returning John's shoes. Oh, by the way, I'm sorry about waking yous up the other night." "Johnny, come out an tawk to me." (...and they would talk until the wee hours of the morning, as if two young boys on a sleep-over... except this time it would be outside, on the front stoop, their chuckles keeping the neighborhood happy and awake.)

Frankie... a man proud of his family, especially proud of his cousin Vincent. Vincent was as "straight" as Frankie was "slanted". Vincent was educated, intelligent, and reserved. Vincent, who in a few moments, was about to leave and begin the five-hour trip to DC, begin his term at Georgetown Law. As his family gathered around, taking turns saying goodbye (a procession that could last up to an hour)... a shout was heard coming from up the street. (In a one block vicinity, at least five of his aunts and uncles and all their children resided.). The shout continued: "Wait!!!" Lo and behold, there's Frankie, running down the middle of the road, bare-assed, a small towel thrown around him, dripping wet: "I didn't want yous to leave without me saying goodbye!" "Hey Frankie, we would have waited for you to put on your underwear!"

The stories about him are a book on their own. The comedian. The Good Samaritan. A saint. He was always helping someone, even strangers. On one Christmas Day, he said: "Ya know, Ma, on the Miami route, there are some guys hanging out on the streets, the homeless. I want them to have Christmas, too." He brought them sandwiches and sodas. "Mom- that just made my Christmas."

One his friends once remarked: "Frankie fed me when I was hungry and had nothing. He seemed to show up at the times I was at my lowest, could just about pay the rent. He would take the shirt off his back for someone, anyone, even strangers." This is the perception that many had of him. New York. Florida. He made a positive impression, a lasting one.

This was the man I fell in love with. This was the man I wanted to marry. A man who could make me laugh, was the center of attention, who dominated every room with his comedic skills. For once, I could sit back and enjoy the show. He could imitate anyone, any accent, any persona whether he became the Spanish bodega owner, the stuck-up Englishman, the Pakistani cab driver. Always with a smile. He missed his calling — his family and friends often said. His talent: to make us all cry because we were laughing so hard. It was no wonder that two of his hero's, whom he emulated daily, were Bart Simpson and Pee Wee Herman.[4] (His third hero, I can't mention. I may end up sinking... into the Long Island Sound.)[5]

---

[4] Pee Wee Herman (Paul Reubens) would be arrested this same year for indecent exposure.

[5] This unmentionable would soon be indicted when his sub-ordinate would break the code and testify against him.

~7~

Bart Simpson and Pee Wee Herman- the man I was dating, the man I fell in love with. Bart Simpson and Pee Wee "I know you are but what am I..." The man who loved me, my Tasmanian devil with a Christian heart. The Pied Piper who had a following of children, adolescents, adults. Nevertheless, there was another side to him that he showed me rarely because he didn't need to- our world was safe. "You're so sweet," he'd say. I couldn't help but be this way (sweet). He adored me. Why?? I didn't deserve his affection and adulation. "You don't understand. I come into contact with so many bad people every day. You're so good. I love you." This is why he wouldn't help me get the money for my co-op. I was having trouble with the banks. "You don't want to be indebted to those guys..." Which guys? We never clarified whom we were speaking about.

Besides his foolish antics and smart aleck persona, my Frankie had no fear...

We went to the movies one night with my brother, JoJo. On the way out from the theatre, there were rats, NYC rats, rats as large as my arm, and they were dancing between the garbage bins, playing tag in the path between the theatre and the parking lot, the path we needed to take. There was no way that I was going to pass by them. No way that I would even think of going near them. Frankie volunteered to go get the car and drive it around to the main road. Of course, he ran right up to the dumpster and tried to scare the rats. "I'm not afraid. One time when I was doing a route, a rat crawled right up my arm!" he yelled to me as he continued to dance around the rats, stomp on their tails, annoy them beyond frenzy.

The same attitude he took with my friendly neighborhood raccoon. A large, an extremely large animal by my city tastes, Frankie would throw things at it, yell at it, run up to it. This raccoon liked my house, the Oak tree in front becoming his home. Frankie would tease me every time I got into the car, "Watch out! The raccoon is underneath!" I'd scream. I'd jump. I'd yell: "Hurray up and open up the door!" Frankie would

fumble for his keys. Hee-hee, ha-ha. "Shit!! You scared me,
Frankie!" I'd shout at him. "Now, now, watch your mouth.
Young ladies shouldn't use that kind of language," he'd say in
his best Mommy voice. My anger would soften as he smiled at
me. I wonder if this kid was scared of anything? Or anyone?

He pissed a lot of them off- wise-guys, hoodlums, men you
didn't want to be associated with. Even the son-in-law of THE
re-known mobster that Rudy Guiliani staked his career in
getting into jail (and eventually did get into jail). "Who the hell
does that kid think he is?" "No- who do YOU think you are,"
Frankie said back, glaring. He should have been back slapped
(with the grip of a pistol), beaten up, or dumped somewhere in
the river with concrete boots... instead: "That kid has balls. I
like him!! Want to work for me?" Frankie, as ever, cocky and
daring: "No- we're gonna to be partners, someday!"

~8~

My mother pulled me aside in her kitchen one night. She had the serious look on her face as if someone had died. "I don't want to be connected. We are nice family and have a good reputation. You can't date him anymore. Just be his friend. I do not want to be connected." "Mom-his family is in sanitation, private sanitation. That's all..."

Frankie had warned me that my friends and my family would question me, drill me, continually ask what he did, especially since he was always disappearing to Florida. "Tell them, I'm a foreman in my Uncle's garage when they ask what I do." (As if anybody believed that as I tried to convince them.) "You're going to be married to the Mob," my friends joked. They mimicked: "We're yous friend whether yous like it or not." My new friends, according to my old straight-laced friends, would be a group of women with big hair, long fake nails, with 1980's hair still prevalent in the 1990's. No way. "That's a stereotype," I said. "He's a foreman in the garage." "Then why is he always going to Florida?" they asked.

He was only selling fireworks. I was smart enough to know fireworks were illegal but it didn't bother me. I could deal with him taking his trips south, spending June in Miami. He was preparing for his biggest season... the 4th of July. I could deal with this little indiscretion. If the Grucci's could throw a party... what was wrong with the little guy having his own celebration?

Everything he did (when I met him) was probably illegal but I never knew, never asked. "You're so sweet. You're so good. I meet such bad people every day," he would say repeatedly to me. He had never gone to jail and he had never done time...[6]

---

[6] He came close, very close. He was traveling across state lines into Florida when he got pulled over for speeding. The police found the guns, three of them hidden in the car. At this time, the State of Florida had just passed a new law. Since Frankie had been an addict, he could not be held accountable. His druggy past had protected him for once. He would go through rehab once again than spend a few wasted years in

"My friends are in "college". Do you know what that means, Rossana?" as he laughed and smiled.

Cable television had not yet immortalized the Italians (did cable TV even exist?). Hollywood had only recently created an Oscar winning movie I had yet to see. It was still whispered (what was whispered?), as not to offend the Italian heritage, the descendants of Verde, Michelangelo, Vespucci, Columbus, descendants who were proud and would not be shamed. I didn't know why my Mom was concerned. Frankie was Italian. Okay- I needed to polish him up a little... but he loved me. Ignore the tattoos. I would make him dress better. I would stop him from swearing (shit- I had my own truck driver mouth to curtail!) Frankie- he was an aficionado of the derelict kind. He had that little bit of dangerous appeal, the bad boy to my good girl but he was mine and only mine. Sort of. I had to share him with many...

He picked me up late one midweek night, around 10:30 pm. As usual, he was always late and I made sure he got the brunt of my bitching. I had already eaten but somehow my appetite was always ravishing around him. No wonder I was getting fat. He took me to a restaurant in Ozone Park on Cross Bay Boulevard. This neighborhood of all neighborhoods. Frankie insisted I sit in the chair facing him: "I need to watch the door." Huhh? I didn't quite understand. And then he sent a bottle of the best scotch "with his regards" over to the next table. The next table. An intimidating group of overweight, ruff at the seams, bad mouthed, hot-blooded men. Italian men. Ozone Park. Connected. Now I understood what my Mother meant!

What the hell was he doing taking a nice girl like me here late at night? I hated these damn guidos. They gave Italians a bad name. They had no class, no manners. And they were all fat!!! And they didn't know how to dress! Did they all own a (legitimate) stake in the Tachini sweatsuit business? If I spoke my mind, which I usually did, I'd probably have a gun in my

---

"college". Drugs had saved his skin. Drugs had saved his ass but did it save him from himself?

face!!! Frankie and I continued to whisper. He wasn't his usual loud, laughing self in the watchful eyes of that group.

~9~

He spent the whole month of June in Florida. He flew me down. We spent a weekend at the Hollywood Beach Hotel, our romantic weekend that turned into a horror story. He had originally planned on taking me to "The" five star hotel in Miami, something "Blue".

My flight arrived three hours late. I was a mess. I hated flying... my sinuses always clogged, my face and feet swelled, my hair became flat. I was a mess and I wore a scowl. Frankie was waiting in the airport with a big grin on his face! Always smiling... The hotel was not what I expected... more of a motel, tacky tourist get up, reminding me of the first time we had gotten together, a time I had let him take me to a hotel, demanded it not be a *screw* motel! At least that had been a Marriott. This room was a ten by ten hole-in-the-wall, mauve and green cracked wallpaper, with a ripped curtain on the window, a corner window that looked into the next room of the L-shaped building, the bed that came out of the wall and continually bounced back up. A horrendous evening. I kept thinking... *Frankie and I will be making love, the voyeurs next door watching with lustful eyes... the bed will suddenly flip up, locking us into the wall, four corners of this moldy bed will become our tomb!* I couldn't get this thought out of my mind and being amorous was the last thing I wanted to be.

I bitched and I bitched loudly. There was no way I was sleeping here with him. We went down to the reception and waited one hour before being told (not taken) where to go. The new room wasn't much better. It was an efficiency unit with a stove that didn't light and the same hidden bed in the wall ...but at least this room overlooked the Atlantic Ocean, the pristine white beach, and bikini clad women and men. The flea- bag Motel. The Hollywood Beach Hotel. We made the most of it. We were together, alone.

I was putting on a little weight thanks to Frankie's late night double dinners. Frankie had promised me some new clothes, a new summer wardrobe. I settled for a stretch pink and yellow miniskirt because he was short on cash. For some reason, he didn't have much money. "It's only money. When you're down, you just pick yourself right up again."[7] I had become accustomed to him emptying his pockets and pulling out wads of cash. I never asked him where he got it. I loved him. It didn't matter.

I was pissed off when I realized I had to fit my big butt into a large since the one leg-fit-all small and the rip-at-the-seams medium wouldn't do! During the next morning's buffet breakfast, just as I was about to get some more eggs... Frankie laughed and giggled: "Sweetheart. You keep sayin how upset yous are about gaining weight. Why are you goin back for a second helping?" How is that for an appetite suppressant? His one and only negative comment to me. EVER!!! I ate the fruit on my plate.

My childhood friend, Lynn, had also flown down with me. She was staying with her college roommate and her husband, a conventional couple by modern standards. Suzanna and Charles had grown up in Hollywood, where most of Frankie's Florida family lived. They knew the same people. Frankie suggested Suzanna negotiate some new business (legitimate business!) with his brother regarding the workman's comp accounts she managed. During dinner, Frankie was always laughing, giggling, making fun of everyone, even my friends. We could not stop laughing as we paid the check and Frankie approached the next table. "Oh, twins!" he said to the woman. "How beautiful. God bless you! My sisters are twins," kissing his fingers to his lips and blessing the babies. I was mortified. My friends were embarrassed. The woman looked bewildered, not knowing what to say. Her husband laughed, breaking the nervous tension that you cut with a knife. Frankie, ever the more jovial, chuckled as the five of us left, smiling...

---

[7] I would remember these words forever, words that could pull me out of a depression, keep me moving forward, always looking for a bright future.

Frankie and Rossana. Cut from the same mold. If my friends had thought I was a character right out of a comic strip, then I can only imagine what they thought about him? It didn't matter. He made them laugh!

I always said I needed a man to shut me up and calm me down. He did that to me and turned me into a lady, treating me with the "utmost respect." Frankie. My Frankie. There was no one like him.

~10~

My Frankie... with his green, green eyes and blonde hair that all the Cubano women loved, his perpetual tan skin (from working outside), the small delicate nose (that had been sculpted from marble), the straight white teeth (always gleaming through the cheshire grin), the broad chest and bulging biceps (that depicted strength and honor). My Frankie– conceited knowing he could make the women drool, whose personality you couldn't help but love. I had to share him. I had to accept this. I had to share him with his mother who he loved deeply and ranked with the Madonna. I had to share him with his sisters who he teased and loved as only a brother could. I had to share him with the world as his friendships spanned from NYC to Florida, across class structures, education levels, and ethnicity. I had to share him because he was loved by many but only wanted to be loved by one. And it wasn't me. He knew I loved him. He loved me. It was a beckoning force, like a magnetic grid, that brought us together. I was the positive to his negative existence, "the bi-polar shall meet." He was only missing one thing...

His life was never meant to be easy... The only peaceful sleep was his nine months in-utero... soon to change abruptly on a day in which he was still in the tranquil surrounding of his mother's womb; on the day her water broke. As his mother crouched in pain, the contractions rapid, as her labor intensified, his father screamed, demanded: "I want dinner, NOW!!!!". How could a woman in labor, a painful labor, possibly make dinner? Luckily, her mother was there to help her curtail her husband's rage.

Poor Frankie. His life... off to a wrong start. His father to blame. Frankie. There was no joy in his birth. There was no joy in his life. His father to blame.

The only thing that Frankie ever wanted, besides me, was for his father to accept him. He yearned for his father's love and tried to earn his respect and trust by remaining "clean". While he was in Florida and worked for his Dad, Frankie tried to make him proud. He wanted to make him proud by keeping a job, staying straight, being the best at what he could do. Frankie was a restless individual who was trying to find himself, trying to find a place in his father's life. If his father could only have accepted him in appositive way instead of as the degenerate that he perceived him to be, Frankie would have felt complete. If his father had only accepted him even half way, understanding his limitations, Frankie would have felt complete. My sweet Frankie. He wanted so much to be loved by this man! An iota of compassion from him would have fulfilled Frankie's every wish.

Even the heat of the Floridian sun could not melt and change this "father". His father was cold, the abomidible snowman, with a frosted temperament that chilled the air wherever he went. His father was cold to Frankie, never once showing him support, pride, simple friendship even though Frankie remained "straight", stayed away from the pleasures that drugs offered, and worked diligently. He never forgot the time his father shunned him, turned his back. The impression remained...

A negative impression indebted into Frankie's mind forever. Frankie had gone into the office of the garage to get a soda, a simple act, a simple need to quench his thirst. Lauri, his father's secretary (soon to be wife), blatantly, vehemently declared: "No worker's allowed in here." She said this in a conciliatory tone, in a demeaning manner like she was in charge and she meant it. No workers? Jesus Christ- his father owned the business. His anger rose. He screamed at her. His anger continued to ignite, a flammable emotion he couldn't control. He backed her into a wall with a verbal tirade. The office turned into a war zone: chairs thrown aside, desks overturned, papers askew. Was she scared? Who knows? Her face ashen, the color of her rats-nest head? His rage caused a few gray hairs to creep up on her bleached blonde mane. Frankie didn't care. He wanted an apology. He wanted his father to back him up. The only thing he wanted was to be acknowledged as his son. Frankie's heart was broken because his father turned his back, showed he didn't care.[8]

Frankie only wanted his love. The "abuse" continued. His father, in his usual inebriated state, looked for any excuse to pick on Frankie. His father knew what he was doing. His actions were pre–meditated. He accused Frankie of stealing a bracelet. His father attacked him, came at Frankie from behind. A fist fight pursued, a one-sided fist fight because Frankie went on the defensive, blocking his father's flailing arms. His father called the police and asked them to arrest Frankie for assault and battery. "Officer, he hit me in the face," his father declared. "He beat me up and attacked me." "Officer. I used ta box. If I hit him there (pointing to his father's face), he'd be on the floor with a broken jaw and cracked cheekbone. He'd have no face left. He wants me out!! I'm leaving. I just want to know one ting. Are yous gonna arrest me or what? 'Cause I ain't looking ova my shoulder!"

Frankie left and Lauri immediately moved in. Any excuse for his father to get rid of him. Any excuse for his father to show his neglect. Any excuse for his father to show Frankie he didn't care. The "bracelet" was found years later. His father never apologized.

---

[8] Frankie's vein popped, throbbed in his forehead, his face scarlet, his eyes wild and strained, his hands clenched in a fistful clutch as he told me this story. I thought he would burst, filled to the limit with hot, sour air. I was scared because he became hysterical with a fury he was not in command of, didn't understand how to control. He finally calmed down when he saw me with my back against the car window, ready to run, end us right then…This was the only time I saw a side to him that wasn't loving, compassionate, kind.

~ 1 1 ~

You may wonder why I have never shared the details of our sex life. It's very simple. It's an intimacy reserved just for the two of us. To those of you who have found your soulmate, you can understand because you've been there, you are there, you should still be there.

It's not about arousal, desire, filling a need or about the physical. It's not about one giving, the other receiving... it's all of those, plus the spiritual commitment, the psychological balance, the physiological embrace. It's about sharing, equanimity.

We are joined in one as body, one in mind, one in our hearts, one in our souls, one in love. It's an inspired unity. Making love- private moments shared by two, experienced as one! To be made love to when you are in love, when he is in love with you is the ultimate experience, a venue of perfection, simple ... divine rapture. I loved him. I love him. I will always love him. And he loved me.

~12~
Hickory, dickory, dock...

July 19th

Tick Tock. Sex was thrown in between everything that was going on. Bank, beach, his mom's, my house... He needed to be somewhere. I was going to me sister-in-law's twenty fifth birthday party at some happening, trendy New York City club. He had an appointment he needed to keep, had no choice but to keep. I was expected, as always, to attend the family functions. I wanted to be with him, to stay in his arms.

Tick tock. We didn't have enough time. My ride was coming soon. We didn't have enough time. Tick tock. I still needed to get dressed. We didn't have enough time. I had yet to jump in the shower. We didn't have enough time. "Pull back your hair. You know how Frankie likes to look at your pretty face," he said to me as I rode him. Tick tock. I never climaxed. We didn't have enough time... and we never would.

10:00 am That Friday began in a way that's hectic. I played hooky from work. I called out sick. I had decided the day before. "You're going to get in trouble. What's going to happen if you lose your job? I'll feel guilty and then no one will be able to support us," he teased. I played hooky from work that Friday. What a joke?

Tick tock. I had to get to the bank to drop off my finalized loan application. I had had so much trouble trying to get this loan for my co-op on Central Park West. I was only borrowing $25,000. Such a small loan. However, it was a co-op and banks weren't so apt to lend money for a coop, even though it was three doors down from Central Park, a primo location on a quiet, tree lined street. Nevertheless, I needed to get the money, any way I could. Frankie had offered to introduce me to someone who could get me the money but he strongly urged me not to. "My friends aren't nice. I want to protect you." He knew how much this apartment meant to me but he still couldn't figure out how our lives together would fit into the scheme of things if I went to Manhattan. Manhattan was another world. He didn't want me to move that far away, especially since it was on the West Side. I might as well move to New Jersey, he teased.

Frank was late as usual, me getting mad. He arrived and I was about to yell at him when... in his arms, he carried a dozen, long stem roses. Red roses. Long stem. This was the first time he actually came bearing roses because he usually had them delivered. (Only the day before, I had been teasing him that he had better keep the romance alive. "How come I never get flowers anymore?" I whined. "You're going to get spoiled. I don't want to spoil yous.") As I was walking into the kitchen with the flowers, Frankie grabbed my face and started kissing me fervently –on the cheek. My mother walked in just at that moment. My face flushed. Frankie replied somewhat to the effect of "I couldn't help myself, Mrs. T. She has such a pretty face. I couldn't help myself. No disrespect!" Off we went finally, to the bank, then the Beach Club.

Tick tock. This day at the beach was like most summer days... it was hot, 95 degrees, sunny. I was getting tan. He was restless. He left me to go play volleyball with the little boys: Robbie, Frank, Dominick, and the rest of that Italian crew. I REALLY WANTED HIM TO SPEND THE DAY WITH ME. After all, I called in sick to work. I really wanted him to dote on me, stay by my side. I gave in. Something made me realize that I bitched too much and that he should have his fun. After a couple of hours, I started to get mad. They were still playing ball. When were they going to stop? Finally! Wait- they're going swimming! They were all walking toward the ocean and were about dive in. I was really mad... but Frankie turned and started to come toward me. "You know I was thinking of you. Of course I wouldn't go swimming without you." He read my mind- I had not yet said one word.

3:30 pm "A strong women's gonna want to marry me," he said. "I'm a strong woman!" I said. "Ahh I don't know. Itsa got to be a strong woman that wants to marry me." "Hey. I'm a strong woman," I screeched! Where was this conversation going? We had left the beach and he was driving around Jamaica, showing me where he grew up, where he worked, where his cousins kept their trucks, the garages, the auto glass store. "This is my neighborhood. If I save enough cash, my uncle will match it so I can be legit. Someday, I going to own a junk yard and make lots of money..." A junk yard? "How do you make money owning that?" I asked. "Scrap metal. It's a great business..." Convince me, I was thinking.

He was driving around as if he was telling me something. It seemed like he was laying everything on the line- giving me my out if I wanted it. "Have you seen *Goodfellows*?" he said. "No," I replied. "You should get it. Rent it. You'll understand me a little better." Huhhh? What did a movie have to do with us?? "Only a strong woman can marry me." he said and looked at me. "I'm strong," I said for the fourth time. "You don't understand, Rossana." he said looking at me, staring at me, serious. So unlike him- he was always joking around, laughing, teasing. We were stopped at a light. He leaned into me. What was he trying to say? What couldn't he say? as if he wanted to tell me... "I'm married. DO YOU UNDERSTAND?" "Yes." I said (but really didn't). It could mean only one thing, I guess. (My mother had said to me recently. I like him but I don't want to be connected. We are not like that. I want you to be safe.) No more words needed to be said. That was that. Our future was decided. "A strong woman's gonna want to marry me." I nudged him- gently.

Tick tock. He mentioned a ring. "It's comin in soon." "I want five carats." "No. Five carats is ugly. They don't shine. My cousin has five and a half carats. Too big for your little fingers. How about three?" Three? As long as it was just one, round (no baguettes). I'd settle for two. I'd settle for anything. We went back and forth, teasing. "The ring's comin in soon," he said.

I loved him, felt it deep inside. I knew- the butterflies were dancing. It didn't matter what he did, who he was. He was in love with me. He was testing me. He loved me but he needed to make me understand. The conversation was never completed. It was left unsaid. I never asked any questions because I really thought I find out later, in time. I didn't need to ask any questions because he would tell me when he was ready. In time.

5 pm: So strange. We went back to his mom's because he had to use the bathroom. We sat at his mom's table. He seemed sad and troubled even though we had just spent a perfect afternoon. "I don't feel good, Mom. I have a pain right here (pointing to the left side of his chest). Look at my eyes. Do ya think I have ta worry?" He was afraid that his eyes were yellow and that he had gotten hepatitis again.

"No, Frankie. Your eyes are fine. On Monday, go see a Doctor. You'll be fine. You probably ate too much." she said. (On Monday, he was going to look for an apartment. He liked living with his Mom but he wanted to be alone with me. He wanted his own place. He wanted his own home. He wanted to be responsible. He had finally found himself.)

We sat down and we talked. The three of us. It was a strange conversation. Frankie did most of the talking... "Mom, if I died, who would ya cawl to do the funeral? Would ya cawl the people at the Beach Club?" "Frankie, why are you talking like this?" his mother said. "Mom, you won't invite Daddy to the funeral. Promise me you won't invite Daddy." "Frankie, stop talking this way!!!" she said back in an affirmative manner.

6:30 pm. We left his Mother's and went back to my house for some time alone. An hour later, I left for the party and he couldn't come with me. I kept thinking that eve, amongst my family and friends, how much I wanted him with me, how much I loved him, how much I wish he could have come and shared in this night.

July 20th. Tick tock. Tick tock

Noon. I called Frankie about five times to try and get a ride to my hair appointment. I knew he had been up late the night before and he probably turned off his phone. I needed a ride. Where was he?? I was getting anxious. I finally borrowed my Dad's car. I hadn't talked to Frankie all day and he hadn't left any messages.

6 pm. I was waiting for Lynn and Dave. We were going on a booze cruise around Manhattan, leaving from City Island. I was excited because I had never gone on one. Frankie couldn't come. It wasn't about the drinking. He had an appointment. I was a little disappointed because I really wanted to be with him. I hadn't heard from him all day. I was surprised because there were no messages. The telephone rang. I thought it was Lynn. The boat was leaving in a half an hour, we still had to drive to the Bronx, and they were late. It was Frankie. "Hey sweetheart. I'm at the club…" The last thing he said to me before the boys pulled him away to play cards (Rumella) was: "I love you." "I love you, too." I said (not ditto).

12:30 am. After the cruise, as we were heading home on the Clearview Expressway, Lynn said: "Let's get Frankie. Come on. I want Frankie to come out and play with us!". "No. It's late," I said. Anyway, we passed the exit and were almost home. "Come on! Let's go get Frankie!" she said. (Okay, Lynn. I've known you my whole life. What's up with your behavior?- I was thinking, not wanting to instigate a fight.) We had been drinking for the last four hours. "Dave- let's go get Frankie!!!" She was adamant, so unlike her. Dave turned the car around.

We went to Frankie's house. It was late. I couldn't ring the doorbell. Dave honked the horn once. We waited. Gina stuck her head out the window: "He's not home." "Do you know where he is?" "No. Do you want to come in and wait for him?" I thought about it. As much as I wanted to spend the night, to wake up in his arms (I loved sleeping in the crook of his arm- his biceps made such a nice pillow), something compelled me to say: "No. Tell him I came by. I'm going to leave him a note." I wrote the note: *I love you. Wish you had been here. –R.* We waited in front of the house another half hour. It was now almost 1:30 am. He never came home. Tick-tock.

July 21st

6:00 am. I woke up early, very early. I couldn't call Frankie just yet because I knew he had been out late, later than me! I'll wait awhile, I thought as I tossed and turned, wanting to get up, wanting to call him, wanting to start our day. Why had I awoken so early? I knew my hangover would kick in later. Tick-tock.

9:45 am. I called the house number. Gina asked me to call Frankie's line. I had a feeling he had his ringer off from yesterday. Tick Tock. Tick Tock. Tick tock. "Can you go get him, please? We are going to the beach." "Okay." She was such a sweet girl when it came to me. She came back to the phone and said: "Frankie is foaming at the mouth. My Mom is giving him CPR. I have to go call the ambulance. I'll call you back."

I went downstairs into the kitchen. My Mom said: "Rossana, you have tears in your eyes. Is everything all right?" I told her what Gina had said. Gina did call back, as promised, screaming, crying. She managed to say, a sixteen year-old child: "I don't know how to tell you this, Rossana! But Frankie's dead!"[9] I hung up. I told my mom. I went upstairs and got dressed. My mother asked if I was okay. "I want to go over." "Do you want me to drive?" "No! I'll drive." We went to his house... only a few miles away but a long, long drive.

I remember walking in and seeing Bobbie (a family friend). I went upstairs. I went into his room. He was lying on the bed. He looked like he was sleeping, bare-chested, on his back, his right arm thrown casually above his head. I remember sleeping in the crook of his arm. I was tempted to crawl into bed next to him. I wanted to lay my head on his bicep, put my arm across his strong broad chest, throw my leg casually over his hip. He was sleeping, that's all. I knew this wasn't right! His mother was at the head of the bed, holding a tissue next to his mouth, wiping away the blood. She looked at me and said: "I'm sorry, Rossana. So sorry." I remember thinking and saying: "I can't see him like this." I ran out, one tear had fallen onto my cheek. I went to the kitchen and drank a glass of water, my saving grace. Why hadn't I called that morning, earlier? He'd still be alive. Why hadn't I waited longer the night

---

[9] She had also left a screaming, crying, hysterical message on my answering machine. A message that gave even my brother goose bumps from head to toe.

before? He'd still be alive. Why hadn't I spent the night in his arms? He'd still be alive. My thoughts running wild as I sipped the glass of water. I got the courage and went back upstairs into his room. I sat on the bed, next to him. He was still warm. Except for the pinkish foam coming out of his mouth, he looked like he was sleeping. Sleeping peacefully. I wanted to crawl into the bed and lay down next to him. I stayed at the foot of the bed as all the screaming women came in, all the friends and family crying, hysterical. I thought, "Don't be like them! You must remain calm!"

This day was hotter than most summer mornings as if the furnace had ignited, the heat turned up to full capacity. I wanted a fan. Why was it so hot inside this room? I sat with my boyfriend and watched him turn blue and cold. I sat and wiped the spittle from his face. I sat and watched his body change. I sat with him as the police arrived, asked me to leave, and searched the room. What did the police want? Why had they intruded on our private moments? Why did they feel it was necessary to interrogate his mother (and everyone) as if this moment was the most opportune? We were all in a state of disbelief.

I found out later it was procedure. They asked many questions, personal questions, questions that would get under anyone's skin. He was twenty-five. Where was he the night before? With who? God, please no drugs... the thought never crossed my mind until it was whispered, the rumors beginning to spread. He died at home. He died clean! He had seen everyone that night. All his friends. All his cousins. He had taken a tour and bumped into them all. The last one he was with was Cousin John. Big John. Please God, don't let it be drugs. I had only known John as a child. I did not know the man he had become. PLEASE, NO DRUGS. Frankie was happy. He was happy with me. No drugs! No drugs. He died clean. He died at home. He died happy, knowing he was loved!! He died being in love with me. He died knowing I loved him, knowing I was in love with him! No drugs... Please, I prayed (as the rumors intensified, spreading quickly).

I went out for air but came back inside every time one of his friends or cousins arrived. I followed them into the room. I needed to see their reaction. The best friend's crying. They were such men yet they didn't care- they cried like little girls. I was watching this through a window. I was absorbing it all as if I was an innocent bystander. I watched as Rosanna came running in, not realizing Frankie was there, screaming, crying, hysterical as she realized what she was seeing. I watched as Gina became distraught. I watched as the whole neighborhood cried simultaneously, one tear dripping down my face. I watched as if I had no part of this.

I went outside. It was hot, the hottest day of the summer that July, hot, humid, 98 degrees. It was hot as a man stood on the lawn and sung opera, beautifully, spiritually, with a voice like an angel. There was an angel, on the lawn, singing... which opera with its tragic undertones? Puccini? Tosca? Madame Butterfly? Carmen? -the strong-willed, destructive siren, who leads men astray by her beauty. Which heartrending score did he choose to resonate, sing beautifully?

I could not listen to the music... I wanted to scream at him and tell him to stop. It was too much! Frankie's Aunt Maria said: "Who is this guy?" Aunt Veronica went up to him, ever bold: "We don't need this right now!" It was too much- the voice of an angel... The angel would turn out to be Brooks- the neighborhood weirdo known for renting porno's to the local boys. In exchange, he promoted their club parties. A mutual exchange. The local boys would hang out at his house and play cards. Brooks! Three months later, he would kill his parents. He then shot his neighbor after calling him up, luring him in with "I'm having a heart attack!" He telephoned each local boy. A few came over. A few rang the doorbell when they saw their friend's cars in the driveway. Brooks- lured them in and shot them dead. His parents. His neighbor. Two young men. Two others would survive- one shot in the back, a paraplegic who would die three years later. The other shot five times, running down the street, calling for help. Brooks. Shot himself dead.

Brooks- the voice of an angel or the Devil incarnate?

~ 13 ~

I went home when I could no longer stand to be in the room with him, when his body had begun to smell, when he turned from pink to blue, warm to cold. It was a good thing I left when I did. I would not be subject to further torment. (Many hours later, the coroner's office finally arrived to take away his body now in full rigor mortis. It was fortunate I left. His body bag was placed on the front stoop, discarded like a heap of garbage, as the van was backed up into the driveway. Where was the bedside manner of these city worker's (who ran through the mechanical motions of getting the job done) when it was most needed? Where was the human compassion?)

I went home and called Lynn. "Where have you been? It's late. Are you and Frankie coming to the beach?" "Frankie is dead." "What? How?" I explained as little as I knew. I decided to go to the beach.

I went to the beach and sat in a chair by the water's edge. I knew what I wanted to do... As I looked toward the ocean, I pondered my fate. Would the coldness of the water freeze my thoughts and turn me back towards the safety of the hot white sands? Or would the tranquility of the waves slapping my feet draw me in deeper and deeper, enveloping my body, closing in, drawing the last breath out of my tormented soul?

I arose and walked slowly, looking back only once at my sun-tanning friend of nineteen-plus years, burning her white Irish skin, noticing signs of blisters. It was a lasting reflection of the sun on her golden copper hair that stayed imbedded in my mind.

I proceeded to dip one toe in...

I wanted to swim. I wanted to keep swimming, let the ocean swallow me up. I had nothing to lose. I wanted to swim and keep swimming beyond the breaking of the waves. The way I use to as a child. The way I use to as a child with him.

I couldn't. I knew that the Point Lookout lifeguards would save me and then I'd be embarrassed, for taking my life, for trying to end it all, for wanting to die. My failed attempt. I'd end up going to therapy, talking about my feelings. I'd be weak. No one would understand. No one could understand. I couldn't be weak- I was always the strong one.

Besides... I needed to take care of his mother. I needed to take care of his little sisters. How could I take care of them if I was frail, pathetic? I was the strong one, always strong. Who was going to take care of me? I was alone. I would get used to it.

That eve, my family thought it best to keep me busy. We were going to the movies to see Billy Crystal in that western comedy, a little levity to tweak my darkened mood. I wanted to go to his house. First of all, I wanted to see Anthony, his brother. I wanted him to put his arms around me and tell me it was going to be okay. I wanted to see the rest of the family as they arrived from Florida... Maybe seeing them was the affirmation I needed to pull me out of my dream? I walked inside, alone, as my family sat in the car.

The conversation stopped, an interruption of thoughts mid-sentence. Everyone just looked at me, wild eyed, staring in disbelief, a look of bewilderment; a look of hope... Anthony walked me outside. "I need to ask you something," he began in a nervous tone. "Frankie said you missed your friend." "Huhhh," I looked at him not understanding. "You know, your friend." "Which friend?" As far as I knew, none of my friends had gone away. Why was he concerned? "You were late. Frankie said you were late." "Late for what?" I really didn't know what he was trying to ask, what he couldn't ask. What was he trying to say? To ask me? I was totally bewildered. "Ya know, you were late with your friend." Ohhhh! "No, Anthony. I'm not pregnant." No wonder everyone had stared at me as if I was the great white hope of the next generation of Frankie's.[10]

---

[10] I wanted to be pregnant. I could be; though, I had just finished my period. Things like that happened. I wished it to be, as my next period never arrived. I demanded to understand on the day I passed a blood clot, lots of blood, lots of tissue into the

~14~

On this suffocating summer's eve, I didn't just feel a presence-the cool air surrounding me, a bone chilling arousal that made me open my eyes. It was the smell. Only those of you that have been with a dying soul or stayed with a dead loved one are familiar with the smell- the smell of decomposure. It is the smell of death. It is a scent that cannot be described in ways to make you understand. The smell of death- not pleasant, not friendly, not nice.

I knew he was here. I knew he had come back to me to comfort me, to tell me he loved me. God had granted him this time as he waited for judgment- soon to head north (or south.) I was scared for I had never experienced something so spiritual or fantastical- not knowing if this was a figment of my imagination, an out of body experience of touch, smell, taste? It was surreal.

"Are you there Frankie? It's me, Rossana." I spoke softly, my voice quivering. At once, these words, this experience, reminding me of a childhood tale, Are you there God? It's me, Margherite (by Judy Bloom). In that story, she talks to God. I was so confused... Was it another childhood tale, a religious story where the little girl is visited by an angel? Was I talking to my angel?

"Are you there Frankie? It's me, Rossana." The stench was overpowering. I thought to myself, trying to calm my fears: "I'll smell the Roses." The roses stood proud, perfectly poised at my bedside. I was mortified- the goosebumps rising from head to toe, my hair standing on end, frozen with fear. Somehow, I managed. Somehow, I got up and leaned over to sniff their fragrance, the aroma comforting my terrified self, calming my nerves, soothing... Red roses. Long stem.

"I'll smell your roses, Frankie." I said aloud. I was compelled to look across the room. I knew he had come, he was here. I

---

toilet at the Beach Club. Our Beach Club. .Had I just lost his baby? The hope of the next generation being flushed away ...I always wonder.

knew he was here with me because the television, silent and dark in its unpowered state, suddenly crackled! sizzled! popped! with light and energy, a brilliant illumination that filled the room, a forceful electrical current that spoke to me, though for only a nanosecond: "I am here. I love you. There will always be a special place in my heart for you."

No one in his or her right mind will understand this. I don't blame you. It's inconceivable, incomprehensible of human thought. I repeated what happened once and only after my little brother, whose brain had been tormented by seizures, looked at me the next afternoon and tried to speak. His face was distraught. His eyes dark with fear. His distorted limbs twisted in pain. His mood sullen. His body language revealed a deep hidden secret. I was concerned and afraid to ask but did: "What's the matter JoJo?"

"Frankie came to me as I was washing the car today," he said in his garbled speech. "I was inside, spraying the windows, when I looked over and he was sitting beside me. He said: 'Hey, Boobie- take care of your sister for me!' With that, he winked and was gone."

I then reiterated my story- to validate its claim or to reassure both of us that our experiences were real? I wonder why he chose to visit JoJo? Why JoJo? Did Frankie designate JoJo as my earthly protector for years to come? Did Frankie know that JoJo would share the same fate-"live fast, die young, leave a good looking corpse"? Maybe it was the foreshadowing of events to come- both only twenty-five, both an unexpected death, both missed dearly by all... Or maybe JoJo was an innocent, one of the last, who could fully see, understand, acknowledge the impact that Frankie's death would leave on me.[11]

---

[11] 1/12/02 Coincidental that "Unchained Melody", the theme song from GHOST is playing as I write this. I cry for my brother as I write this. I miss him. He was supposed to take care of me. "JoJo, whose going to take care of me now? You promised. You promised Frankie."

~15~

July 21st.

This day changed my life forever, a day that stole from me the twinkle in my eye, a day which snatched the spunk from my soul, a day which grabbed and held prisoner my emotional being...

July 22nd.

I received a letter from the General Manager of the Hollywood Hotel, offering us a free weekend due to our inconvenience in June. I had written to them a few weeks back. How ironic. A free weekend for two, good for one year.

July 23rd/24th.

The Wake was grand, a festival honoring their fallen hero, my hero, my love. It was elegant, a room filled with huge floral arrangements that covered all four walls, two deep. The wake... how they screamed at piercing levels, cried loudly, became hysterical, not understanding, not wanting this to be...the wailing wall- yet the women were not covered in veils but shrouded in heartfelt misery. I remained calm and watched. I didn't want to be like that, like them. I didn't want to speak to anybody as they lined up for hours-over 700 people- paying homage to their friend, my friend.

The wake that his Dad was allowed to come to, participate in as if he needed the support of friends. Rosanna picked up his flowers, flowers that stood perched at the coffin's bedside and moved them to the back. One of Frankie's cousins introduced me to this man. (He asked to be introduced to me.) I wanted to scream, at the top of my lungs... "NO!! Don't let this man in. He does not deserve to mourn!!" Frankie hated him. Frankie said only four days earlier that he didn't want this man here.

As a further insult, his father's family (the aunt that never said hello, the uncle that turned his back) demanded they also be allowed to attend the services, to be included with the family, to <u>simulate</u> grief. They never cared about Frankie. Why were they causing us all so much pain?

That is when the line was drawn. Only his Dad. This "allowance"- a special privilege bestowed on him from his ex-wife was stressed to him in a private conversation on the stoop of the funeral parlor. It was reiterated by the son-in-law of that re-known mobster I mentioned earlier. It was stressed in a way that his father (and his father's family) understood. Capisce. His father. He did not deserve to be labeled as such: Father. Dad. Daddy. I hated that man! Who did he think he was, attending his son's funeral, when he never once gave him an ounce of compassion? I should have smacked him in the face. For Frankie. I should have created a scene (long overdue) but I couldn't. I was a lady.

~16~
On Megan

I was in a triangle, sort of. Frankie was always speaking about his best friend, he had tons... this was different: his best girl friend, Megan, whom he met during summer school. She's this. She's that. I was jealous. I couldn't help being so. He spoke so highly about her. "Don't worry. We're friends. There's always been a special place in my heart for you..."

I finally met her at the wake, on the second eve. She came up to me and introduced herself, as Irish as I am Italian. Her blue eyes were as bright as my once shining golden eyes. I couldn't help notice her beauty. She was as different from me as day is to night. Yet... we had that one common bond: we loved the same man. It was more than that... We were IN LOVE with the same man. I knew this. I could see it in her eyes.

She was exactly like him- the crude mouth, the abusive and troubled childhhod. I, at this time, the "lady", with my wonderful and loving family.

She was his clone... in mannerisms and dress. I was his alter ego. She accepted him as he was. I tried to change him and mold him into something better.

She gave him her clean needles so he would not get sick.[12] I would never have condoned this behavior. I would have demanded he check himself into a clinic.

I was jealous when I first heard her name, kept hearing it... but I realized that he loved me. I knew he loved me. I wonder if it was because he was Italian, proud of his heritage? She wasn't Italian. I was. That's why they were friends and would only remain as such.

He wanted children. She didn't. I did. Five to be exact.

---

[12] Megan was a diabetic. The needles were for her own use.

Yet, it was I, he loved so deeply. Yet, it was she, he opened up to so completely. There were things she knew... that I could never understand. Yet there were things I asked and pried... that she would NEVER do so. There were things he could never tell me because it "was for my own protection". I found out later, she knew it all!

To her- he lived "by the gun and should have died that way." Something that his other friend, Rico, also believed: "He should have gone out with a blaze of glory..." To me- he lived from the heart.

For she was the best friend... someone he would always have. Yet I was the girlfriend... for whom he wanted to marry. I shared the intimacies... yet she was the one he'd always be affectionate to. We should have been enemies, as women usually are when it comes to the affairs of the heart, the affairs of a certain shared someone... yet we became friends. As someone said, "she was my competition"... yet there was no animosity between us.

They said I was the strong one, and I know it seemed strange that at his funeral, at the graveside, she broke down and cried... and it was I who held her and told her it would be all right. At his graveside, this somber event, as everyone looked downward... a moment suspended when I looked up into the eyes of his cousin and best friend Andrew, standing across in this crowd of mourners. We were one in our thoughts, pain, and solitude. One tear slid down my cheek, as I held his gaze. "Why?" we both asked-in a moment shared between us.

Megan never realized that she was the strong one... for she showed her true emotions. I only hid them... She accepted his death as it was- a simple tragedy. I still look for answers to questions I won't ask.

She was the best friend. I was the girlfriend. We were in love with the same man. He was Frankie.

WHAT WERE THE PARALLELS THAT MADE OUR PATHS CROSS?????

~ 17 ~

My life, moving fast into a positive realm, suddenly disrupted as I discovered the meaning of death. Death was new to me. Frankie had left me. Death is hard. Why did the first person to die in my life have to be him? Death is difficult. Death can suddenly sneak up on you...

Death. I had never known it. Death. I was now reminded of it every day... On *"Nurses"*, one nurse sarcastically said to the other: "Drop dead!" (and she did). The show continued to depict death and all its elements: the funeral, grief, loss. However, this had comedic undertones. On *"Sisters"*, the show depicted the one year anniversary of their Dad's death. Surprise. The other woman shows up. No comedic undertones but the same portrayal: funeral, grief, loss.

At some point in time, Demi Moore was making the rounds on the talk show circuit promoting her newest, *"The Butcher's Wife"*, speaking about her past success with *"Ghost"* (the movie we both loved). The underlying theme: psychic powers. The psychic phenomenon I knew existed. I had experienced. Then ...*"Life Goes On"* tells the story of a boy dying of Aids. He says: "Live fast, die young, leave a good looking corpse." Concurrently, airing on *"Eerie, Indiana"*, the young girl says those same exact words. Why?

Death is hard. Death was new to me and was being thrown in my face.

I still had those magical pills hidden away, protected, safe for tomorrow, September 21st. On this night, the last night I would be with my family, we went to the movies to see *"The Commitments."* Everyone. I had planned it this way. My mind wandered...I knew I would soon be out of harm's way, feel content.

I woke up late the next morning. The cemetery was over an hour away. Once again... my body's time clock protected me from the sin I was about to commit. It was late; too late to do anything. Angela's (Angie's) letter would be my saving grace. She was attending George Washington University.

...I know you don't want to hear it but you really must keep going ahead and go on with your life. You have so much to offer and so much to give. Don't give up now. My god, you are only 26 years old! ... I don't want to lecture you; that is not my style but I'd like to give you some advice...Be strong and keep your head up high... Don't lose your faith in God because he will be there for you always...

I continued to close myself away from the world, to find peace in my solitude, to turn my back to God. Out of nowhere, <u>it</u> invited itself into my life. Out of nowhere, it hit me. Soon depression descended graciously on me as if it took its rightful place and expected no more. I continued to not be me.

My family wanted to buy me the co-op. I lost interest. I didn't want to work anymore. There were too many issues that I had to face daily, weekly, monthly that began to snowball. I quit. (I didn't' know that I could have taken a leave of absence. I didn't understand my rights as an employee.) I needed to be alone.

I found a letter from my mother, sitting on my pillow...

I lay awake at night, thinking of you in your room. I want so much to hold you in my arms, take all the pain you have and make it disappear...It is not easy for a mother and father to see their child suffer, you are so much a part of us and looking at you locked in your sorrow, it is like having a knife in our heart... When God took Frankie, I screamed in my heart to God-why? Please God, take an arm from my body but make the pain disappear from my Rossana....

When you were little, I was sometime angry at the world for making you the middle child. But you won!! You made life for yourself, far more educated and interesting than your childhood friends. You grew up the most knowledgeable of all my children. I am so proud of you. Under your quick temper and your bitching, there is a big heart that always comes true for your little brother, your sisters, me and Daddy and even the Housekeeper...Please forgive me that besides feeling for you, I do not know how to help you get back on track. ...Please help us to help you...I have tons of thoughts but I stop here.

A child is forever a part of her parents' body and soul!

Love, Mommy

It was still so difficult to want to go on with my life. I didn't understand why this was happening to me. Why did Frankie have to die? I wanted his memory to live on. I looked for ways to recall, reflect, remember... At some point in time, I wrote a letter to Joe Pesci. He reminded me so much of Frankie, in looks, in the characters he played, in his mannerisms, the way he spoke. Joe Pesci- my Frankie in 15 years...

...I was very disheartened to discover you had at one time decided to forgo your acting career. I read an article outlining your career; subsequently, the promo's for "The Super" were playing. I must say, that in my eyes, there are many similarities between your character and Frankie... In the promo: "Joe knows dancing", that was my Frankie and his two left feet. And who can forget "Joe knows women"...that definitely was Frankie. The promos made me smile again for I had not in such a long time. The promos made me remember...

If you combined every character you have ever portrayed, that was my Frankie. He was a "Wise-guy" (Goodfellows), in every aspect. He strongly believed in omerta but unlike you, he would have never gotten himself shot in the face. If he had lived, he would have truly depicted the next generation of wise guys...

In "My Cousin Vinnie", you played an intelligent character though you were perceived otherwise, an out of place New Yorker set in the deep south. My Frankie: smart, clever, quick-witted, gifted... even though he had barely finished 8th grade and eventually got his GED. He definitely could make someting out of nuttin! He could come up with ways to make us see something that wasn't so easily understood. And those love scenes...reminded me of ours.

Even "Raging Bull"... Frankie took a stint at a career in Amateur Boxing, at the Atlantic Avenue Gym in Brooklyn. He boxed with unrelenting prowess and liked to spar, liked to fight, liked to win. He possessed that passionate rage that he took out in the ring (a rage that inherently came from his father's neglect).

Like you, Frankie was a comedian, known for his positive demeanor....They say that life imitates art or vice /versa. You must keep on acting... Through you, I can live vicariously and remember.

I love Joe Pesci. Every time I see him in a movie, I remember... He reminds me of Frankie.

~18~

His mother's dream brought his death into perspective. It leant the credibility to my own internal suffering. She begins... "One month after he died, I heard this voice, coming from within me. *I'm all right. I'm all right mom. I'm all right.*' She continues, "In the dream, I'm sitting in the kitchen with Anthony and the twins. We were crying and crying. I heard his voice, '*Mom! Mommy!*' I looked up. It was him. I looked down, away. I was frightened. '*Look at me, Mom. Look at me. Don't cry. Don't you see. I'm so happy.*' His eyes were blue, like when he was born. A deep, brilliant shade of blue. He was radiant as if the sun shined continually on him, behind him, from within. '*I'm so happy...*' and then he faded."

Then my dream... In my dream... a dream that I had, many months after he died... "Last night, I dreamed about Frankie. I haven't been able to dream about him so far- not even daydreams. I just have images that flash in and out of my mind. In this dream, I remember, I was mad at him because he hadn't called in awhile. He always called. Three times a day. This trip to Florida, he hadn't called. I couldn't find his phone number. I couldn't find his name. I looked and looked, in both phone books, but he wasn't there. I finally pulled out a phone book, old and dust covered. It said *Frank- Jamaica* scribbled in a childish handwriting and some number. No one answered. It kept ringing and ringing. I called the operator to find out if the number was disconnected or just no one was there to pick it up. She didn't tell me. I remember thinking how mad I was at Frankie and I was going to say to him 'What's going on Frank? Out of sight, out of mind? Is this it?' And then, when I couldn't find his name or number, in that same book, I remembered... Frankie is dead. He would never call again."

His Mother and I believe that he died that Friday. His physical body was left on earth to make amends, to be with us, to share, to make that lasting impression. He joked with Gina that last night. As usual, he teased her and tormented her as

late as it was, "Come on Gina, stay up with me and talk."
"Frankie! It's late, tomorrow..." Tomorrow would not be. He
saw everyone, his family, his friends, friends he hadn't seen in
years. He was everywhere on that last day, all over Queens,
the old neighborhood, the club, everywhere people bumped
into him. "We just saw him," they would say. "We just saw
him, yesterday," they would cry.

His Mom believes that God said: "It's enough, Frankie. You
don't have to go through this anymore. You're at peace. You
will remain in peace for eternity..." But God took him from me.
I wish that I could have embraced God and his doctrine.
Instead, I turned away from the Church. God took him from
me. I know he is at peace but...

~19~

I still could not escape my pain. When he died, I carried the pain with me, not only mentally but also physically. My heart had been ripped out-the ache evident in every breathe I took. Heartache- its figurative meaning stronger than its literal one. The physical anguish so real– felt more than 100 times, 1000 times, infinite multiplicities than pain felt when you sprain an ankle, break an arm, pop a dislocated shoulder back in place. An emptiness that no matter what I did, it couldn't be filled, a hole that went through me –front to back, back to front.

My heart had been ripped out, as if two hands took hold of my breast, fingers digging deeply in, sharply, tearing sinew, breaking bone...Grabbing. Pulling. Yanking. Ripping out. I felt the pain daily, in every waking hour, every restless night. Day after day, weeks turning into months- it continued- chronic- worsening...sometimes- I just didn't want to, couldn't move- clutching where my heart once raced.

I had never known this before in the innocence of my life- the life that had been running smoothly with very few obstacles and challenges. I didn't know how to overcome this. I had too much pride to ask for help. I needed to help others- his mom, his sisters. After all, I was the strong one. Why did I feel so beaten up and weak? The excruciating, physical pain! Until...

~20~

The baby was born.

I was angry at the world. I was angry with myself. I didn't want to participate in life. I had lost all sense of hope, of love, of happiness. I hated my sister Diana for once again stealing the show, all eyes on her. Hate is a strong word. I felt it. She was pregnant. During her baby shower, I took refuge in the kitchen. I didn't want to be involved even though my name was on the invitation. This was supposed to be my year... with Frankie.

On one blustery January night, there was a blackout. The transformers had blown up around the corner. Chiara and I were scared and called 911 when we saw flames shoot through the telephone wires. We were embarrassed when the Firemen questioned us. Luckily, Chiara used her flirtatious skills to get us out of trouble. These Firemen were cute; even I couldn't help but notice.

Anyway, Daddy and I stayed home while everyone else went to wait in the hospital as Diana began her labor. We lit candles on my grandma's coffee table and read by the candle light. I didn't want to go to the hospital.

The next day, I was forced by my Mother and Father to go Booth Memorial. I didn't want to. I had no desire to share in our family's good fortune. Something happened to me. I softened when I saw the baby and she was put into my arms. I melted and thawed just a little bit when I realized how precious she was, how tiny, how fragile. Caraline Grace. She was so beautiful, especially in comparison to my sister, who looked like a truck had just run her over.

I started to move forward, slowly, carefully. I had no choice to begin life again when I was asked to take care of Caraline when Diana returned to work.

Caraline- brought me back to life, my savior for the time being...

~21~

It is ironic that he died of an enlarged heart- a measure of his infinite love for me, a finite ending to a cerebral galaxy of emotions he now understood, he now accepted, he now embraced.

The memories of my youth are good ones- laughter-filled, teenage frolic as my pubescent body matured into womanly curves, free to experiment, boyfriends galore. Ms. Popularity. I sang and danced through year after year of close-knit family ties- confetti thrown from rafter heights upon gleeful parents open arms to welcome the New Year over and over again. I wish I could say the same for him...

Black. White. No gray if not for the love of his mother...

The shouting matches escalated to pitches heard by the neighbors down the block. Smack! Crunch! Crack! as fatherly hands struck out in the only way they knew- to bond by beating him, demoralizing him, over and over again. This tormented post- teen temperament motivated itself into a heroine induced carefreeness, the temporary escape, the momentary drugged bliss of not caring, not wanting to feel anything, kept needing a fix, wanting a fix, doing anything for a fix... until me.

Until me- I became his fix- the only thing he wanted or needed.
Until me- he waited vehemently through his tortured childhood
Until me- the anger softening

He had not known love, did not know how to love, how to be loved... until me. (Yet he was loved by many.) I am blessed knowing this, knowing I made an impact, a positive one in his life, knowing that joy and sorrow were juxtaposed... side by side, these parallel emotions raced until one day they would meet, intertwine, combine, then separate into opposite ends of the spectrum...

For in heaven, he was at peace. For on earth, I was lost...

... <u>In the devil's playground</u>

It was a tormented soul
Who wandered this earth
Seeking comfort however brief
In arms of strangers reach.

It was the tormented soul
In heaven's lair
Looked downward earthly
At his lover's despair.

Like the Greek myth's playground
Pushing boulder to the summit
Inches reach
Downward plummet.

To begin once again
Over and over
No final ending
Just a new friend, lover.

It was the devil's doing
Laughing so
"He's protected, peaceful
But she's spiraling below."

Give her hope
Before her eyes: men
One thing they want
Their hearts pretend.

She keeps going
The unconditional fool
Devils still laughing
At heart's broken bloody pool.

It was the tormented soul
Who wandered this earth
A cyclical path
Future bleak.

The devil continues to tease
His evil bearing
She continues to love
Defying, daring!

~22~

Red roses... long stem.

Their scent, sweet and fragrant. Red roses, no more. Red roses, flowers that would carry so much meaning in my life.

When we buried him, I wanted to stay. I wanted to jump in. I know you have seen this in all those made-for-TV La Cosa Nostra movies. The despondent mother. The despondent wife. ... jumps into the grave, to be with her loved one for eternity. I wanted to be with him.

I took the red roses, breaking off their delicate petals carefully, and threw them inside. "I want him to sleep on a bed of roses..." I said to no one or the few who still lingered near. I just kept looking down into the open ground. Would the roses somehow make him...? I don't know... rise again? I wanted to be with him. I wanted to...

I was told to leave. I was pulled away. I wanted to stay. There. With him. Forever...

One year later, I bought one dozen... dozen red roses. Long stem. I went early to his grave, not early enough though those magical little pills were in my pocket. There would be too many people lingering about. Not early enough as if my extra few hours asleep had been planned to disrupt my day, disrupt my life, disrupt the end to my life.

I walked around the serenity of the empty cemetery and lonely gravesites and stole the urns scattered about. Oops. Sorry. I needed them. Stole them — that's sacrilege. Borrowed them, borrowed them from graves whose flowers were as dead as their honorees.

One dozen dozen. Red roses. Long stem. How beautiful. His graveside –144 roses, a bed of roses... You could barely see the marble stone, its pinkish tone, the perfect back drop... How beautiful. I wanted to lie down and be with him forever.

The beauty before me- life. My life- he would want me to live. The magical pills were close by. MY RELEASE from THIS TORMENT ON EARTH. Release- soon to be ecstasy, heavenly ecstasy... I would be with him again...

On a bed of red velvet, draped casually on a sea of green. A bed of red velvet, soft, luxurious, that you could see as you drove up, as you drove near. A bed of love. I wanted to die that day — to be with him. I would sleep peacefully near him. On him. As we use to do.

Red roses. Long stem.

~The end~

Epilogue
The Significant Insignificant

*Why is it that you play with lust,
frolic with desire, but have to
work so hard at love?*

Once again the "Pop-up Princesses", Kim and Robin (Ying and Yang), Marybeth, and Chrissie... needed something to amuse their frenetic, never-have-enough-time beings. Those "Pop-ups" as they deemed themselves. What the Yaya's couldn't convey and the Sweet Potato Queens failed to master, the Pop-up Princesses took the crown, the reigning glory of their southern belle/southern bitch ways and would not relinquish it to anyone, especially those who got in the way of "fun". They were more conventional, mid-30-year- old beauties, whose personalities of the moment depended on which way their hormones were fluctuating... The "Pop-up moms", the ladies who danced on bar stools, gyrated to the disco beat, sashayed in-between the lines of men two deep, teasing the little boys who watched with mouths open and astonished faces... Pop-up moms who could pop-up and be anyone that the circumstances called for... Pop-up moms –whose husbands accepted them for their wild ways... knowing they would never cross the line into a sinful, cheating existence. Pop-up moms... educated women, good mothers, wonderful wives, great lovers... Pop-up moms- beautiful, trendy, mischievous... Pop-up moms- my friends...

One of them commanded a party, some festival to celebrate whatever event they could make up as an excuse for their follies. Since the "nasty t-shirts night" had almost raped some of their chaste married state, they knew that this event, though summer's onset, must be somewhat contained. In order to curtail (somewhat) their wanton ways, they knew they must include all of the "others"- those middle aged (at 30) preppy prisses who still wore the pink and green sorority of their youth, the women who never left their LL Bean existence. The "others"- who conformed rather than set the pace for any new adventure. The "others"- who couldn't wait to spread a little gossip as they stood poised with pasted smiles and perfectly powdered faces. The "others" who state again and again how "everything's perfect, ya'll" as their creative husbands found ways to work "late at the office". It would be an interesting night...

And of course, no party would be complete without "sub-5" (as I was affectionately called)... My-self, always the life of a party, yet, I acted and carried myself in a lady-like manner befitting "a northern woman of stature" (or I should say lack of stature since my barely 5 ft height simply could not match up to the models who surrounded me). The venomous femme fatale had hidden herself once again and chose to camouflage herself into the girl next door, promulgating my position as a single woman... since I could not be protected by the ring that encircled my friends' fingers. (I explained to the Pop-ups, once, that if I acted in their fool-hardy manner, my actions would be misunderstood and could get me in trouble, real trouble.) ...So once again, I was in my car, my reliable PT cruiser, a "woody", a car that exemplified my personality... heading south with my customary pit stop in D.C.

This time, I was ready to confront John since our emails and phone calls had resumed a regular occurrence... John- how confused he seemed. Why couldn't he just leave me alone? I kept getting drawn back into his life.

I got dressed that night as if it was my last great seduction... My subconscious was exercising without caution as it somersaulted and flipped its way into the forefront of my thoughts, its on-going cheer of "You can look but you can't touch (and you never will...)" my motivation factor, a factor which psyched me up and kept me thinking positive. It was as if this last maneuver, a well thought-out play in action, would determine once and for all, the winner (or loser) in this game of cat and mouse, the game that usually began with "catch me catch me if you can", ending with a quick, no reason given "see ya!" I was over him and I wanted to show him what he could never possess. I felt good. My self-esteem was idling high although not quite at a level I needed it to be. Again, the cheer kept motivating me to cross the finish line, one way or another... The black silk dress with its jersey fabric that clung... looked ever-so-perfect for this little imaginative tete a tete... Something wasn't right, as I made my way to the front door and caught my reflection in the French doors... Maybe it was just too "out there"? I was "too out there" for this conservative DC suburb. At the last moment, I threw on a pink, silk wrap. There was something about the way it covered me, yet, accentuated my curves into a hot fuschia silhouette...

I guess I stood out- I knew I did, especially as I walked past the outside windows of the darkened bar and heads turned. I had not yet entered into the smoky pool hall (our intended meeting place) yet I knew the evening was in my favor... This night would fulfill my urge to scratch at and bloody the scab that was forming, that frustrating itch, the thorn in my side that kept aching... that little inkling desire for revenge. This night would put me on a path of independence, the getting-to-know-me stage I knew I dressed with on occasion but needed to make uniform. Getting to know me again.

I walked up to John. I kissed him hello. I turned down a drink. At that moment, he turned around and looked at me. I was still focused on John. He looked at John, turned to me, surmised the situation for a brief moment and proceeded to direct his attention to John: "Is she your significant other," he asked, already knowing the answer... "No, she's my insignificant other," John replied without hesitation to this stranger.

... Later that night, during dinner, John hinted he would be taking a three-week vacation in the Fall. As usual, my intuition got the better of me and I asked: "Are you getting married." It seems John was "thinking about getting engaged." Thinking about. Humn... He had his doubts... She was very young. A mere 22 to his wise 43. It would never work.

He made his move that night. Finally, John made his move- a kiss that I would remember but casually try not to own. Try. ...*That kiss pulsated through me* as I drove the hour and half south to my friends party. That kiss that I could not get out of my mind... That kiss. *A kiss that awoke a latent sensuality. A kiss, the desire rising as if the recipient were afraid to let it end.* Our kiss. One kiss that got me going. He made his move, but it was too late. I would simply not be the woman to sow his oats. What was he thinking?

The insignificant (John) became more significant when he rejected me, not because he didn't love me- quite contrary. I was too sexy to be his and only his. He told me this, as an afterthought to his revelation about his intended nuptials, the child bride he would soon call wife. He told me I was too sexy. "It won't work. I thought about it. I thought about us. It won't work." he said. I was too sexy. He couldn't control his jealous being and to have me would mean placing me in a box just for his viewing... The insignificant (John) became most significant when he graciously bowed and offered my hand (and subsequent body) to another... The insignificant did not remain significant much longer...

My knight had finally come, galloping bareback to my rescue... In tarnished armor. His name was Paul.

I waited a few days to digest the John saga. I waited a few weeks before I finally emailed Paul... "So..." -is all I wrote. Paul couldn't quite place me. But that simple one word message began a long three-week conversation of getting-to-know-each-other, before our first date. He sent me daily cards via email. It was scary... always roses. One red rose. A bouquet of roses. A field of roses. Red roses. Long stem. He exuberated a haunting power. I was mesmerized by his innate warmth and human compassion for others, others not so fortunate.

I hated dates but for some reason this one seemed so easy... Paul reinvigorated my waning desire... that desire to beloved (not coveted). Remarkably, he seemed to exemplify a "staying power". Could he possibly be the one for me? I hated dates, yet this one seemed so easy. It seemed so easy and began a tumultuous affair, the love affair that I always wanted, a two-sided love affair.

...I discovered that we had something in common. A year in our lives that had been dramatically altered. A year that we would always remember but love to forget... 1991.

1991. He was thrown from his car as it somersaulted through the sand, escaping its steel embrace... yet the momentum did not keep him from harms way as his spine met the full impact of one lonely pine... smashing the vertebrae into an infinite brittle mass... He died. He lived. He was told "you will NOT walk" yet his conviction proved worthy. "Yes, I will."- with one small step, ever the patient being, his mind strong, his body followed... His body healed with a miraculous recovery that Hippocrate's students did not, could not, understand.

1991. "HE" chased me in my gleeful youth, waited patiently for me through "HIS" troubled teenage years, finally captured me at the onset of my career...when I could do anything... but "HE" left me, one day... My life, moving fast into a positive realm, suddenly disrupted as I discovered the meaning of death. "HE" left me. Death is hard. Death is difficult. Death can suddenly sneak up on you...

At 12:01 am, on that day which changed my life forever, a day which stole from me the twinkle in my eye, a day which snatched the spunk from my soul, a day which grabbed and held prisoner my emotional being... I heard once again three words I had been waiting for.

At 12:01 am, 11 years to the day... a day which left its dark mark burned into my heart... He whispered: "I love you, Rossana". He spoke slowly and deliberately as he held me... "I am the dream. You are the dreamer," he whispered.[13] Had my dreams finally been acknowledged? I was overcome with emotion, responding by pulling away into a corner of the dark room, my body collapsing, my heart palpitating uncontrollably, the nausea rising as I could taste the bitter bile in my throat... I waited so long to hear these three words... My body reacted... I was about to throw up. It didn't matter. He still wanted me. He had been waiting for me. He knew. He just knew as he held my hand... Had he picked the lock that had sealed shut the closed chambers of my heart? He held my hand just so... the human touch- a far greater healing passion...

Why is it that you play with lust, frolic with desire, but have to work so hard at love? Paul answered: "Because love is forever..."

Forever would come sooner than I thought.

(to be continued...)

---

[13] These words are from a Town and Country advertisement.

ABOUT THE AUTHOR

HER NAME IS Rossana, simply Rossana. One of six. A typically large Italian-American, Catholic family. She grew up in the heart of New York City, within 45 minutes drive of the sandy ocean beaches and 30 minutes to the downtown Village scene. Queens. The middle child, she somehow managed to escape the conventional lifestyle which her siblings live by. Creative, single her- where does she fit in?

She's the girl you might hate. You'd be hard pressed to figure her out. "What does she have that I don't?" you may ask. Like a chameleon, she changes colors to blend into whatever environment suits her purpose; raging redhead, ditzy blonde, or maybe the studious brunette. All her. The twinkle in her eyes reveals mischievous secrets she fails to keep hidden. She's the girl who can throw on vintage frock and wear it as if it is the height of haute couture.

You may find her a bit eccentric, but she would tell you that she's just close to the cutting edge. Avant-garde is how she should be perceived for within the woman lie many intriguing characteristics. She has been described as both witty and wise. However, her garrulous tongue might cause your blood to boil at times. Often she can talk and listen simultaneously and carry on multiple conversations at once (an innate family characteristic). This may be an effort of her subconscious to live her life to its fullest. Men love her (which is why they are her best friends). Women? The decision is split until they get to know her. She smiles a lot even though she has been thrust through the gates of hell. Bubbly, outgoing, adventurous. Why? Because she never wants to say "If only I had..."

She enjoys travel and is either coming or going somewhere exciting. She spent numerous summers (and winters) in Italy (every year) as her Sicilian mother longed for an Italian son-in-law. (Her mother is still longing...) As a back up plan, there have been several excursions throughout Europe. Perhaps, her most interesting adventure, most recently, was a mission to Africa. She built homes for the poor and camped in a remote region of the "Bush". She was lullabied by the sounds of nature- the rhythm of the bell frogs, the hyena's laughs as they danced around the dying embers, various catcalls from the flight of the birds, and the roars of the lions as they tiptoed at night. Imagine that? A city girl placed amidst nature's wildest.

She shows the real her. Her friends say she wears her heart on her sleeve. Perhaps. But only to accessorize the scarlet letter emblazoned across her breast.

She spent over 12 years in the fashion industry. "Let me into your closet. Give me some of your discretionary income and you will be transformed into a new woman (or man), a new you- the trendy, sophisticated, sexy (still comfortable) mini-van mom (dad). I assure you." Some say that she should consider being a decorator. Be careful of inviting her into your home. It won't look the same. She enjoys designing (and sewing) window treatments, selecting colors and textures, rummaging through fabric swatches, appointing furniture and so forth. She also enjoys the "hands on" experiences: stripping and staining antiques in need of TLC, doing Venetian stucco faux finishes, painting murals and replacing fixtures. Having a great love for art, she also enjoys charcoal drawing and painting- both in oils and water color, especially nudes. Her favorite medium, although she's not very good at it, is Fresco painting (the antiquated art of painting in wet cement.

"With fervor, I seek to give love to life and life to love."

Printed in the United States
1241700004B/1-39